Popular Science Library

EDITOR-IN-CHIEF: GARRETT P. SERVISS

THE STORY OF CHEMISTRY

The Nature and Structure of Matter—How Chemistry Is Utilized in Our Present Day Economic and Industrial Development

By

HIPPOLYTE GRUENER

*Professor Emeritus of Chemistry,
Western Reserve University,
at Cleveland, Ohio*

COLLIER BOOKS
SINCE 1875

ILLUSTRATED

P. F. COLLIER & SON CORPORATION
PUBLISHERS   NEW YORK

PREFACE

THE emphasis throughout this work is upon the general principles underlying the subject of chemistry. Without this emphasis the reading of the wonders and the achievements of the science may develop into mere pastime. The most important portion of the text, therefore, is that dealing with general chemistry, the groundwork upon which all the rest is based. In the treatment of the subject are interwoven descriptions, general principles and applications to ordinary life, selected with a view to building up the reader's understanding and correlating it with his ordinary experiences.

Following upon the discussion of the principles of general chemistry comes the division of organic chemistry, which requires extended treatment. It is not a different science, but the subject matter is special, and it seems, in its orderly progress and in its applications to living matter and to certain industries, almost to be a field in itself. After the principles of general chemistry have been mastered, organic chemistry has for many a special fascination.

Industrial operations in which chemical principles are involved (chemical industries) are constantly increasing in number and scope. They are touching our lives in increasing degree and commanding ever-widening popular interest. The more significant of the chemical industries are discussed, either in the regular text or in the special chapter devoted to the topic. They are somewhat sharply differentiated with respect to their inorganic or organic nature. Among the former are the extraction and manipulation of metals, the recovery of salts, the alkali and acid industries, ceramics and electrochemical processes.

The organic industries are even more striking, partly because they are less familiar, partly because one could imagine that there is no limit to their possibilities. Prominent among the organic industries are: the great petroleum industry; the coal-tar industry, much less significant in volume, but spectacular for its relation to such products as dyes and synthetic drugs; sugar, starch and its alteration products; cellulose and its derivatives, such as cellophane; the fermentation industries, reaching out into altogether new directions; the fascinating chapter of synthetic rubber, textiles, and plastics; fats, oils, paints and varnishes; new solvents.

Certain special branches of chemistry, analytical and physical (including colloid) chemistry can be here dealt with in only a brief manner. A glimpse of these is nevertheless enlightening; without their inclusion the broad subject of chemistry would be incompletely treated.

A chemical interpretation of certain other fields of interest follows. On the inorganic side there is included geochemistry, the chemistry of the earth's crust; on the organic side, the chemistry of foods (including that of the vitamins and the hormones). Further, there is given a brief survey of the contributions of chemistry to agriculture and sanitation.

The glossary will be found convenient for reference.

HIPPOLYTE GRUENER

CONTENTS

CONTENTS

LIST OF PLATES

CHAPTER I

THE NATURE OF CHEMICAL CHANGES

WHEN a chemical action takes place, and a chemical change results, the effect is often apparent to the ordinary observer. But the reasons why this change takes place, and the manner of its taking place are so far from apparent that it presents serious difficulties to the novice in chemistry. Iron rusts, it changes, it ceases to be the strong metallic substance we are used to. It is converted into a brown brittle powder which is only a nuisance. The mechanic has no interest in the rust; for him the iron has been destroyed, he drops all thought of it and looks for new material. For the chemist the matter is different. He must know what is happening, and why: what the iron has changed to, and what is involved in the process. If questions like these are fully answered, the knowledge gained will quickly lead to the appreciation and solution of the next problem, and thus our understanding of chemistry has made a beginning. In all chemical considerations we must follow with care every circumstance. If, like the mechanic, we say that the iron is gone, and the discussion closed, we shut ourselves out from one of the first chemical principles, namely the study of the *change* which has taken place. It is often difficult for the beginner to realize that the change which seemingly destroys the object before him, does not end the discussion, but is in reality the subject matter of his thought. A serious difficulty met with at the outset of the study of chemistry is that there are rather few common experiences, in any sense clearly appreciated, upon which we can draw for our material for chemical discussions. Chemical happenings of a familiar nature are few in number. The following array includes most of them: combustion, or burning of fuel or other matter; rusting or corrosion of metals; decay and fermentation of animal and vegetable matter; plant growth and food assimilation by animals; explosions; and a more or less vague experience with the corrosive action of chemical substances, as acids and alkalis. In all men's experiences the attention is usually given to nonchemical phases of the event, with no penetrating thought as to what lies at the foundation of these experiences.

The reason for men's neglect of chemical thoughts lies in part in the fact that the chemical aspect of familiar experiences has apparently no practical meaning. Further, in the familiar chemical changes, some of the reacting substances and products are gases, and therefore escape observation. But probably the greatest difficulty lies in the nature of the changes. Chemical forces act at small distances, and the unit masses involved are so minute that it is with great difficulty that we can form a mechanical picture or conception of that which is happening. Without some mechanical conception our mental processes are indeed slow. We make progress by applying our past experience to the present problem. Correlating our experience of large readily appreciated masses with the minute masses and distances of chemistry is a matter of very great difficulty, and is the one great stumbling-block in the early conquest of our subject.

Chemistry is often described as the study of the nature

of matter and the changes which it undergoes, but a more complete and suggestive description has been given as follows: Chemistry is the study (a) of the nature and composition of matter, (b) of the changes in its fundamental nature which matter undergoes, (c) of the causes of these changes and the influences controlling them, (d) of the energy changes involved, and (e) the laws found to govern them. In order to make this concrete let us take a familiar and important chemical happening, namely combustion, or burning, and, as a special case, the burning of sulphur. We will first describe the action, and then interpret it with the above points in view.

In order for sulphur to burn, it must be lighted, that is, heated sufficiently to start the burning. As it burns, the sulphur unites with the active constituent of the air, oxygen, and in doing so develops enough heat to give what is called a blaze. The sulphur disappears, and we know that a limited supply of oxygen is soon exhausted, and in place of these two a new substance appears, a gas with a well known pungent odor. This gas is made up of both sulphur and oxygen, and its weight is the same as the combined weight of the two. Its name, sulphur dioxide, indicates its composition.

In this simple process much of what is stated above is illustrated. (a) First as to the composition of matter. We can see that the oxide of sulphur, which results from the burning of the sulphur, is made up of simpler parts, namely oxygen and sulphur, and is therefore a complex substance, called a compound. It will develop presently that by no known process can it be shown that sulphur and oxygen are complex. They seem to be simple substances, incapable of resolution into any constituents,

These then are "elements," and may be considered the fundamentals of chemistry. (*b*) In the process of the union of sulphur and oxygen, which we call burning, we see a characteristic change: its opposite is the separation, called decomposition, of a complex into its simpler parts. (*c*) We say that sulphur and oxygen exhibit affinities for each other, and under the influence of the heat applied, when the sulphur was set on fire, the affinities asserted themselves so that they combined. (*d*) In the burning heat is developed. This means that energy is being liberated. In chemical changes we are concerned with energy in the form of chemical energy, heat, light, electricity, and mechanical energy. They are all intimately related. Chemical energy and heat are the forms which will receive most of our attention.

In a cursory view of chemical manipulations the term "mixture" often comes into consideration. A mixture of some sort is a necessity if we wish to cause two substances to combine or to interact. Without mutual contact chemical action does not occur, for it, unlike magnetism and gravity, asserts itself only at minute distances. The chemist is interested in single substances, elements and compounds, and concerns himself with mixtures only so far as they favor or interfere with this end. The distinction between "mixture" and "compound" will be discussed later.

In order to familiarize ourselves somewhat more fully with some phases of the subject of combustion, let us consider the combustion of charcoal and of gasoline. Chemically the material of charcoal is called carbon, and it is the same as that of ordinary hard coal and of soot. It is an element, like sulphur and oxygen. Ordinarily carbon does not alter in the air, and we say that its affinity under ordinary conditions is slight, otherwise it would at all times unite with the oxygen of the air. But when carbon is heated sufficiently it burns, that is, unites with the oxygen, for that is what the process of burning or combustion is. The charcoal and oxygen concerned both gradually diminish, and in their place is a colorless, odorless gas, carbon dioxide, so inconspicuous that it needs special tests for detecting it. But in the use of stoves and furnaces, the escape of this gas must be provided for, and is one of the functions of the chimney. The burning of gasoline is more complicated, for gasoline is made up of two elements, carbon and hydrogen. The presence of the former is evident in many ways; the hydrogen is less evident without further study. Both of these elements, carbon and hydrogen, have affinity for oxygen when heated, hence their combination burns readily. This burning means that each element present unites with oxygen much as it would were it by itself. Each forms its own oxide. Carbon forms carbon dioxide, mentioned above, and hydrogen forms water, which is made up of hydrogen and oxygen. This is indicated by its formula, H_2O.

These points are made a bit more graphic if they are represented by a simple form of symbolism, called the chemical equation.

1. For sulphur burning, $S + 2O \rightarrow SO_2$, sulphur dioxide.
2. For carbon burning, $C + 2O \rightarrow CO_2$, carbon dioxide.
3. For gasoline burning, $CH_2 + 3O \rightarrow CO_2 + H_2O$.

Another familiar chemical experience is the corrosion of metals. Some metals, particularly iron, have affinity for oxygen, even at ordinary temperatures, but more so when heated. Hence they corrode, that is, become covered with a layer of oxide, which is a combination of the metal with oxygen. Silver will not tarnish with oxygen, but does unite with sulphur which is occasionally present in the air. If we wish to understand these changes better we may again use equations.

$$2 Fe + 3 O \rightarrow Fe_2O_3, \text{ iron oxide.}$$
$$Cu + O \rightarrow CuO, \text{ copper oxide.}$$
$$2 Ag + S \rightarrow Ag_2S, \text{ silver sulphide.}$$

The possibility of a change involving compounds by which they are resolved into simpler parts, an action the opposite of union, must logically follow, and decomposition is as common a phenomenon as union. Ordinary experiences illustrating simple chemical decompositions are not common. Perhaps a helpful illustration is that of a log of wood placed upon glowing embers. It is not difficult to appreciate that the wood is altered. Part of it is seen to pass off as a gas, and as the gas becomes ignited, it forms the flame. Another part, if the combustion does not go too far, is seen to remain behind as charcoal. Theoretically the conception of decomposition is not difficult, after the idea of union is appreciated. It may be visualized by assuming a reversal of the equation of the preceding paragraph.

$SO_2 \rightarrow S + O_2$, sulphur dioxide when decomposed into its constituents, yields sulphur and oxygen.

$$CO_2 \rightarrow C + O_2 \text{ and } Fe_2O_3 2 \rightarrow 2 Fe + 3O$$

In our discussions it will be seen why a reaction which results in a union will not actually be likely to reverse itself. Different groups of substances are usually involved in the two types of reactions, union and decomposition.

Therefore, following upon a consideration of the (*a*) nature of matter and (*b*) the changes which it undergoes, comes a discussion (*c*) as to the causes of these changes. When we contemplate the causes underlying mechanical and to some extent other physical phenomena, we can readily satisfy ourselves as to the relation of cause and effect. In chemical changes no such relations are apparent, and we must develop a new interpretation. This is conventionalized as follows. When under proper conditions two elements react to form a compound, they do so because of an inherent attraction for each other, which attraction is called "chemical affinity." In the beginning of our study we must take this conception empirically, basing it upon our knowledge of simple experimentation. In more advanced studies of chemistry there will be formed amplifications of this idea. For our elementary study this meager conception must suffice.

It may now be seen why a compound like sulphur dioxide formed by the union of sulphur and oxygen does not readily resolve itself into its elements. The same affinity which causes the sulphur and oxygen to unite causes them to remain together. To show decomposition we must then use for illustrations compounds which are made of elements with comparatively low affinities for each other.

We have also (*d*) energy changes involved in chemical changes. A conspicuous accompaniment of chemical unions is heat development. It is a law of nature that energy cannot be created or destroyed. Hence it is evident that the energy of the heat liberated, as for example when charcoal burns, must have been inherent somehow in the original charcoal and the oxygen of the air with which it united. We call this the chemical energy of the two substances, and when they unite, we say that the chemical energy is converted into heat energy and is then liberated. It is axiomatic that in order to again separate the carbon from the oxygen an equivalent amount of energy must be reintroduced. Inasmuch as any system which possesses energy can lose it more readily than a system lacking energy can gain it, reactions involving liberation of heat are altogether more common in elementary considerations than those which require an addition of energy.

This relation of chemical energy and heat is a vital factor in the realm of foods and the industries. The energy value of food, expressed in part as heat, is pretty well understood. The greater portion of the energy of our industries is derived from the heat liberated by the burning of coal, that is, from the chemical energy of the coal and of the oxygen of the air.

In this connection the interrelation of the common forms of energy may be emphasized. We are mostly concerned with the relation between chemical energy and heat. The familiar magnesium flash light brings light energy into consideration, as does also the influence of light in the storing up of energy in the growth of plants. The electric battery illustrates the connection with electrical energy, and the force of chemical explosives illustrates the relation to mechanical energy. Thus chemical energy, heat, light, electricity and mechanical energy are all seen to be related, and their interchangeability must be kept in view as a fundamental principle.

The last topic (*e*) in a study of chemistry, the laws

governing chemical changes is an involved one. It will be touched upon in part in the sequel. On the whole this is the field of physical chemistry, to which a chapter will be devoted later.

When we study chemical changes, and form chemical compounds, we are often confronted with these questions. Have we really performed a chemical change, or is it merely a physical change which has taken place? And when two substances are put together, have they really combined, or have they only formed a mixture? After some progress has been made in this study, such questions cause little confusion. At the beginning, however, the distinction must be carefully drawn, and methods applied for determining the nature of the change.

Physical changes come under the titles of mechanics, heat, light, sound, electricity and magnetism. It will be noticed that these are all concerned with the energy changes of a body, rather than with the nature of the substance of that body. A piece of iron is in motion or comes to rest. Its energy is important, but the body is always the same iron. When heated, platinum wire glows, and water is converted to steam, but upon cooling the change will be seen to have left the matter unaltered. Light may traverse a transparent medium, or be reflected by a bright surface, but it makes no impression on the nature of the matter. A wire will vibrate and give out sound, or be conducting electricity, but later will be seen to be absolutely unaltered. The following statement covering such cases is crude perhaps, but will serve as a very usable formula. A physical change is one of such nature that when the influences bringing about the change are removed, the substance involved reverts to its original form. In a chemical change the substance is permanently altered. For example, when the sulphur was heated in the air it was permanently converted into a substance, sulphur dioxide, of an altogether different nature.

The case of the difference between a mixture and a compound may be shown by the usual laboratory illustration of iron and sulphur. If we mix iron filings and sulphur powder and examine the product, we will notice, if we use care enough, that the iron is still present as iron, and the sulphur as sulphur. A magnet attracts the iron and leaves the sulphur; while, if the mixture is shaken up with water, the heavier iron may be separated. If we now heat a mixture of sulphur and iron the mass is seen to glow and all individual characteristics of the sulphur and iron are gone. We may formulate as follows: In a mixture the different constituents preserve their individuality and may be separated by proper mechanical means; in a compound the constituent elements have lost their individuality and have become merged into a new substance with its own set of characteristics.

It will be convenient to state three canons by which we may decide whether a chemical change has taken place. They are: (a) in a chemical change heat is usually developed or absorbed; (b) after the change the substances involved show different characteristics; (c) in chemical changes the proportions of reacting substances involved are always definite. If there is an excess of one constituent it simply remains behind like so much inert matter.

CHAPTER II

NATURE AND CONDUCT OF MATTER

IF we make a survey of substances which come under our observation, including those of a less common nature, found only in certain industries and chemical laboratories, we may notice that they fall into two classes, one of simple substances, the other of their compounds. The simple substances, or elements, include the metals, and a number of nonmetallic substances, as carbon, sulphur, and oxygen. In all ordinary experiences elements are incapable of chemical subdivision or simplification. Although our ideas of the elements have been modified since the discovery of radium, a topic to be discussed fully in a later chapter, we may assume the integrity of the elements in all our elementary studies. In general, changes can be accomplished only by adding to them. Compounds include substances which may be divided, which in fact are made up of two or more elements. Elements unite to form compounds, as the sulphur and oxygen united to form sulphur dioxide, and compounds can be resolved into their constituent elements. These ideas are fundamental and our nomenclature is based upon them. The name silver sulphide is thus interpreted at once, and we may at a glance receive considerable information from it.

The element, being the simplest form of matter, may be used as the basis for the study of our subject. About ninety such individual substances, or elements, have been identified, and each is a starting point for a whole set of compounds. But in spite of the vast array of individuals which such a fact suggests, the whole subject is simplified by the very ready grouping of all the elements and their compounds, so that they may be comprehended within comparatively few divisions. The elements fall into two classes, the metals and the nonmetals. The exact chemical characteristics of the metals must be left for later study, but the usual impression of what constitutes a metal is correct as far as it goes. Malleability, high specific gravity, opacity, and conductivity for heat and electricity, are the most outstanding features of metals. These are all physical properties but the chemical properties which characterize metals also belong to substances possessing these physical properties. The common metals conforming to these conditions are zinc, aluminum, manganese, chromium, iron, cobalt, nickel, tin, lead, copper, arsenic, antimony, mercury, silver, gold, and platinum. From a chemical standpoint, however, the list is not complete and another group of metals must be added, the common members of which are sodium, potassium, calcium, and magnesium. These metals conform to the usual ideas of metals in most respects, but they are not heavy and possess such high chemical affinities that they cannot be used for ordinary purposes.

The second class of elements consists of the nonmetals. The name is a weak one, as is also the description that these elements do not possess the properties of metals. It is nevertheless convenient. The physical properties of nonmetals are varied, but when we come to their chemical properties we find that they stand out strongly as a group.

Oxygen and hydrogen are conventionally mentioned

as the first of the nonmetals. These two elements, however, stand by themselves. This is especially true of oxygen, the most abundant of the elements, and the most general in its relations. Outside of laboratory experiences, oxygen is known as a gas, a supporter of combustion, essential in life processes, the cause of corrosions, such as that of iron. In the laboratory it has peculiar relations to hydrogen, to the metals and to the nonmetals, and these relations will be referred to with great frequency. Hydrogen is a gas so light that it is used for filling balloons. It is well known to be very combustible, in its combustion uniting with oxygen to form water. As will be seen presently, it is, like oxygen, in a class by itself.

The following are the typical nonmetals.

Carbon, the element making up the major portion of charcoal, coal, graphite, and the diamond. Carbon is the fundamental element of living organisms.

Nitrogen, a gas, the inert constituent of the atmosphere. In compounds of vital importance in the animal and vegetable world.

Although these four elements are rather dissimilar, there are advantages in grouping them together. They serve as good illustrations for studying chemical reactions, for their reactions are typical, and come within the range of ordinary human experience, so that we may illustrate from them freely. These four elements are sometimes called the "organogens," because they are the main elements which go to make up organic matter. Organic matter is of somewhat complicated composition, so that its study requires special attention. This branch of chemistry is studied under the name of "Organic Chemistry."

Fluorine, chlorine, bromine, and iodine form a group

of elements so similar that they must be considered together. Their names are not unfamiliar, but iodine is the only one likely to be familiar as an element. Chlorine is a constituent of common salt, and is the most important of the group. They are called halogens, meaning salt formers, because they are constituents of typical salts.

Sulphur is a common element, found free under certain conditions. It is well known that it is found in combination in some mineral waters, as an impurity in soft coal, and in many ores of metals.

Phosphorus is associated with matches. It is exceedingly inflammable, hence dangerous as well as useful. It is a constituent, as may be surmised, of the minerals called phosphates.

Boron is found in borax and boracic acid.

Silicon is the fundamental nonmetallic element of the mineral world. The great mass of the minerals of the rocks of the earth's crust consists of silicon and oxygen, sometimes including also certain metals. Its compounds are not active under ordinary conditions, hence, in general, they interest the chemist to a lesser degree than they do the mineralogist.

As was stated above, all terrestrial matter is made up of elements, and theoretically can be resolved into these and built up from them. But many of these elements are rare and the great bulk of the earth's crust is made up of a small proportion of them. Eight elements, oxygen, silicon, aluminum, iron, calcium, magnesium, sodium, and potassium, make up more than 97 per cent, ten more make up over 2 per cent, and all the rest are comprehended within the narrow range of one-half per cent. One must be careful not to obtain false impressions from these relative values. Sulphur, for example, makes up only one-tenth per cent of the earth's crust, yet the absolute amount is considerable, and where conditions have been favorable for its concentration, it is found in abundance. Most of the common metals, also, are present in relatively small amounts, yet like sulphur, seem abundant when concentrated.

The classification of the elements into metals and nonmetals is a fundamental one, dominating the whole range of chemical study. It will be seen presently that the metals are on the whole positive electrically, while the nonmetals, either by themselves or associated with oxygen, are negative. It may readily be surmised that the positive metals and the negative nonmetals have an attraction for each other. They readily unite to form the group of neutral substances known as salts. Typical illustrations are: Positive sodium with negative chlorine forms sodium chloride, neutral. Positive calcium with the negative sulphate group, forms calcium sulphate, neutral. The conception of early chemists that all matter was made up of mercury (the metal) and sulphur (the nonmetal) was a crude symbol of this fundamental relation.

In anticipation it may be briefly stated here that nonmetals form compounds with hydrogen, or with hydrogen and oxygen, of very definite characteristics, the "acids." Acids are so outstanding that the idea of acid is almost the only chemical thought that has filtered into the world without. To balance the formation of acids formed from the nonmetals, we will find "bases," formed from the metals. These two classes of compounds possess opposite characteristics, and unite readily to form the class of neutral compounds called salts.

In summarizing the conduct of matter we may distinguish the following types.

a. Direct union of the elements to form compounds; an example is the combustion of carbon in oxygen. $C + O_2 \rightarrow CO_2$.

b. The union of simple compounds to form more complex compounds, as the union of acids and bases to form salts.

Beyond these preliminary statements the subject must be postponed to a later place (Chapter XI) where it will be discussed in full.

The reader must be reminded that every chemical reaction is theoretically reversible. However, inasmuch as the conditions under which we usually work favor a given reaction, it is true that only one type of action takes place at a given time. At the beginning we will avoid any discussion of doubtful reactions.

CHAPTER III

THE STRUCTURE OF MATTER—MOLECULES
AND ATOMS

SULPHUR, water, and oxygen have been mentioned in connection with typical chemical reactions. They represent the three physical states of matter, the solid, liquid, and gaseous. From the standpoint of chemistry this difference is an incidental one, although we never lose sight of it. Chlorine, bromine, and iodine are three elements of very great chemical similarity, yet the first is a gas, the second a liquid, the third a solid. The physical state of any one of them may be more or less readily altered.

The minor influence, from the chemical standpoint, of the physical state is illustrated by water, the most important of all compounds. Whether we deal with it as ice, as liquid water, as gaseous water, *i. e.* steam, we must always consider it the same chemically, namely the compound composed of two parts of hydrogen and one of oxygen.

From the practical standpoint, there are often advantages in the liquid state. Substances in that form are handled more readily, and contacts with other substances are attained more easily. For this reason solutions either in water or in other solvents are frequently utilized. The gaseous condition, on the other hand, is the ideal condition for the study of the structure of matter, to which study we will now proceed.

17

If a gas is placed in an open vessel, it will be noticed that it spreads out in all directions, and presently diffuses to every portion of the room. If we are in the open, the diffusion goes on indefinitely. The gas may be heavy or light, the result is the same, although in the former case more time will be required. This diffusion will take place in spite of obstacles. As gases are not so familiar to the ordinary observer the illustration may be extended to include volatile liquids like ether or gasoline. As they readily pass over into gases they represent the same phenomenon. Gasoline is dangerous because of its great diffusibility. If left in one place, it may fill all the surrounding space with its vapor and thus produce the danger of accidental ignition.

What does this diffusibility mean? It is most readily explained by assuming that gases are made up of little particles, called molecules, all alike, independent of each other, moving about freely with energy enough to cause them to move on and away until they meet with some barrier. This molecular hypothesis offers such a satisfactory explanation of the conduct of gases that we do not need to inquire into the physical and mathematical confirmations which can be adduced. We will assume it without anything further, except a definite summary.

Gases are made up of large numbers of small molecules, far apart as compared with their actual size, moving rapidly and freely in straight lines until they meet with an impediment, when they take another direction. The pressure exerted by a gas is due to this molecular activity. When a gas is heated the molecular activity increases, when cooled it diminishes.

Liquids are readily converted into gases, and even before

they are thus converted, liquids show some properties similar to those of gases. Hence we must assume a somewhat similar structure for liquids. Gases are, roughly speaking, 500 times more diffused than the liquids from which they come. Hence it is evident that in liquids the molecules must be nearer together and their molecular activity less.

Solids are only slightly more compact than liquids, but their molecular activity must be appreciably less, as evidenced by their rigidity, and their slight tendency to give off vapor. That they possess molecular activity is evidenced by their expansion and contraction under the influence of temperature changes.

We may picture the molecular motion of a solid to be like that of people in a dense crowd. Motion is possible, but impeded in every direction. In a liquid the motion is like that of individuals in a thin crowd. Motion is rather free, but no individual can move far in any direction without meeting an obstacle. In gases the motion may be compared to that of a swarm of insects, each individual moving with great freedom and only occasionally meeting with another.

Molecules are very small. One cubic centimeter of a gas contains so many that their number is expressed by twenty figures. The common comparison of the magnified drop of water is useful for obtaining an impression of their size. If a drop of water were magnified to the size of the earth, the molecules would seem as large as baseballs. The speed of the molecules is very great. Those of hydrogen, the most rapid of all, move at the rate of about a mile a second. Others move more slowly, their speed being in the inverse ratio of the square roots of their molecular weights. Thus the oxygen molecule moves one-fourth as fast, and the chlorine one-sixth as fast as the molecule of hydrogen. When molecules meet an obstacle, either other molecules or a restraining wall, they rebound without loss of energy, that is, they are perfectly elastic. The pressure of a gas is due to the "bombardment" of these molecules against the confining walls. Heat increases the motion. From certain chemical and physical considerations it is clear that in equal volumes of all gases under similar conditions the number of molecules is the same.

The relation of molecular motion to heat is an intimate one. When a substance is heated the speed of motion of the molecules is increased, and when we subtract heat the speed of molecular motion is decreased. The increased speed of molecular motion causes the molecules to strike harder and more often against their neighbors and the gas expands. If expansion is resisted, the pressure exerted by the gas increases, for the pressure is caused by the many blows of these molecules striking against the restraining walls. The activity of the molecules of a liquid is less than that of the molecules of a gas. If we heat a liquid, the activity at once increases, and if we continue the heat, the liquid is finally converted into a gas. A solid has still lower molecular activity than liquids; upon heating this increases, the body expands, presently melts, and finally is converted into a gas. In bringing about these changes heat is converted into molecular motion; and if the changes are reversed the molecular motion is reconverted into heat in exactly equal measure. From all these considerations it is clear that heat and molecular motion are intimately associated, and are readily convertible, one into the other. Water as gas, as liquid, as solid, has always the same molecules, moving more or less freely. It is apparent that the molecule is constructed of simpler units, for by chemical means we are able to break it down. The smaller constituents of the molecules are the atoms, the real units for chemical considerations, as the molecules are for physical considerations. Two or more atoms of different elements unite to form one molecule, and chemical reactions are usually the reactions of the atoms. This has already been shown in our discussion of the combustion of carbon, sulphur, and hydrogen. The equation $C + 2O \rightarrow CO_2$ means that one atom of carbon unites with two atoms of oxygen to form one molecule of carbon dioxide. The equation $2H + O \rightarrow H_2O$ means similarly that two atoms of hydrogen unite with one of oxygen to form one molecule of water. We need some form of picture to make this real, so that devices like these are often used to represent the molecule of water.

$$\boxed{H|O|H}; \quad \boxed{H} - \boxed{O} - \boxed{H}; \quad H - O - H; \quad O\!\!<^H_H$$

These are simply more graphic representations of the formula H_2O. They should not be studied as an end in themselves, as they may not represent true pictures; but they are often so useful, particularly the last forms, that they are practically indispensable in our consideration of the structure of a molecule.

All matter is made up of molecules and the molecules in turn are made up of atoms. In the molecule of water there are two hydrogen atoms and one of oxygen. The molecule of carbon dioxide, CO_2, contains one carbon atom and two of oxygen, and so on. These facts about molecules apply to elements as well as to compounds, for the elements are also made up of molecules. The atoms making up such a molecule are always of the same kind. Two atoms to the molecule of an element is a frequent number, so that for oxygen the formula is not O, but O_2, indicating that in ordinary oxygen the molecules contain two atoms. Ozone is an unusual form of oxygen containing three atoms to the molecule, O_3.

In general, then, O_2 is the formula to be used to represent ordinary molecular oxygen, and the written equations must frequently be doubled in order to apply an even number of atoms for the molecule. The knowledge of this fact will be assumed as understood in the following pages, although it will often seem desirable to deviate from this correct practice for the sake of simplifying the illustrations used.

Physics and chemistry often approach each other closely. For our purpose we may assume that physics uses the molecule as its unit, while chemistry delves into the molecule, breaking it down and building it up, its unit in such cases being the atom. Naturally at many points chemistry must take cognizance of both considerations.

THERMOMETRY AND THE METRIC SYSTEM

In all scientific discussions it is desirable to use the universally adopted units of weights and measures instead of the English units. The confusion is unfortunate, but by frequent reference to the table of comparisons the inconvenience may be minimized.

The Fahrenheit scale in thermometry registers 180 degrees from the freezing point of water to its boiling point. The freezing point was set at 32 degrees above zero, for a reason which proved quite inadequate, so that we have the unusual numbers 32 degrees for freezing, and 212 degrees for the boiling point of water. The centigrade scale assumes the freezing point of water for its zero, and the boiling point for 100 degrees, a much more natural and simple arrangement for scientific work. The transference of a temperature from one scale to the other is not difficult. One degree Fahrenheit is 5/9 of 1 degree centigrade. The only confusion comes from the necessity of adding and subtracting the arbitrary 32 degrees of the Fahrenheit scale.

The metric system of weights and measures is based upon the standard meter, one ten-millionth part of the earth's quadrant at Paris, approximately 39.37 inches. All other units are derived from this by decimal multiplications and divisions. In simple chemical work only three sets of these measures are used.

Length. The meter, 39.37 inches = 10 decimeters (4 inches) = 100 centimeters (0.4 inch) = 1,000 millimeters (1/25 inch).

Volume. The liter is a cubic decimeter. It is equal to 1.06 quarts. 1 liter (L.) = 1,000 cubic centimeters (c. c.), about 1/16 cubic inch or 1/30 fluid ounce, virtually the same as the milliliter (ml).

Weight. The kilogram is the weight of 1 liter of water under standard conditions. Its weight is equal to 2.2 pounds. 1 kilogram (K.) = 1,000 grams, (g.) 1/28 ounce, or 15 grains.

The most used units are the cubic centimeter and the gram. With respect to water these are equal, but for all other liquids corrections must be applied to bring them into comparison.

CHAPTER IV

HYDROGEN, OXYGEN, AND WATER

ALTHOUGH oxygen is preëminent among the elements, it is expedient to devote our first study to hydrogen. It is the simplest of the elements in physical as well as in chemical properties, and it therefore lends itself well to an introductory study.

HYDROGEN

Hydrogen, abundant as it is in compounds, is not familiar as an element to anyone who has not performed a few chemical experiments, nor does it occur as an element in nature in any noticeable way. In combination, however, we find it in water, from which fact it received its name (water former). It is found in all animal and vegetable matter, which has assimilated hydrogen in the form of water. Hydrogen is found in petroleum combined with carbon. Finally, all acids contain hydrogen.

In all these compounds of hydrogen the presence of that element is only approximately apparent. One might say that gasoline seemed to contain hydrogen because it is gaseous and combustible, but hydrogen is not apparent in water or in acids, and we know of its presence there only by liberating it. In general, we may never be certain of an element in a compound judging merely from external appearances, although now and then we have some indications; lead is heavy and so are its compounds; magnesium is light, and so are its compounds. We must,

JOSEPH PRIESTLEY (1733-1804)
THE DISCOVERER OF OXYGEN

ANTOINE LAVOISIER (1743-1794)
THE FOUNDER OF MODERN CHEMISTRY

DIMITRI IVANOVITCH MENDELÉEFF (1834-1907)
THE AUTHOR OF PERIODIC CLASSIFICATION

(See page 187.)

however, always be cautious in drawing conclusions from such facts. When we say that water contains hydrogen, we must carefully distinguish this meaning from the meaning of such an expression as "the water contains salt." In the one case we mean that hydrogen is a constituent, in the other case that salt is a foreign substance not strictly related to the water.

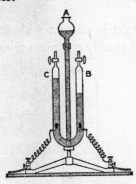

ELECTROLYSIS OF WATER

Water mixed with sulphuric acid is poured into the apparatus at A and the two arms B and C filled completely. When the current is passed, a gas is seen to pass from each of the electrodes and to collect above them. In a few minutes it will be seen that the one gas, hydrogen, is twice as abundant as the other gas, oxygen. The gases may be drawn off at the jets and tested.

In order to obtain hydrogen in a free state we need only to select a compound of hydrogen and decompose it. Water is the first to be considered and we find that water may readily be separated into hydrogen and oxygen by means of the electric current. In electricity, we constantly deal with the positive and negative conditions. Constituents of compounds are often found to be positive or negative when the compounds are in solution, and if the poles of a battery are introduced into the solution, these substances are attracted to the poles of opposite nature. Water is made up of positive hydrogen, and negative oxygen, and is therefore susceptible to electrical action. It can be electrolyzed, that is, decomposed by the current, and hydrogen will be liberated at the negative pole, and oxygen at the positive pole. A U-shaped tube keeps the two gases apart. Two volumes of hydrogen are liberated and one volume of oxygen, a fact suggested by the formula of water, H_2O.

If water is brought in contact with an active metal, as calcium, this metal readily combines with the oxygen, and

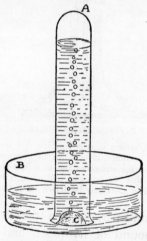

PREPARATION OF HYDROGEN BY THE ACTION OF CALCIUM ON WATER

The tube A is filled with water and inverted without loss of water in the dish B. When a piece of calcium C is placed in the water under the tube, action takes place and the liberated hydrogen rises in the tube, displacing the water.

the hydrogen is liberated and may be collected in any convenient way. This method is simple and clear, for not only is the hydrogen apparent, but the presence of the calcium oxide formed may readily be established.

The reaction is: $H_2O + Ca \rightarrow CaO + 2H$.

The most convenient manner of preparing hydrogen is by the treatment of an acid with a metal. Acids are made up of two parts, hydrogen and a nonmetallic part, and the latter tends to unite with active metals. Hence, when

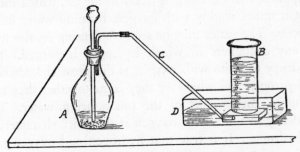

APPARATUS FOR GENERATING HYDROGEN AND OTHER GASES

Zinc in a convenient form (granulated) is placed in the flask A. It is covered with water, and sulphuric acid gradually added. The hydrogen is liberated from the acid, and on account of its great volume passes out of the flask and is collected by displacing the water from the inverted cylinder B. C is the delivery tube and the arrangement of D is called a pneumatic trough.

an acid is treated with a metal, it is decomposed; its non-metallic constituent unites with the metal to form a salt, while the hydrogen originally present is left in the un-combined state, and on account of its gaseous nature escapes from the liquid in bubbles. Zinc and sulphuric acid are the substances most used for preparing hydrogen. The zinc combines with the so-called sulphate, forming zinc sulphate, while the hydrogen is liberated. The zinc sulphate may be seen as a crystalline salt if the residue from the action is allowed to evaporate. As the gaseous hydrogen is liberated, it is conducted by tubes to inverted cylinders from which the air has been displaced by means of water. As the hydrogen enters, the water is driven out, and the cylinders are presently filled with the invisible hydrogen gas.

Hydrogen is a gas free from color and odor, not soluble in water and so light that it is used to fill balloons. It is not poisonous, but does not support life. When a flame is applied, hydrogen burns freely in the air, which means that it unites readily with oxygen, forming water in the process. The water may be seen condensing on the walls of any containers in which hydrogen is burned. This tendency to unite with oxygen is the great characteristic of hydrogen and whenever they come together they tend to unite, the product of the union being water. This tendency to unite with oxygen is the chief characteristic of hydrogen. It is true that hydrogen and oxygen may be brought together, both in a free state and in many compounds, without any interaction. When, however, an impulse is supplied, for example heat, the union may take place, in the case of the free elements, with great violence. Hence in all dealings with hydrogen its mixture with air must be handled with care so that it may not become ignited. Neglect of this precaution is a cause of many minor laboratory accidents. The mixture with pure oxygen is extremely dangerous and should be made only with the greatest precautions. Hydrogen is the lightest substance, not alone as a gas, but also in its atom. Consequently the relative weight of all atoms is referred to hydrogen in an approximate way. The most important relation of this kind is that between oxygen and hydrogen. The ratio is 15.879 to 1. But greater convenience is obtained by making the first number an even 16 and allowing the second to deviate from unity, so that the ratio really used is 16 to 1.008.

Oxygen

Oxygen received its name (acid former) from the fact that it is an important constituent of acids, yet some acids contain no oxygen. It is the most important of the elements. It makes up more than one-half of the earth's crust and enters into compounds in more important ways than any other element. In particular, it is found in the uncombined form, mixed with nitrogen, in the air. The presence of such a great mass of an active element can be explained only on the ground that it exists in excess, and is left over after all possible substances have united with it. A calculation of the amount of oxygen existing free in the atmosphere as compared with the amount in combination in water and the rocks of the earth's surface can be only speculative. It will show, however, that the existence of life on the earth (dependent as it is on free oxygen) is possible by only an exceedingly narrow margin.

Oxygen occurs in the combined state in water, and like hydrogen, in many plant and animal substances which are built up from water. So also many inorganic substances have water in their composition and hence contain oxygen. There are many oxides, both natural and artificial, which of course contain oxygen.

Oxygen makes up about 50 per cent of the great mass of the earth's crust. Its abundance will be illustrated by the following representative list.

Weight per cent

The atmosphere	23
Water	89
Quartz	55
Granitic rocks, about	50

Organic material	Weight per cent
Carbohydrates, about	50
Proteins, about	16
Fats	3-4

Oxygen may be prepared readily enough on a small scale by heating certain compounds which contain oxygen and decompose rather readily. Potassium chlorate is the best for laboratory purposes, and the liberation of the oxygen is facilitated by the presence of manganese dioxide.

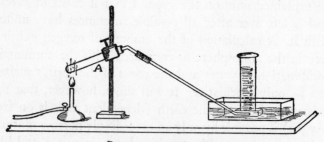

PREPARATION OF OXYGEN

Potassium chlorate mixed with manganese dioxide is heated in the brass tube A. The gas passes off as it is generated, and is collected in the usual manner by passing into inverted cylinders from which the air has been displaced by water.

The oxygen is collected in the same way as is hydrogen, over water.

A method of no practical value, but of historical interest, is that of heating mercuric oxide, which decomposes simply into mercury and oxygen.

$$HgO \rightarrow Hg + O$$

It is by this experiment that Priestly discovered oxygen, in 1774, a discovery which gave Lavoisier the clue to the process of combustion, and laid the foundations of modern chemistry.

Oxygen is required by the industries on a large scale, and is prepared more economically by other methods than those mentioned above. These are described in the chapter on industrial chemistry. The source of oxygen in these methods is either air or water.

Oxygen is a colorless, odorless gas, only slightly soluble in water. We must carefully distinguish between the oxygen which is a constituent of water, and which ceases to show the properties of oxygen, and the gaseous oxygen which is in actual solution. If ordinary cold water is gently heated, it will be noted presently that small bubbles appear, which consist of the air, partly oxygen, which has been in solution in the water. Water dissolves some oxygen. The amount is small, approximately 1 per cent by volume, but it is of practical moment in that it is enough to supply fish life, and, under conditions not too unfavorable, to cause the oxidation of impurities which find their way into water.

Chemically the properties of oxygen are very striking. Anything which burns in air will burn much more brilliantly in oxygen because there is no diluting action due to the nitrogen. Sulphur, charcoal, phosphorus, magnesium, even iron, will burn in oxygen with a brilliant display. Oxygen unites directly or indirectly with almost every element, forming oxides, which are usually important substances. As it will unite with single elements, as carbon or sulphur, so it will unite with combinations of such elements, as carbon disulphide, CS_2. The process of respiration, in animal life, brings about the union of oxygen with the carbon and hydrogen originally supplied by foods. With hydrogen or gaseous hydrocarbons it unites so readily that, when a mixture is ignited, there is a very violent explosion.

Liquid oxygen has ceased to be a rarity. It is of a pale blue color. Because of its highly concentrated form, it must be handled with precautions, as it supports combustion with violence.

Ozone is a modified form of oxygen. The ordinary oxygen molecule contains two atoms, but the ozone molecule contains three, this being indicated by O_2 and O_3 respectively. Ozone is exceedingly active, not because it contains more oxygen, but because it tends to pass over into ordinary oxygen, $O_3 \rightarrow O_2 + O$, thus liberating an oxygen atom, which is oxygen in its most reactive form.

WATER

Among all the compounds which elements form, water is preëminent. It is not only very abundant, but is physical and chemical properties are such that it concerns a large number of phenomena in which we have the greatest interest. It would not be too much to say that its properties control the progress of chemical reaction, not alone as applied to ordinary chemistry, but as applied to the chemistry of living things, both plant and animal, and we may add to this the influence exerted by water in geological ways, in physiography and geography, and the combined influence of all these on human life.

The *physical properties* of water are exceptional. It is one of few inorganic liquids, and a liquid medium is best suited for chemical reactions, whether in the laboratory or in living organisms. It is liquid within narrow limits, $0°$ to $100°C.$, or $32°$ to $212°$ F. It has great solvent action, especially for inorganic compounds. On organic compounds this action is limited, but those that have a chemical relation to water, such as the alcohols and organic acids, are soluble. This great solvent power of water is very important in chemical reactions. The saying of the early chemists that substances do not react except when in solution can hardly be considered strictly correct, but it is full of suggestion. Solution is important even when it is very slight, as in the case of marble, which reacts readily with acids when water is present. Ionic reactions, a set of reactions of the utmost importance, are dependent upon solution in water.

In other respects the physical properties of water are outstanding. It has the highest specific heat, that is, ability to absorb heat, of all substances. This influences such facts as the tempering of climates by the Gulf Stream, and enables water to be used to advantage in heating and cooling. It counts in the equalization of the temperature of the animal body. The capillarity of water also is high, illustrated by its rising in the soil from the water table below, to supply plants with moisture.

Latent heat. When a liquid is converted into a gas, or a solid into a liquid, there is a marked increase in the activity of the molecules. This means an increase of energy, which comes from without, in the form of heat. Hence a liquid boiling away, or even evaporating slowly, or a solid melting, absorbs heat from its surroundings. In the reverse processes this heat is given out again. The heat thus absorbed or given out by the change in molecular activity seems to be hidden, or latent, as ice water and the ice from which it is formed are both at 0°C. So also water ready to pass into steam, and the steam rising from it are both at 100°. These statements are amplifications of the discussion in a previous chapter of the relation between heat and molecular motion. All substances show this phenomenon of latent heat, but among them water stands very high, another fact important in the function of water in equalizing temperature.

Other physical properties. Water contracts irregularly upon cooling. After reaching 4°C., it expands, and upon passing into ice, this expansion is so marked that the ice is lighter than water and floats. This irregularity, as yet unexplained, is of the greatest importance in nature, for it results in such conditions in bodies of water that only the upper layers freeze solid in winter, and with the varying seasons the important circulation due to changing temperatures is increased.

A number of physical properties of water remain still to be mentioned. We usually say that it is colorless, odorless, and tasteless. Water in large masses has a distinct blue color particularly noticeable in ice. The color of seas and lakes involves other features, not altogether satisfactorily explained. Pure water seems to have a flat taste, due perhaps to the dilution of the saliva, or to the lack of taste ordinarily associated with drinking water.

The *chemical properties* of water are as outstanding as are the physical. Three types of chemical reaction involving water may be mentioned, in addition to the action on substances which we ordinarily call solution. Solution is in some respects so important that it requires special treatment.

Water of crystallization. Many substances form compounds with water in which each portion seems to preserve its individuality, yet both are merged into one. In such cases the combination has a definite crystalline form, and at times another color. If the water is removed, which may easily be done, both crystalline form and color are changed. A striking example of this is copper sulphate. This is a white powder, its formula, $CuSO_4$. When water is added to it, it forms beautiful blue crystals, known as "blue vitriol." The formula of these is $CuSO_4 \cdot 5H_2O$.

Water of chemical union. The more active oxides of metals and of nonmetals unite readily with water. Two examples will illustrate. Calcium oxide unites readily with water to form calcium hydroxide. $CaO + H_2O \rightarrow Ca(OH)_2$. This is the once familiar operation called slaking of lime. Again water unites greedily with sulphur trioxide to form sulphuric acid, $SO_3 + H_2O \rightarrow H_2SO_4$. In these cases the union is an intimate one and both constituents lose their identity, yet water has entered into the compound and can be extracted therefrom. In the case of the metallic oxides the substances called bases are formed, in case of the nonmetallic oxides, the acids, both compounds of the utmost importance.

Hydrolysis. Water forms many combinations with certain double compounds, in that the hydroxyl portion,— OH, of the water unites with one constituent, and the hydrogen with the other. The double compound is thus cleft in two, and the term *hydrolysis* (cleaving by means of water) is applied to this operation. In the upbuilding of plant and animal material, and in the digestive process, this relation is of very common occurrence.

Water by itself is rather stable, as is evidenced by its great abundance. It can be decomposed into its elements, hydrogen and oxygen, by the electric current and by excessive heat. Certain elements unite with the hydrogen, others with the oxygen, each liberating the other constituent. Finally, water is somehow decomposed in building up animal and vegetable tissue, so that often the hydrogen and oxygen are completely separated.

The *composition* of water has been determined with the greatest care, as the ratio of the oxygen to the hydrogen therein is the most important ratio of chemistry. It was formerly supposed that the oxygen was exactly 8 times as heavy as the hydrogen, and since the hydrogen is double, one unit or atom of oxygen would be 16 times as heavy as the single unit of hydrogen. This has been shown to be only approximately correct. The ratio is 15.879 to 1. So far as the volume relations go, it has been clearly established that the two parts of hydrogen and the one part of oxygen obtained when water is electrolyzed, mean that the water molecule is made up of two atoms of hydrogen held together by one atom of oxygen, a condition represented by the formula H-O-H.

Ordinary potable waters contain a number of foreign substances, which in ideal cases are really advantageous. These are firstly the gaseous constituents. One liter of Lake Erie water contains about 30 c. c., that is 3 volume per cent of gases. Of this about 1/20 is carbon dioxide, 1/3 oxygen, and the rest nitrogen. So far as taste and safety go these are advantageous. In fact the oxygen is the first essential for the purification of water. And this small amount is enough for waters which are not seriously defiled. Ordinary waters contain a number of solid substances, most commonly salt, acid calcium carbonate (lime), calcium sulphate, and corresponding magnesium compounds. These, in amounts not excessive, seem to be harmless, and in the opinion of many improve the flavor, though this is a matter of usage. Those used to hard waters consider the taste of soft water flat, while those used to soft waters find that the hard waters have a metallic taste. There is organic matter present, due to contact with vegetation, leaf mold and such substances. This is not in itself bad, unless the organic matter is excessive or contains dangerous bacteria. Bacterial, not chemical, pollution is the ordinary danger which menaces water supplies. Sanitary purification has for its object the removal of disease germs and turbidity, and seldom affects the mineral matter actually in solution.

The above picture of hydrogen, its relation to oxygen and the nature of water may be accepted as representing the facts ordinarily observed in our experiences. However, even at this early stage of our study an account of heavy hydrogen, indicated by D, and of heavy water, D_2O, should be included.

Heavy water. A sensational discovery of recent years has been that of hydrogen of atomic weight two, and consequently of its compound with oxygen, D_2O, deuterium oxide, heavy water. The separation of this heavy portion of hydrogen and of water is by tedious processes of fractional evaporation and electrolysis, by which the lighter portions are allowed to progressively escape or to be decomposed. A convenient source of the water has been from the cells in which water has been electrolyzed (for the manufacture of hydrogen and oxygen) for a long period of time, with frequent additions of fresh water, while the residues in the cells were never emptied, so that the heavy water accumulated. This heavy water differs only slightly from ordinary water, and has a slightly higher boiling and freezing point. The interest in these discoveries lies in part in the more accurate knowledge of long known common substances, and in part in the fact that both deuterium and heavy water, being in a sense marked as distinguishable substances, lend themselves to the solution of many chemical and biochemical questions.

Hydrogen Peroxide. Besides water, hydrogen and oxygen form another compound, hydrogen peroxide, H_2O_2. It contains in its molecule a second atom of oxygen, which is very readily split off, with the formation of a residue of water. This represents the most interesting feature of this compound, for the oxygen thus liberated is in an active form, and is effective in bleaching and disinfecting.

CHAPTER V

CARBON AND ITS COMPOUNDS

CARBON, like hydrogen and oxygen, is met with frequently. Both as an element and in compounds it is connected with innumerable substances in common use, and its chemistry is part of the familiar happenings of everyday life. Carbon is very abundant in nature, occurring in the free state in diamond, graphite, and in anthracite coal. (The various forms of soft coal are probably intricate compounds of carbon and hydrogen, high in carbon content, and despite their black color containing no free carbon.) In combination it is found in carbon dioxide, a gas found in small amounts in the atmosphere, and frequent in emanations from the ground, either as the pure gas or mixed with water. Carbon dioxide is a constituent of the very abundant limestone rock. Petroleum is a mixture of compounds of carbon and hydrogen. All organic matter has carbon as its basis, as is apparent from the fact that, when charred, the black carbon may be observed. Carbon forms so many compounds of this last type that we must devote an entire subdivision of our subject, Organic Chemistry, to their study.

The *diamond* has a number of points of scientific interest. It has a distinct crystalline form, is exceedingly hard, refracts light brilliantly, and in the end is simply made up of carbon. Further, human appreciation of an object so beautiful and so rare has put this gem in a class by itself. The qualities which make it valuable are its beauty, its durability, and its rarity. One feature of its beauty is the above mentioned high refracting power, and stones are cut in order to bring out this quality. Its great hardness makes the diamond valuable industrially for cutting glass and stone, for which of course imperfect diamonds are selected.

The second crystalline form of carbon is *graphite,* well known as the "lead" of pencils, also called black lead and plumbago when powdered. It is often confused with lead by the unthinking, but there is no relation between them. The name graphite, "to write," refers to the quality of making a mark upon paper. Graphite is slippery to the feel, and is used as a lubricant. Its permanence—for, in spite of the fact that it consists of carbon, it burns with the greatest difficulty—enables it to be used for such purposes as stove blacking and crucibles. In recent years graphite has been made from ordinary carbon by the high temperature of the electric furnace.

That the diamond and graphite are really composed of carbon can be clearly established. Each form can be converted into the other form: even minute diamonds have been prepared from ordinary carbon. All three forms are converted into carbon dioxide upon heating in oxygen, the product being absolutely the same in each case.

This is only one of a number of instances in which we find one element appearing in a number of different forms. Such forms are called allotropic forms, and the relation between them is called allotropy. Oxygen and ozone offer such an illustration, and the various forms of phosphorus and sulphur offer others. The explanation of this is not known certainly, except in the case of ozone.

The forms of ordinary carbon are endlessly more interesting than the diamond or graphite. They consist of coal, and artificial forms, as charcoal and coke. To understand the nature of these we will study the changes involved in the making of charcoal and apply what we learn there to the coal deposits of nature.

Charcoal is derived from wood, the chemical material of which may be represented by the formula $C_6H_{10}O_5$. If we heat wood out of contact with the air, so that there will be no burning, we will gradually drive off the gaseous constituents, hydrogen and oxygen, although in the process a considerable amount of carbon escapes in combination with them. But the bulk of the carbon will be left as the black solid, called charcoal, free from the gaseous elements of the original wood.

Coal. Let us apply a similar process of reasoning to the great coal deposits of nature. Coal comes from wood tissue much as charcoal is derived in the above operation from wood, by removal of the gaseous constituents. This has taken place in the absence of air, under the influence of pressure and heat perhaps, and through long intervals of time. In the case of hard coal, or anthracite, the process is almost complete, and besides the ash (purely foreign earthy material) there is little besides carbon present. Other forms of coal may be considered intermediate between the original wood and the final anthracite. The series of products formed strikingly shows this increasing carbonization. The steps which may serve to illustrate the gradual change are: wood, 50 per cent carbon; peat, 55 per cent; lignite, 73 per cent; bituminous coal 84 per cent; anthracite, 93 per cent. Each substance represents a decrease in the gaseous constituents, and a corresponding increase in the carbon remaining. Peat plainly shows the original fiber from which it was formed, and lignite is so called because it often preserves the woody structure. There are large deposits of lignite, not so desirable as coal, but available when the coal supplies become exhausted. In the various forms of coal proper, the external resemblance to the original wood is obliterated.

Coke. For many purposes, particularly the extraction of iron from its ores, soft coal is unusable because of its gaseous constituents and its softening upon being heated. These defects are remedied by the preliminary conversion of the coal into coke. Coking coal is the same process as charring wood. By applying heat, the gaseous constituents, much hydrogen, some oxygen, and small portions of nitrogen are expelled, along with a considerable amount of carbon which escapes in combination with them. The coke is the residual carbon and contains the original ash of the coal. Coke is in a sense an artificial hard coal, though less compact, and serves many of the purposes of the latter.

The coke-making process has another interest besides the production of coke. The gases thus expelled are in part permanent, and in part can be condensed to liquids. The permanent gases, when properly handled, form illuminating gas, while the condensed products form coal tar. Further, among these products there is formed a considerable amount of a nitrogen compound, ammonia, NH_3. It will be seen presently that nitrogen compounds are of unique importance, and should be preserved in every way possible. Coke making, then, has these three classes of by-products, gas, tar, and ammonia, and in the cruder methods of making coke they are wasted, as they are allowed to burn with no advantage but to get rid of them. The tendency to save these has increased in recent years and this is done in the by-product coke ovens.

The greatest use of carbon in the form of coal or coke is for fuel, the burning of which converts the chemical energy into heat, by uniting the coal with oxygen. This affinity for oxygen results in another great use of carbon, the extraction of the metals. Many metals occur in their ores in the form of oxides. Hematite, the famous lake ore of iron, is iron oxide, Fe_2O_3. To obtain the iron the oxygen must be removed, and heating with carbon, usually in the form of coke, serves this purpose best. A few other uses of carbon may be mentioned. *Lampblack*, made by partial combustion of compounds rich in carbon is used as a black pigment in paints and inks. It is very durable, as at low temperatures carbon is not affected by any ordinary reagents. *Bone black* and *charcoal* are very porous, and are used for absorbents. The most striking case of this is the use of charcoal from certain sources in gas masks. The porous carbon is very efficacious in absorbing poison gases. *Gas-black*, a form of carbon obtained by the partial combustion of natural gas, has been serviceable in improving the quality of rubber tires.

Smoke. When hard coal burns the reaction is simple. The carbon simply unites with the oxygen of the air supplied to the fire. Carbon dioxide is formed and passes out at the flue. The ash is inert mineral matter which is accidentally present, and which is not affected by the burning of the coal. When soft coal is burned the operation is much more complex. When this coal is first placed upon the fire, the heat of the fire expels the hydrogen and oxygen still remaining in the coal, along with some carbon, and these escape as gases. As soon as they escape they become ignited and burn. As they burn, however, they are not likely to meet with a sufficiency of oxygen and in addition they are cooled. Then the hydrogen in these gases burns by preference and the carbon is liberated as soot. The prevention of the formation of soot or smoke is accomplished by the avoidance of either one of the conditions which result in smoke, namely gas formation and partial combustion. If a fuel is used containing no gaseous constituent, such as hard coal or coke, there can be no smoke, as the carbon never assumes a finely divided form. Again, when a gas-containing fuel is used, the liberated gas, as it begins to burn, is caused to meet with enough oxygen (in the air), so that it will burn as a whole and no carbon be deposited. In practice, excess of oxygen is obtained by diminishing the amount of gas liberated at any one time. This is in its turn accomplished by means of mechanical stokers, which feed the coal into the fires very gradually. Each small installment of coal gives off no more gas than can be entirely consumed before another portion of gas is supplied.

COMPOUNDS OF CARBON

The first compound of carbon to engage our attention is *carbon dioxide*. This has been mentioned repeatedly as the product formed when carbon unites with sufficient oxygen. It occurs in the atmosphere to the extent of about 0.03 per cent, a seemingly small amount, but corresponding to a weight of 10 to 12 tons over every acre of land. Lime water exposed to the air soon shows the presence of carbon dioxide by its milky appearance. Carbon dioxide may be formed by burning carbon in air or oxygen. The latter method is practically unavailable on account of the cost of oxygen. The former has a serious defect in that four parts of nitrogen are mixed with every one part of oxygen in the air. Hence this method is used only when the admixture of nitrogen does no harm. The usual method is the treatment of carbonates, like those of calcium and magnesium, with an acid.

Carbon dioxide is a colorless gas, half again as heavy as air, in small quantities odorless, but if a full breath is taken, an odor will be distinctly noticeable. It is so soluble in water, especially under pressure, that it forms carbonated waters, which have a pleasant acid taste.

Carbon dioxide in the atmosphere. Carbon dioxide is liberated from the earth in many places, especially in springs as at Saratoga, and Apollinaris, near the Rhine. Others sources by which the carbon dioxide in the air may be increased are by respiration of animals, fermentation, combustion, and decay. Withdrawal is by plant assimilation, and absorption when rock disintegrates. The carbon dioxide in the animal shells which are converted into solid rock is permanently withdrawn from the atmosphere. The influence on climate of varying amounts of carbon dioxide in the air is a much debated question. It is said that larger amounts would cause the air to become a better blanket for preserving the warmth which the earth receives from the sun. A complete loss of carbon dioxide would eliminate the possibility of life on the earth. Within the range of men's study no appreciable differences have yet been observed.

Carbon dioxide in the air brings up the question of the carbon cycle in nature. Plants are capable of absorbing this substance, and by means of the energy absorbed from the sun, to split off the oxygen, which is thus returned to the air. The carbon is built up into the plant tissue of which starch and cellulose are the most typical. We may assume that in this compound the hydrogen and oxygen balance each other, so that all the chemical energy of this substance lies in the carbon. When the animal consumes this compound for food, the carbon is burned by the respiration process and forms carbon dioxide, which is exhaled into the atmosphere. The cycle is now complete, and is repeated indefinitely. $CO_2 \rightarrow C$ of plant tissue→animal food→CO_2.

Carbon dioxide has considerable application and is made in large quantities. Its first use is for carbonated beverages. It has a pleasant taste, and being more soluble under pressure, the gas escapes when this pressure is relieved. Carbon dioxide is the leavening gas liberated in dough, either by the fermentation by yeast or by baking powders. Its importance in this case is solely because it can be conveniently generated as wanted.

Solid carbon dioxide has been known for many years, but only recently has it become a common refrigerating agent. The refrigeration is due to the rapid volatilization of the solid carbon dioxide, which has been produced, like liquid air, by modern engineering methods. As with other refrigerants, its efficiency is based upon physical properties, namely the ready passage from a state of low molecular activity to that of a higher state, the gas. Chemistry, however, is concerned with the sources of the carbon dioxide, and its harmless nature as it passes off as the gas. The dry ice industry represents an almost unique feature in that the combustion of carbon serves two purposes, the preparation of a desired compound and the utilization of the energy derived from the heat in solidifying the gas.

Carbon dioxide cannot burn, as it already contains all the oxygen with which it can combine. Nor do common substances burn in it, as the oxygen is so firmly held by the carbon that it will not separate from it to join other substances. With water it forms a very weak acid, called carbonic acid, but the combination is so unstable that it is problematical whether it really exists. By virtue of its nature as a nonmetallic oxide, it combines readily with the more active metallic oxides, in the presence of water, forming the so-called carbonates.

Carbon monoxide, CO, is another compound of carbon and oxygen. It is formed when carbon unites with an insufficient amount of oxygen. The conditions for its formation are especially favorable in charcoal, coke, and hard coal fires, and the blue flame playing over the top of these fires is due to the final burning of the carbon monoxide formed in the lower layers. It is a poisonous gas and causes many accidents. An especial illustration is the presence of carbon monoxide in the exhaust gases of the automobile engine and consequent danger of poisonous action when in confined spaces. The question of a dangerous accumulation in city streets has not yet been satisfactorily answered. Its greatest interest to the chemist is on account of certain general principles illustrated by its relation to the more common dioxide. The dioxide is the normal compound, formed by the complete satisfying of the affinities between carbon and oxygen. In the monoxide these affinities are only partially satisfied. Hence the monoxide tends to unite with more oxygen to form the dioxide. This is the reason why it burns. The explanation of its poisonous action is also connected with this condition. Normally the red blood corpuscles must unite with oxygen to carry this gas to the tissues. When carbon monoxide is inhaled, it attaches itself to the red corpuscles, on account of its unsatisfied condition, and makes so firm a combination that they can no longer function with oxygen.

The hydrocarbons. Carbon unites with hydrogen to form about two thousand compounds. There is no comparable set of compounds among other elements, and this unusual variability of composition lies at the basis of the broad field of organic chemistry. The many combinations between the two elements are due to three kinds of variation.

1. There is a difference in the proportions of hydrogen and carbon present in the molecule. Such differences are shown by two sets of comparisons, C_2H_2, C_2H_4, C_2H_6, and the series CH_4, C_2H_6, C_3H_8, C_4H_{10}.

2. In some cases the proportions of carbon and hydrogen are the same, but the actual size of the molecules differs. Such a case is that of acetylene, C_2H_2, a gas, and benzene, C_6H_6, a liquid. The two compounds differ greatly in their chemical characteristics.

3. The molecules are of the same complexity, but within the molecule there are subtle variations. In a complex molecule like $C_{10}H_{16}$, it is conceivable that there might be many arrangements of the carbon and hydrogen, each arrangement resulting in a different compound. Such differences of arrangement occur, and each form shows some difference from the others, although this difference may not be great.

Illustrations of these hydrocarbons are common. Marsh gas, methane, CH_4, is a constitutent of natural gas. The individual constituents of gasoline, kerosene, paraffin, turpentine and coal tar benzenes, commonly called benzols, are examples. They are gases, liquids or solids, depending upon the complexity of the molecule; C_2H_2, acetylene, is a gas: C_6H_6, benzene, is a liquid; $C_{10}H_8$, naphthalene, is a solid. They are all colorless, many have noticeable odors, and they are insoluble in water. The great value of many of them lies in their combustibility, particularly in their being converted into gases just before burning, gasoline in carburetors, kerosene and paraffin at the tips of wicks. The liquids and solids are conveniently handled, and the gaseous condition is obtained as wanted. The benzenes have a value as being the raw materials from which coal tar products are prepared.

Organic Chemistry, to which considerable attention will be given later, is the study of these hydrocarbons and their derivatives. They form these derivatives in endless variety, by the substitution of other elements for the hydrogen. When the substituting element is a halogen, we have such compounds as chloroform and iodoform; when it is oxygen, we have the alcohols, aldehydes, and organic acids, the sugars, fats, and countless other compounds. The introduction of nitrogen gives aniline, and with many complications the important proteins.

CHAPTER VI

COMBUSTION AND ITS ACCOMPANIMENTS

COMBUSTION is only one special form of union between two substances. Our conception of a substance burning is that as it burns it gives out heat and exhibits a glowing mass. The two occurrences are intimately associated, as the glow is simply the result of the heat. We may say, then, that combustion is the union of two substances, with so great a development of heat that these substances glow. Inasmuch as one of the substances is usually oxygen, we may restate our propostion thus: ordinary combustion is the union of a substance with oxygen, with so great a development of heat that the substance glows. It may be more crudely stated thus: combustion is the union of two substances accompanied by heat and light.

We know that a fire must be "started." This means that the chemical union does not take place until the substances involved are heated. The intensity of heat required varies considerably. Phosphorus ignites when heated to a temperature just above lukewarm, and this is one reason why it is so dangerous as well as so useful. Sulphur will ignite from a small spark, carbon must be heated to a glow before it burns, and magnesium must be heated still more. We see then that before a substance burns it must be raised to a certain temperature, varying for different substances. This is called the kindling temperature.

An important factor in the readiness with which substances ignite is the size of the portion of substance which is heated. A needle and a bar of iron are of the same material, but the former is so small that when placed in a flame it is quickly raised to the temperature

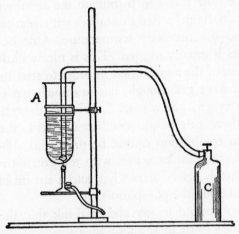

BURNING PHOSPHORUS UNDER WATER

Phosphorus may be burned under water when the three conditions of combustion are met. The water in A is heated to the kindling temperature of the phosphorus, and oxygen from the cylinder C is passed down through the water. The phosphorus burns readily.

of its surroundings. With the same amount of heat applied the iron bar will be heated only slowly. Therefore a shaving, presenting a small mass for heating, will ignite more quickly than the block of wood from which it is cut. Magnesium ribbon ignites readily, a block of magnesium can be set on fire only with great difficulty. This idea applies particularly to gases. On account of their fine state of division a small portion is easily heated to the kindling temperature. A burning match plunged into kerosene will be extinguished, but if the kerosene is first converted to a gas, the burning match will ignite it. One great danger of gasoline lies in this circumstance. It passes off as a gas readily, and hence is in the fine state of division favorable to ignition.

We are now ready to formulate the requirements for combustion, namely, two substances with affinity for each other and the necessary temperature. One of the two substances is usually oxygen. This is nicely illustrated by the maxim of the autoist, that in order to start his engine, "he must have gas enough, not too much gas (meaning enough oxygen) and a spark." Without these three conditions there can be no combustion, with these three conditions combustion cannot be prevented. Phosphorus may be burned under water, with the greatest readiness, if the water is heated somewhat, and a stream of oxygen is directed upon the phosphorus.

It is our custom to say and to think that the various combustibles burn in the air. In a practical way this is true, because ordinarily the air surrounds the burning object, but in strict truth both substances are uniting and are equally related to the action. By a little ingenuity air can be made to burn in an atmosphere of illuminating gas quite as readily as the gas will burn in the air.

Spontaneous combustion is caused by the gradual development of heat, due to some chemical change, and the accumulation of this heat until the kindling temperature is reached. Linseed oil combines with oxygen spontaneously, and in doing so develops heat. Cloths soaked in linseed oil thus expose a favorable surface to the action of the oxygen of the air. If these are somewhat closely massed, so that the heat due to the oxidation of the oil cannot be dissipated, the conditions for spontaneous combustion are ideal. The heat developed by the initial oxidation accelerates further oxidation, thus progressively

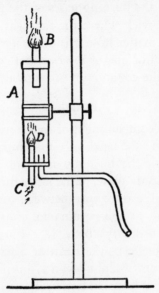

EXPERIMENT FOR SHOWING THAT, IN THE COMBUSTION OF A GAS, THE UNION OF THE GAS AND OXYGEN IS MUTUAL

The cylinder A is kept filled with gas, which, passing through the tube B, is lighted. By using some care the upward current of air, entering at C, may be made to burn at D. In the upper flame, gas is burning in air; in the lower flame, air is burning in gas.

developing more and more heat until the whole is raised to a temperature sufficiently high for the mass to burst into a blaze.

All the methods of extinguishing combustion illustrate these three conditions. The shutting off of air by smothering a fire concerns the oxygen. Water cools the burning body. Cooling is often accomplished by pulling a fire to pieces, when the loss of heat, due to radiation, exceeds the rate of heating due to the burning. Blowing out a candle flame is successful in part because of cooling, but mainly because the burning gases of the flame are blown away from the wick where the new gas supply is being generated. No matter how it is done, it will be seen that it is the removal of one of the essential conditions which is the cause of the cessation of the combustion.

FLAME

A frequent accompaniment of combustion is flame. To understand flame we need only to compare the burning of charcoal with the burning of wood. In the former case there is a steady glow, in the latter the lambent flame. We know that the difference between the two materials is simply in the gaseous content of the wood. We see therefore that ordinary flame is a burning gas. The burning of kerosene in the form of a flame is preceded by its gasification. Sulphur which burns with a flame vaporizes before it burns. Hard coal often shows a flame, which is due to the burning of the gaseous carbon monoxide formed before the final combustion. Unless a gas is present the combustion takes the form, as in charcoal, of a steady glow.

The simplest flame is that of burning hydrogen. It shows a conical form, the interior of the cone consisting of the hydrogen emerging from the jet, the rest of the cone consisting of the burning hydrogen, glowing on account of the heat liberated. If we now consider a flame of ordinary illuminating gas, composed of carbon and hydrogen, we see that the flame is more complex. In the interior is a region of unaffected gases. On the exterior

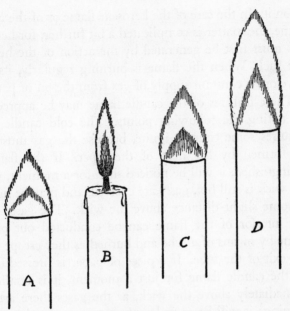

A COMPARISON OF FLAMES

A, the hydrogen flame. The inner cone represents hydrogen not yet burning, the outer cone the hydrogen in the process of burning. B, the candle flame, which is similar to the flame from burning oil. The brown inner region represents gases which have not yet begun to burn. The luminous portion is the cone of partial combustion luminous on account of the glowing carbon. At the bottom and around the entire flame is the region of complete combustion, shown by the blue flame which in the upper regions is difficult to distinguish. C, the ordinary gas flame, essentially the same as B. D, the Bunsen flame, in which the middle zone of partially burning gases is eliminated.

is a region, inconspicuous, of complete combustion, where everything is finally combined with oxygen. Between is a region wherein the combustion is partial. The hydrogen burns, leaving the carbon for a moment in a free condition, and it is the glow of this free carbon which makes the flame luminous. If a cold object is placed in this middle region, some of the unburned carbon will be deposited upon it. In the case of the kerosene flame or of the candle flame, the matter is complicated a bit further, for here the gas must first be generated by the action of the heat on the fuel. When the flame is burning regularly, its heat develops a constant supply of gas from the oil or paraffin.

These features of the candle flame may be appreciated by noting the following points. The cold candle wick requires some time to ignite, because the gas must first be formed by the heat of the taper. If the flame is extinguished, it will be noticed that, for a moment, while the wick is still hot, gases are evolved, and may be lighted at some slight distance above the wick. The gases from the interior of the flame can be conducted out of the flame by means of a tube and burned as they escape from the exit of the tube. If a piece of paper is pressed down on the candle flame for just a moment, it is unaffected immediately above the wick, as the gases there are not burning; it will be coated with soot immediately around this, on account of the free carbon in the middle region; it will be charred in a circle due to the heat from the combustion, mostly in the outer region.

LUMINOSITY OF FLAME

The luminosity of a flame is ordinarily due to the glowing of a solid. In ordinary flame the solid is carbon, liberated for an instant from its compound before it is burned to carbon dioxide. Hydrogen burns with a nonluminous flame, as there is no solid present. Methane (natural gas), CH_4, includes a proportion of carbon too small to give much luminosity. The same is true of the two alcohols, wood and grain, CH_4O and C_2H_6O, which are used for fuel for special purposes just because they

MADAME CURIE, WHO, WITH HER HUSBAND, DISCOVERED RADIUM IN 1898

AIRLINER *HINDENBURG*, FILLED WITH THE INFLAMMABLE GAS HYDROGEN, WAS DESTROYED BY FIRE WHEN
ABOUT TO MOOR AT LAKEHURST, N. J., MAY 6, 1937

liberate little carbon. Acetylene, C_2H_2, on the other hand, has so large a proportion of carbon that it burns with a brilliantly luminous flame. Any gas which is to be used directly for illuminating purposes, if not already rich in carbon, must be enriched by the introduction of compounds high in carbon content. The modern solution of this problem, however, is the introduction of the mantle, made of certain metallic oxides. The gas is burned with an abundance of air, the flame being virtually a Bunsen flame, and very hot, all the energy of the fuel being directed to the development of heat. The light is obtained by the glowing of the mantle, the whole arrangement being more or less ideal, if only the mantles were not so fragile. The magnesium light owes its brightness to the glowing of the magnesium oxide formed.

A common form of electric lighting, the filament, owes its efficiency to the glowing solid. The fundamental difference is in this case that the glow is induced by physical means, the resistance to the current. Illumination by the chemical means of combustion has taken a very secondary place in compact communities.

THE BUNSEN FLAME

The Bunsen flame owes its efficiency to the introduction of a current of air at the base of the burner. The reaction of the ordinary gas flame is, as was shown above, divided into two steps, with consequent spreading out of the flame and of the heat effect. The air introduced in the Bunsen burner results in the elimination of the middle region of the flame, so that the gas burns at once, with a smaller flame, and the heating effect is concentrated in time and space. The result is a smaller, hotter flame, which does not deposit carbon. The difference when the air holes are closed is apparent at once. The Bunsen burner is probably the most useful piece of chemical apparatus which we possess and is adapted to gas burners, even oil burners, in a variety of forms.

COMBUSTION OF ELEMENTS AND COMPOUNDS

When an element burns, it unites with oxygen. When a compound burns, each element present unites with oxygen. Carbon disulphide in burning forms carbon dioxide and sulphur dioxide. Methane burning forms carbon dioxide and water. The combustion may be interfered with, as happens so often in the case of carbon and hydrogen compounds, by lack of oxygen or by cooling. But if these conditions do not apply, all the elements are completely oxidized. When an element is present which has a low affinity for oxygen, as nitrogen, the more active elements burn, and the nitrogen is simply left in the uncombined state. The practical effect of these facts is that no matter what compound of carbon, hydrogen, oxygen, or nitrogen may be completely oxidized, either by rapid burning or by the slower process of decay, the final result is the same, viz., carbon dioxide, water, and free nitrogen. Hence burning is a final way of disposing of organic rubbish. The combustion products are unnoticeable and are normal constituents of the atmosphere.

EXPLOSIONS

Explosions are often the result of very rapid combustion, and hence may be considered here. The simplest case is the explosion of a mixture of hydrogen and oxygen. We know that when hydrogen and oxygen combine much heat is liberated by the union. When hydrogen burns at a jet, a very small portion burns at any one moment, and the heat therefrom is dissipated as fast as it develops. If, however, the hydrogen and oxygen are mixed previous to lighting, the union takes place with great rapidity throughout the mass, and all the heat of union is developed instantaneously. The result of this is an expansion of the water vapor formed, so great, and so sudden, that the disruptive force is tremendous.

It is generally assumed that volatile liquids like gasoline and ether are explosive. This is a misconception, for they are ordinarily stable substances. Their evil reputation for explosiveness results from their volatility and their combustibility. They are, on account of the former fact, likely to form a mixture with the air, and if this mixture is lighted we have a repetition of the conditions mentioned above—a sudden development of heat, resulting in a violent expansion of any gaseous matter present, water vapor, carbon dioxide and the nitrogen of the air.

The same effect is accomplished by other conditions in the use of the old-fashioned gunpowder, a mixture of charcoal, sulphur and potassium nitrate, KNO_3. When the powder is lighted, the charcoal and sulphur burn, combining with the oxygen from the unstable nitrate, and the final result is a mixture of gases, mainly carbon dioxide and nitrogen, which are highly heated by the burning. Their formation and expansion is the cause of the explosion, which is not very violent unless the gases are pent up, and suddenly burst through the confining walls.

A third type of explosions is caused by the disruption

of certain organic compounds containing nitrogen. This element causes the whole to be unstable and allows chemical changes to take place practically instantaneously. The most important explosives of this type are: nitroglycerin, $C_3H_5(NO_3)_3$; guncotton, $C_6H_7O_2(NO_3)_3$; picric acid, $C_6H_3O(NO_2)_3$; and trinitrotoluol, $C_7H_5(NO_2)_3$. It will be noted that these all have a somewhat similar composition. The nitrogen causes them to be unstable, the oxygen can unite with the hydrogen and carbon, and everything concerned is within the same molecule, so that the decomposition takes place with the utmost suddenness. The first of the above may be taken as typical. It decomposes as follows: $2C_3H_5(NO_3)_3 \rightarrow 6CO_2 + 5H_2O$ (gaseous) $+ 6N + O$, which means that nitroglycerin is changed instantaneously from a compact liquid into a voluminous mixture of gases. The violence of the disruptive force is due to the suddenness of the gas formation, and this in turn to the fact that all the reactions occur at infinitely small distances, all within the same molecule.

CHAPTER VII

NITROGEN, AIR, AND NITROGEN COMPOUNDS

HYDROGEN, oxygen, and carbon are generally considered the first three constituents of organic matter. Nitrogen enters as a fourth into the composition of compounds like the proteins and their derivatives. These four are therefore naturally classed together, not for their chemical similarity, but because of this relation to the products of living matter. Nitrogen does not rank among the most abundant elements of the solid earth, yet it is so available in the air that as an element and in its compounds it is very conspicuous in our lives. It makes up four fifths of the air, but is less noticeable there than the more active oxygen. In recent years, processes for converting the free element into compounds give assurance of a supply. Nitrogen compounds hardly exist among the minerals, but soils contain small amounts, and the Chile deposits of sodium nitrate, $NaNO_3$, are enormous. The latter are nevertheless appreciably depleted by the vast inroads made upon them. The chief organic compounds of nitrogen are the proteins, the main constituents of animal tissue. The chemical changes in these proteins in the processes of digestion, assimilation, and excretion lead to other nitrogen compounds of especial interest to the physiologist.

Nitrogen may be prepared readily from the air by the removal of the oxygen. For this purpose phosphorus may be burned in a closed volume of air. As it unites with the oxygen, the white fumes of the oxide of phosphorus appear. They may be made to go into solution in water, when the nitrogen will be left, showing the properties which are already familiar from an acquaintance with

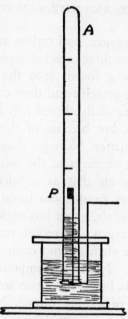

EXPERIMENT SHOWING THE PREPARATION OF NITROGEN FROM AIR AND ALSO THE PROPORTIONS OF OXYGEN AND NITROGEN IN AIR

The tube A, filled with air, is inverted over the dish of water. A piece of phosphorus, P, is introduced, and in the course of twenty-four hours all the oxygen present unites with it. The resulting oxide of phosphorus dissolves in the water, and only nitrogen remains. It will be seen that one-fifth of the air has disappeared.

the air. It is a colorless, odorless gas, slightly lighter than air, and slightly soluble in water. Chemically it is inert, combining directly with rather few substances. When a combination is established, it is usually unstable, simply because the nitrogen in it has a low affinity for the other constituents. Compounds which are unstable and reactive are of the utmost importance from the chemical standpoint. Stable substances may have their uses, but they are not the substances with which the chemist accomplishes his results; nor would they be best suited to the delicate changes necessary in the vital tissue of plants and animals. Nitrogen compounds exhibit great instability and reactivity, and in the composition of foods and of explosives they are of great importance. So great a place did these two features assume that "the nitrogen question" had a permanent place in chemical interests. The essential point of the question was the fixation of nitrogen, namely, the converting of the inert gas nitrogen into compounds which men could use. On the whole, the tendency of nitrogen is toward the free condition, in which state it is useless. Nitrogen once in combination should be carefully preserved in that condition, and a regular and plentiful new supply of nitrogen compounds should be established by the methods of manufacturing and of agriculture.

The Air

The air is not a compound of nitrogen and oxygen, but a mixture. This fact is apparent from a comparison of the properties of air with those of compounds of nitrogen and oxygen. The latter have characteristic properties, in part highly corrosive, essentially different from those of their constituents, while air has simply the properties, somewhat toned down, of each of the constituents. When air is liquefied the nitrogen evaporates much more readily than the oxygen, and a separation may thus be readily accomplished. If air were a compound it would act simply as one unit.

The composition of air may be determined by carefully subtracting the oxygen from a known volume of air, and measuring the remainder. Air is thus found to consist of 21 per cent by volume, or 23 per cent by weight of oxygen. In all ordinary considerations of air the 1 per cent of argon present is not noticed. In fact it escaped detection until the year 1894, when Rayleigh and Ramsay discovered it. The discovery of a new constituent of air, present in such large amounts, made a great sensation and has stimulated research in that general direction. As a result a number of similar gases have been found in small amounts, all with somewhat the same properties as argon. Argon is inert, and so far has not been found to combine with any other substance, or even with itself. In the molecule of argon there is only one atom.

In the atmosphere there are normally found water and carbon dioxide besides the oxygen and nitrogen. The water content is very variable, the content on a cold day and on a warm day being very different. At — 10° C. (14° F.) saturated air consists of about 0.2 per cent water; at 30° C (88° F.) it may contain six times as much. It should be remembered that air is dry or damp, not in accordance with the amount of water which it holds, but in accordance with the amount of water it is still capable of taking up. The carbon dioxide, three parts in ten thousand, 0.03 per cent, is rather constant in open spaces, but in closed spaces, where animals are breathing or fires burning, the increase in the proportion may be marked. No harm, however, can be directly attributed to the increased amounts ordinarily met with.

Liquid air is prepared in considerable amounts for the production of low temperatures and for the preparation of oxygen and nitrogen for industrial purposes. The principle of liquefying air is a combination of compressing and cooling. The necessarily intense cooling is accomplished by the expansion of air previously compressed, for the expansion of a compressed gas results in cooling much as does the evaporation of a liquid. Liquid air is a colorless liquid, which evaporates with great rapidity, and in doing so abstracts heat from anything with which it comes in contact. The Dewar flask, familiar as the thermos bottle, is used to hold liquid air, for the vacuum between the two walls of the flask prevents the entering of heat. The temperature of liquid air under ordinary pressure is about $-170°$ C. ($-300°$ F.). The nitrogen, being more volatile, boils away first, and presently liquid oxygen is left as a pale blue liquid. The low temperatures achieved by means of liquid air have extended greatly the range for chemical and physical experimentation. Formerly the investigation of many compounds was hampered by their gaseous condition. Many of these are now brought into control by their liquefaction by the cooling effect of liquid air.

COMPOUNDS OF NITROGEN

Nitrogen combined with Hydrogen. Ammonia, NH_3, is formed with some difficulty by the direct union of the two elements. Commercial ammonia came, until recently, from very indirect sources. It is a light gas of well-known odor. The gas is familiar, but since it is usually handled in its water solution, called aqua ammonia, or ammonia water, and rather incorrectly, ammonia, the fact may not generally be appreciated that it is a gas. The strong solution at ordinary temperatures holds from 300 to 400 volumes of the gas.

One great use of ammonia is in artificial freezing. Ammonia is rather easily converted to a liquid by pressure and ordinary cooling, such as by running water. This liquid ammonia can be caused to evaporate rapidly, for it is normally a gas. It then absorbs heat rapidly and has

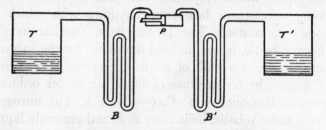

DIAGRAM OF THE AMMONIA ICE MACHINE

T and T' are the tanks in which the liquid ammonia is placed. It is taken from these tanks and returned to them alternately. P is the pump by which the ammonia is withdrawn from one tank and forced into the other, in the first case accelerating evaporation and cooling, in the second reconverting the gas to the liquid for the next operation. The chilling of the expanding gas is applied by means of the coils, B and B', alternately.

therefore intense cooling effect. This is not peculiar to ammonia, but ammonia is the most convenient of the gases of this type. When ammonia is converted to a liquid, its latent heat is allowed to dissipate into the air or into cooling water. When the liquid reverts to a gas, the containers are so arranged that it takes it latent heat from the object which is to be cooled. The diagram will show how this is accomplished.

Liquid ammonia is contained in the tank T, and by means of the pump P the gas is withdrawn from above it, causing rapid evaporation, and hence rapid absorption of heat. Refrigeration is accomplished by allowing the pipe conducting the cold ammonia gas to chill the spaces or objects to be cooled. For making ice this pipe chills a salt solution stored in great tanks. This brine will not freeze until chilled to about —20° C. (0° F.). Into this brine square cans of distilled water are suspended until their contents are frozen solid. As the gas is pumped out of the tank T it is forced into the tank T'. In this compression process the heat which it has just taken up is again liberated, and is carried away by ordinary cooling means, running water for example. At the end of the operation the apparatus is ready again, in inverse order, for another freezing operation, the liquid ammonia now being accumulated in T'.

Refrigeration is a purely physical process. The compounds, however, which serve to accomplish this require chemical discussion. Ice, solid carbon dioxide, liquid air and ammonia have been discussed. For domestic mechanical refrigeration, now so common, sulphur dioxide and methyl chloride, CH_3Cl, are better suited than any of the above. Their advantage lies purely within physical and mechanical considerations.

Ammonia has one chemical property in which it differs from all other common substances. It combines directly with water thus, $NH_3 + HOH \rightarrow NH_4OH$, properly written $(NH_4) OH$, because the so-called ammonium group acts like a single atom of a metal. The compound, called ammonium hydroxide, is very similar to sodium hydroxide, caustic soda, or lye, and it is used similarly for cleansing purposes. It is, however, much milder in its action. Ammonia also unites directly with acids to form

salts, very similar to those of sodium. In all these combinations, ammonium, NH_4, acts like the single metal
atom, sodium.

Nitrogen combined with Oxygen. Nitrogen forms a
series of compounds with oxygen. These illustrate very
nicely the law of multiple proportions. With the same
amount of nitrogen present in each of these compounds,
the oxygen increases in regular steps, as demonstrated in
the following list:

1. Nitrous oxide, N_2O.
2. Nitric oxide, N_2O_2, more correctly NO.
3. Nitrous anhydride, N_2O_3.
4. Nitrogen peroxide, N_2O_4, (or NO_2).
5. Nitric anhydride, N_2O_5.

Nitrous oxide is a colorless gas, which is the well known
"laughing gas" of surgery. The second compound is
remarkable in that it, a colorless gas, unites directly on
contact with oxygen, to form NO_2, which is of a strong
brown color. The readiness with which these two pass
into each other by gaining and losing oxygen, is distinctly
unusual, and causes them to be used as carriers of oxygen,
especially in the manufacture of sulphuric acid. The gas
with less oxygen takes oxygen from the air to form the
peroxide. The latter surrenders oxygen to sulphur dioxide
SO_2 converting it to the trioxide SO_3, itself being reduced
to NO. On further contact with air this again forms the
peroxide, and thus the process continues, as long as oxygen
is supplied.

The most important of these oxides is the fifth, nitric
anhydride, N_2O_5. The name means literally that it is
nitric acid without water, but the chemist is more inter-

ested in reverse idea, namely in the fact that the compound unites readily with water to form nitric acid.

$$N_2O_5 + H_2O \rightleftarrows (H_2N_2O_6)\ 2HNO_3$$

It is a white solid, with a powerful corrosive and oxidizing effect. By itself it is hardly more than a chemical curiosity. Its main interest centers in its relation to nitric acid, the chief of all nitrogen compounds.

Nitric acid is a colorless liquid, but unless mixed with considerable water, decomposes gradually and becomes yellow. The yellow color is then indirectly a sign of high concentration, and fuming nitric acid, as it is called, is a very powerful and dangerous reagent. Nitric acid has for its greatest use the making of explosives. The essential point of these explosives is that the molecule is capable of disintegration, with the consequent formation of gases. To disintegrate, a molecule must be unstable, and the presence of nitrogen is the readiest way of accomplishing instability. The common explosives contain either the nitrate, NO_3, group, or the nitro, NO_2, group. Both are introduced by treating the original substance with nitric acid mixed with sulphuric acid. The latter negatives the effect of the water which is formed as a by-product.

Nitric acid is also used as a source of oxygen, for it decomposes readily, as do most nitrogen compounds. It will not readily yield pure oxygen, but is convenient for adding oxygen to other compounds.

A discussion of an acid is not complete without some mention of the salts which the acid forms. The salt has the same structure as the acid, but the hydrogen is replaced by a metal. HNO_3, nitric acid, is readily converted into KNO_3, potassium nitrate, or $NaNO_3$, sodium nitrate, or

$AgNO_3$, silver nitrate, and so on. These salts as a class have three main applications: They supply oxygen to other substances, as does HNO_3, and upon this fact the use of potassium nitrate in gunpowder is based. They supply nitrogen for fertilizer purposes. Sodium nitrate is the salt used almost exclusively for this. They form convenient soluble compounds with the metals when the metals are desired in combination; as silver nitrate, $AgNO_3$, in electroplating.

The necessity of nitric acid in making military and engineering explosives is one of the features which has given rise to the nitrogen question. The other is the need by plants of nitrogen in the combined form. Nitrogen compounds for making explosives must be in the form of nitric acid or a salt thereof, and when the explosive is used, the nitrogen is liberated as free nitrogen. Hence the compounds used for these purposes must always be replenished. For many years the natural deposits of sodium nitrate in the north of Chile supplied this need, and the supply will still last for some time.

Nevertheless the problem of the fixation of nitrogen has been given serious attention in recent years, and it may now be said that the problem is solved. The methods which have been applied for nitrogen fixation are several.

1. Uniting the oxygen and nitrogen of the air by means of electric discharges. This has been profitable only where water power is available for the generation of the electricity. Such conditions obtain in Norway. Lower oxides are first formed; these pass over on the addition of oxygen (of the air), water, and lime into calcium nitrate. The calcium nitrate can then be converted into any desired form.

2. The cyanamide process consists in causing free nitrogen to combine with calcium carbide. This compound may be used to supply the soil with nitrogen capable of absorption by plants, or ammonia, NH_3, may be obtained from it and applied thus, or converted into nitric acid.

3. Under conditions not easily attained, nitrogen and hydrogen can be directly combined to form ammonia. This is the synthetic Haber process. The ammonia may be applied as a fertilizer, in the form of a salt. For purposes of making explosives, it must be oxidized and thus made into nitric acid. Both these steps represent great achievements of modern chemistry. The results are accomplished along the lines of "greatest resistance" so to speak. The chemical chances of success are not large, but slight as they are, they have been used as the basis of successful manufacturing processes.

4. The last of the more important methods is, strictly speaking, not a method of fixation, but of saving the small proportion of combined nitrogen which is stored up in coal. Soft coal is destructively distilled in large amounts for making coal gas and coke. The nitrogen present escapes as ammonia, and if this is all saved the total is considerable. For explosives the ammonia must be oxidized as in the synthetic ammonia process. Most of the ammonia now obtained in this manner is devoted to agricultural needs.

For agricultural purposes nitrogen in practically any compound is available, for one compound passes readily over to another. This will be more clearly illustrated by the diagram on the following page, which shows the nitrogen cycle.

THE NITROGEN CYCLE

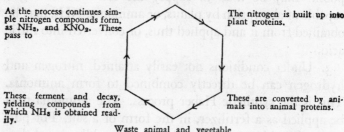

Fully oxidized nitrogen compounds, as KNO_3 and $Ca(NO_3)_2$.

As the process continues simple nitrogen compounds form, as NH_3, and KNO_2. These pass to

The nitrogen is built up into plant proteins.

These ferment and decay, yielding compounds from which NH_3 is obtained readily.

These are converted by animals into animal proteins.

Waste animal and vegetable matter including bacteria.

The nitrogen compounds of any ordinary type will fit into this cycle and serve their purpose. It would seem possible that when once there were nitrogen compounds in sufficiency, the cycle would be maintained and the agricultural needs always provided for. There are, however, many sources of loss, such as farm waste, decay under unfavorable conditions, and fire, and in all these the nitrogen escapes, so to speak, from the cycle. There are ways by which the atmospheric nitrogen is drawn into this cycle, to a slight extent by electric discharges in the atmosphere, more by the fixation of nitrogen by leguminous plants. The beneficial effect of growing and plowing under a field of clover is well known.

THE INERT GASES

TABLE OF THE INERT GASES

Name	Symbol	Atomic weight
Helium	He	4
Neon	Ne	20
Argon	A	40
Krypton	Kr	84
Xenon	Xe	131

In 1894, Rayleigh and Ramsay, having noted a discrepancy in the weights of nitrogen obtained from the air and from chemical compounds, followed up this clue which led to the discovery of argon (the name means inactive) present in the air to the extent of 0.9%. Argon is an inactive gas, and no combination with any other element has been certainly established. It is now prepared on a considerable scale and is used to fill electric light bulbs, in order that the filament need not be in a vacuum, and yet not subject to any possibility of chemical action.

The discovery of this abundant substance which had for so long eluded the observation of chemists made a profound impression, and resulted in a keen stimulation to research. In course of time helium, neon, krypton and xenon were discovered, all inert gases, which fitted into the general classification of the elements to be later discussed.

Of these gases helium holds the greatest interest, both from the standpoint of pure science, that is, in the structure of the atom (Chapter XX), and because of its utilization in airships. The use of the highly inflammable hydrogen for aircraft has resulted in many calamities. The discovery of helium in natural gas in Texas to the extent of 1%, has made its recovery in large quantities possible. The name helium (meaning sun) was first used in 1869 to designate an element noticed by means of the spectroscope in the atmosphere of the sun. When the new gas was discovered about thirty years later its identity was established by the same means.

Neon is familiar on account of its use in neon lights. The others have no practical application.

CHAPTER VIII

SULPHUR AND ITS COMPOUNDS

SULPHURIC acid from the standpoint of the industries is probably next to water the most important compound, and a study of chemistry can make little progress without a knowledge of its preparation and properties. Sulphur, the essential element of this acid, along with several of its chemically indispensable compounds, must be included in this study.

Sulphur, the element, is well known. It can be obtained in several allotropic forms. If sulphur is heated to its boiling point and cooled suddenly by pouring into water, it takes on a gummy form which only slowly reverts to the original brimstone. Sulphur occurs free in nature, in spite of the fact that it is reasonably active. Its occurrence free is due to recent formation and more or less accidental protection from union with oxygen and metals. In Louisiana the sulphur occurs several hundred feet below ground, and is brought up in the molten condition accomplished by forcing down superheated steam. As sulphur melts at 114° C., it requires a temperature above that of ordinary steam to liquefy it.

Sulphur is found also in combination with metals. Sulphides of copper, mercury, zinc, and lead are very important ores. Their value lies usually in the metals which they contain, yet the sulphides of iron and zinc are used as sources of sulphur for making sulphuric acid. It also occurs in a number of abundant sulphates; as

Na_2SO_4, $CaSO_4$, and $MgSO_4$, sulphates of sodium, calcium, and magnesium.

The physical properties of sulphur are familiar. There is one popular misconception, namely, that concerning the odor of the element. Its odor is almost inappreciable, but when burned the odor of the oxide formed is very noticeable, and this is usually attributed to the sulphur itself. Chemically, sulphur is marked by two affinities, that for metals and that for oxygen. The former is often the cause of the tarnish of metallic objects, especially silver. It accounts for the sulphide ores in nature, and is the cause of many difficulties in the preparation of metals for the industries, as the presence of sulphur is usually injurious. Its affinity for oxygen results in the formation of the much-used sulphur dioxide, SO_2, and sulphuric acid, H_2SO_4.

The uses of sulphur are for making the old-fashioned black powder, and similar pyrotechnic mixtures; for making spraying solutions for fungicides; for vulcanizing rubber; and especially for making its oxygen compounds.

COMPOUNDS OF SULPHUR

Hydrogen Sulphide. This gas is not formed directly by union of hydrogen and sulphur, as the affinities are not sufficiently strong. It is prepared indirectly by the simple reaction between iron sulphide and sulphuric acid. It is a colorless gas, with a fetid odor, known to those who have visited sulphur springs. Such spring waters contain the gas, since it is markedly soluble in water. The gas burns readily, as might be expected, forming sulphur dioxide and water. Hydrogen sulphide is a much used laboratory reagent, as it forms characteristic compounds with many of the metals. The differences in these compounds lie in their varying colors and solubilities, so that by its means many of the metals may not alone be detected in the form of compounds, but these compounds may be separated from one another. It is and indispensable laboratory reagent. (Formula, H_2S).

Sulphur dioxide. When sulphur burns in the air or in oxygen, gaseous sulphur dioxide is formed. It is colorless, but when formed in this way traces of the trioxide give it the familiar bluish cloudy appearance. It is rather soluble in water and forms with the water an acid called sulphurous acid. When, however, this acid is formed in considerable amounts it breaks down into water and the dioxide. Hence such a solution acts indifferently as either sulphur dioxide or sulphurous acid. The great characteristic of sulphur dioxide, as also of sulphurous acid, is its tendency to unite with another atom of oxygen, forming sulphur trioxide and sulphuric acid respectively. There is no essential difference, for sulphur trioxide with water forms sulphuric acid. To this chemical activity is attributed the bleaching and disinfecting action of sulphur dioxide, although it is likely that much of it is due to union not with oxygen, but with other constituents of the color or the bacteria. By far the greater portion of sulphur dioxide prepared in the industries is simply as an intermediate product in the manufacture of sulphuric acid, to which we will now turn our attention.

Sulphuric acid is the foundation of the greater portion of the acid industry. It is an old saying that the amount of sulphuric acid used by any civilization is an index of its progress along modern lines. There are, to be sure, some signs that it may become less indispensable. However, in a recent census of chemical products, sulphuric acid received the first attention.

Sulphuric acid may be said to be made up of sulphur trioxide and water. $SO_3 + H_2O \rightleftharpoons H_2SO_4$. It may be separated into these two constituents with some precautions, and this feature of its structure frequently asserts itself. The exact formula of sulphuric acid is,

$$\begin{matrix} H-O \\ H-O \end{matrix} > S \begin{matrix} =O \\ =O \end{matrix} \cdot$$

This shows how the various atoms are held together in the molecule. It indicates that the molecule is a unit, yet that the hydrogen is directly held to oxygen only, as in water, and sulphur to oxygen only, as in sulphur trioxide. In the great majority of reactions, however, in which sulphuric acid takes part, the so-called sulphate group (SO_4) remains intact. The hydrogen is readily displaced by metals and sulphates formed. For such reactions the formula H_2SO_4 represents the structure best.

The reactions of sulphuric acid which enter into simple relations are three.

1. The possibility of decomposing into water and sulphur trioxide, and subsequently losing oxygen. When heated with substances which have affinity for oxygen, this reaction takes place.

$$H_2SO_4 \rightarrow H_2O + SO_3; \; SO_3 \rightarrow SO_2 + O$$

2. Sulphuric acid has a striking affinity for water. This is noticeable whenever the two are mixed, for much heat is developed. So much, in fact, that care must be exercised and thorough mixing accomplished in order to distribute this heat through the mass. As a result of this affinity the acid absorbs water vapor from air and other gases

which may be passed through it. It extracts water from substances which contain water, either free or combined. And it even extracts the hydrogen and oxygen from many substances such as sugar, as though they were really present as water. It is used for this reason in the making of explosives. The making of explosives depends upon the action of nitric acid upon certain organic compounds and water is a by-product. The water thus formed would dilute the nitric acid and diminish its action, and sulphuric acid is therefore added to absorb this water.

3. The third and chief reaction of sulphuric acid is its marked acid action, that is, its tendency to form sulphates with metals and metallic compounds. The list of these reactions is a long one and they are applied in many ways. They are all alike in that the hydrogen of the acid is in each case replaced by the metal involved. In simple cases, when the metal is free, the hydrogen escapes free, but in every other case it combines with that which had been in combination with the metal.

Chemical equations will be discussed later, yet even at this stage they may serve to clarify the above account.

$$Zn + H_2SO_4 \rightarrow ZnSO_4 + H_2$$
$$ZnO + H_2SO_4 \rightarrow ZnSO_4 + H_2O$$
$$ZnCO_3 + H_2SO_4 \rightarrow ZnSO_4 + H_2CO_3$$
$$ZnCl_2 + H_2SO_4 \rightarrow ZnSO_4 + 2HCl$$

Since sulphuric acid is the fundamental acid it must be prepared in some fundamental way. Other acids can be prepared from it, but sulphuric acid itself must be derived from some original source.

It has already been stated that this acid is made up of sulphur trioxide and water, $SO_3 + H_2O \rightarrow H_2SO_4$.

The addition of water presents no difficulties, so that the problem is to prepare the sulphur trioxide. When sulphur or certain abundant compounds of sulphur are burned the sulphur unites with oxygen to form sulphur dioxide,

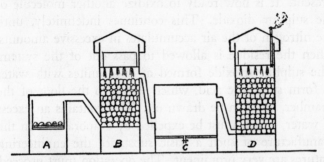

THE CHAMBER PROCESS FOR THE MANUFACTURE OF SULPHURIC ACID

In A sulphur or a compound of sulphur is burned with an abundant supply of air, and sulphur dioxide is thus formed. The mixture of sulphur and dioxide with a great excess of air (oxygen) is passed upward through the tower B, which accomplishes several purposes. This tower is filled with inert material, down which the desired liquids are made to trickle in fine streams. Among the uses of this tower is the cooling of the gas, sulphur dioxide, the introduction of the nitrogen oxide catalyst and of water. C represents one of a number of chambers, in which the union of oxygen and sulphur dioxide takes place, followed by the union of the resulting sulphur trioxide with water. Steam is introduced here, to supply an abundance of water. The sulphuric acid thus formed is drawn off from the bottom of the chamber. When the nitrogen introduced in the air becomes excessive, the desired reactions cease to take place, and the remaining gases are passed out through the tower D, where the useful oxides of nitrogen are in great part recovered. The walls of the chambers, connections, and towers, are lined with sheet lead, which is affected comparatively little by the acid.

$S + 2O \rightarrow SO_2$. The addition of one atom of oxygen to this yields the sulphur trioxide, and it is this step which presents the only real difficulties. It is accomplished by the help of catalysts by one of two methods.

(1) *The Chamber Process.* In this process sulphur dioxide, air (oxygen), nitrogen peroxide, and steam are

allowed to react on each other in huge leaden chambers. The oxide of nitrogen acts as an oxygen carrier, in that it first yields oxygen to the sulphur dioxide, and immediately recombines with an atom of oxygen from the air present. It is now ready to oxidize another molecule of the sulphur dioxide. This continues indefinitely, until the nitrogen of the air accumulates in excessive amounts, when the residue is allowed to pass out of the system. The sulphur trioxide formed at once unites with water to form sulphuric acid, which settles to the floor of the chamber, and can be drawn off. This contains an excess of water, which must be expelled by evaporation. In the manufacture of such a basic substance the engineering features are very prominent. The operation must proceed on a large scale; it must be continuous; there must be a minimum of waste; heat must be economized; by-products must be recovered; the handling of the acid is difficult. The making of sulphuric acid is a vast affair, and a chamber system covers much ground. Yet all the details are worked out to such perfection that this process, elaborate as it is, is carried out with certainty of success and the product is placed upon the market at a price so low that the acid may be used as raw material in many other industries.

(2) *The contact process* is much simpler. The sulphur dioxide mixed with air passes over heated catalysts, finely divided platinum being very serviceable, and the two are thus caused to unite. Catalysts are easily injured by foreign matter, which is likely to be present in the sulphur dioxide, and this presents the chief difficulty in the method. The sulphur trioxide is then united with water to form the acid.

Sulphuric acid is a heavy colorless liquid which flows in a sluggish stream. Hence it presents the appearance of an oil and is often called oil of vitriol. It dissolves in water in all proportions.

The first characteristic of an acid is its power to form salts with metals, and such a typical acid as sulphuric acid

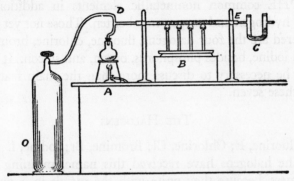

THE CONTACT PROCESS FOR MAKING SULPHURIC ACID

Sulphur dioxide generated in the flask, A, is mixed at D with oxygen from the cylinder, O. The mixture is passed over the heated platinum catalyst in B, and the two gases are now combined to form sulphur trioxide, which may be shown by disconnecting at E. The sulphur trioxide may be passed into the water in the U tube, C, and thus converted into sulphuric acid.

shows this property in a marked degree. Most metals form salts with sulphuric acid. Sodium sulphate and iron sulphate are types. They are usually well crystallized salts, with color only when the metal introduces color. The typical sulphate of sodium has the formula Na_2SO_4. If, however, only half the amount of sodium is applied, the acid salt, sodium hydrogen sulphate, is obtained, $NaHSO_4$, half acid and half salt, and partaking of the properties of both. This acid salt is a crystalline solid, with a sour taste and a regular acid action. It is often very useful in that it represents sulphuric acid in a solid form.

CHAPTER IX

THE REMAINING NONMETALLIC ELEMENTS

THE common nonmetallic elements in addition to hydrogen and oxygen number ten. Those not yet considered are the four halogens, fluorine, chlorine, bromine, and iodine, besides phosphorus, boron, and silicon. It will not be necessary to discuss more than the main features of these seven.

THE HALOGENS

Fluorine, F; Chlorine, Cl; Bromine, Br; Iodine, I.

The halogens have received this name, meaning salt formers, because they unite with the metals in a simple manner to form salts, $Na + Cl = NaCl$, sodium and chlorine = sodium chloride, common salt.

Fluorine, although rather abundant in nature, is of minor moment for our purpose. The other three present an excellent example of a group of elements, in which the resemblances are very striking, and what differences there are, very regular. Such a group bears very definitely on the question of the nature of the elements. Their resemblances and differences are of such a regular nature that we simply cannot accept as final any idea that different elements have no ultimate connection.

The other three elements of this group occur in nature in somewhat similar manner, in compounds only, and frequently associated. Their properties show their relationship in that the three elements are very similar, or when they differ, vary in a regular way. The physical state is characteristic and is suggestive of all their relations. Chlorine is a gas and is the most active; bromine is a liquid and comes next in activity; iodine is a solid and is the least active of the group. The atomic weight of bromine, 80, is a mean between those of the other two, 35.5 and 127. The color of chlorine is marked, that of bromine more so, and that of iodine still more. The affinity of all for hydrogen and the metals is very great, but it varies in the regular order. Chlorine has the greatest affinity, and will remove hydrogen or a metal from combination with the others. Bromine ranks next. The affinity for oxygen is of the reverse order, that of iodine being greatest. So regular are all these properties, that a knowledge of any two of these elements would enable us with great certainty to tell the properties of the other. Fluorine is a fourth member of this group, coming before chlorine. Its properties are such as one would expect from its position.

Chlorine, the most abundant of the group, is a heavy greenish yellow gas of great chemical activity. Its affinity for hydrogen is comparable with that of oxygen, and a mixture of hydrogen and chlorine explodes with some violence when ignited. They even unite under the influence of strong light, and hydrogen will burn in an atmosphere of chlorine. This affinity results in the use of chlorine for bleaching and disinfecting.

Organic substances are usually colorless. Only such have color as possess a rather complicated structure. If therefore a colored substance loses any of its constituents, or they are altered in any way, the new substance is likely to be free from color. Most colored substances are made up of carbon, hydrogen, oxygen, and often nitrogen. The easiest of these to remove is hydrogen, so that any substance likely to unite with hydrogen may be a bleaching agent. Hydrogen peroxide, through the active oxygen which it supplies can act thus, but chlorine is the most used. Its action is simple, in that it simply withdraws some hydrogen from the coloring matter, and the residue is colorless. Chlorine needs water for a catalyst, else it cannot bleach. The by-product of bleaching with chlorine is hydrochloric acid, HCl, an injurious substance, hence bleaching is often accomplished by means of bleaching powder, made by adding chlorine to lime. It is as effective as chlorine.

The action of a disinfectant is probably similar to that of a bleacher. Chlorine is efficient in this respect, and its use in improving public water supplies has been a great public boon. The amount used is less than one part in one million, and although its presence is sometimes noticeable and therefore objectionable, it annually saves many lives by the destruction of typhoid germs.

Bromine is less active than chlorine, but resembles it otherwise very closely in all chemical respects. It is a heavy liquid, easily convertible to a gas. It is used in medicinal and photographic preparations, in the manufacture of dyes, and as a disinfectant. Its greatest use is in medicine and in the preparation of ethyl gasoline. *Iodine* is still less active than bromine. It finds extensive application in the chemical laboratory and in medicine.

All the halogens form typical compounds with hydrogen. *Hydrochloric acid* is easily the most serviceable. It is a fairly heavy gas, very soluble in water, and it is this aqueous solution which is used in the laboratory. It is an active acid responding in all respects to the tests applied to acids. It is prepared with ease by treating sodium chloride with sulphuric acid, and collecting the gaseous hydrochloric acid in water. (The commercial acid is known as muriatic acid.)

$$\text{NaCl} \quad + \quad \text{H}_2\text{SO}_4 \quad \rightarrow$$
Sodium chloride (salt)   sulphuric acid
$$\text{Na}_2\text{SO}_4 \quad + \quad 2\text{HCl}$$
Sodium Sulphate   gaseous hydrogen chloride
(Hydrochloric acid)

The gas is so soluble that its solution in water acts as a powerful acid, and in its use consideration of the water may often be omitted. Hydrobromic acid and hydriodic acid are very similar to hydrochloric acid, but less stable. They have no practical application. Hydrofluoric acid, also similar in many respects, is marked by its powerful physiological action and the fact that it attacks glass, and is therefore used for etching that otherwise resistant material.

The group, or "family" of the halogens will find parallels among the metals in the sodium and calcium groups. They represent a striking similarity in physical and chemical properties, and when they differ in the intensity of their chemical activity, the difference is regular. So true is this that from the consideration of any two individuals the properties of the other members of these groups can be foretold.

The halogens have a low affinity for oxygen, but with precautions all but fluorine can be brought into combination with it. These compounds are unstable, and for that reason useful. $CaOCl_2$, bleaching powder, is of this nature, and readily gives up its oxygen or its chlorine according to conditions. Potassium chlorate, $KClO_3$, is another oxygen compound of chlorine, valuable because on heating it yields oxygen.

PHOSPHORUS

P

Phosphorus is striking on account of its great affinity for oxygen. Its compounds are vital in plant and animal growth. Otherwise the characteristics of the element and its compounds conform to nonmetals in general. Phosphorus may be prepared in two allotropic forms, the red and the yellow. It will be recalled that oxygen, carbon, and sulphur may also occur in different allotropic forms. The yellow form of phosphorus is the form usually associated with that element. It is a waxy solid, igniting with great ease and burning violently, on account of its great affinity for oxygen. The glowing of phosphorus when exposed to the air is usually attributed to its slow oxidation. Yellow phosphorus must be kept under water, partly because of this slow oxidation, and partly because of the danger of its becoming ignited. The other form of phosphorus, the red, is much less active. It may be handled freely and is not poisonous as is the yellow. Yet when ignited it burns fiercely. Each form may readily be converted into the other.

The most interesting use of phosphorus is for friction matches. The match of sixty years ago consisted of a stick of wood upon the end of which a bit of yellow phosphorus was placed. Hence these matches glowed in the dark. When rubbed, the heat of the friction was sufficient to ignite the phosphorus, and the combustion was communicated to the wood by means of a coating of sulphur. Later matches improved greatly upon this arrangement, particularly in the elimination of the sulphur, which gave off the disagreeable odor of sulphur dioxide when burned. The modern match involves the following features: The tip consists of a phosphorus compound, phosphorus sulphide, held to the stick by means of glue. A layer of paraffin carries the fire to the wood and the wood is powdered with a mineral substance to quench any spark after the match is extinguished.

The safety match is ingenious. Its effectiveness is based upon the fact that red phosphorus and potassium chlorate produce a very inflammable mixture. For the purposes of safety the red phosphorus is placed upon the friction surface of the box and the potassium chlorate, mixed with some combustible substance, as antimony sulphide, is placed upon the match. The match therefore ignites only when rubbed on the special surface.

Compounds of phosphorus. Phosphine, PH_3 is a curious gas, in structure comparable to ammonia. It is poisonous and highly inflammable. As ordinarily prepared in the laboratory an impurity therein causes it to ignite spontaneously.

The oxide of phosphorus, P_2O_5, and its corresponding acid, H_3PO_4, and salts, play an important part in the study of chemistry and in the realm of nature. When phosphorus burns, this white oxide formed can be collected. This has a powerful affinity for water, forming phosphoric acid, $P_2O_5 + 3\ H_2O \rightarrow 2H_3PO_4$, a sirupy liquid somewhat resembling sulphuric acid. So great is this affinity for water that the oxide may be used for drying gases, and for extracting water from such compounds as sulphuric and nitric acids.

From phosphoric acid, salts called phosphates are derived. Sodium phosphate, Na_2HPO_4, has medicinal applications. Another salt, trisodium phosphate, Na_3PO_4 (called T. S. P.), has wide application for cleansing purposes. Calcium phosphate, $Ca_3(PO_4)_2$, demands especial attention. It is the chief constituent of bone, and its development in the animal body is a point necessitating constant attention. The indispensability of phosphates in fertilizers is common knowledge, and in the industries mineral calcium phosphate is the source which supplies this. The phosphates of Florida are relics of animal life, and now, through their use as plant fertilizers, they are being brought back once more into the realm of living organisms.

BORON

B

Boron is of limited interest only. However, as several of its compounds are in common use, its chemistry should receive some attention. It is a typical nonmetal although neither the element nor its compounds show great activity. It forms an oxide, B_2O_3, which in turn forms an acid, H_3BO_3, a solid, and a salt, $Na_2B_4O_7$, the common borax. Boric acid has medicinal qualities and is used as a preservative. Borax has some uses, particularly as a cleansing agent. Its use as a flux in brazing, as a constituent of glasses, glazes and enamels, is based upon the presence in borax of the nonvolatile boron oxide, which unites with various metallic oxides to form fusible compounds, comparable with salts. The occurrence in nature of boron compounds is picturesque. In California, in the famous Death Valley and in the Mojave Desert it is abundant. In certain regions in Italy (Tuscany) steam arising from fumaroles contains recoverable amounts of boric acid.

Silicon

Si

In laboratory chemistry silicon plays a very minor part, but in the realm of geology and mineralogy, as well as in the great industries included under the head of ceramics, silicon dioxide and silicates play a major rôle. Of other compounds of silicon only "silicon carbide," SiC, the well known carborundum, need be mentioned as particularly important.

The leading silicon compound is silica (quartz), silicon dioxide, SiO_2. This is found in a variety of forms, and is known by many names. Quartz, crystal, rhinestones, agate, flint and many other forms are familiar, particularly sand and sandstone. The subject of silica could occupy a long chapter by itself. The compound is very insoluble in water, hard, and chemically inactive. Although it is very infusible, modern industry has achieved the shaping of many pieces of apparatus, useful because of resistance to chemical changes.

During geological periods, involving high temperatures and pressures, and long periods of time, changes of great variety have taken place. The list of silicon minerals and rocks is a long one. Except for the carbonates of calcium and magnesium the amounts of all others are insignificant by comparison. A short list of the chief minerals with their formulas will emphasize the fact that after oxygen, silicon is the most abundant element in nature. (26%.)

Silica, SiO_2
Potassium Feldspar, $KAlSi_3O_8$
Sodium Feldspar, $NaAlSi_3O_8$
Calcium Feldspar, $CaAl_2Si_2O_8$
Mica, $H_2KAl_3Si_3O_{12}$
Talc, $H_2Mg_3Si_4O_{12}$
Clay, $Al_2Si_2O_7$ or $H_2Al_2Si_2O_8$

Silicon will come into discussion again when the chemistry of steel is dealt with. Silicon dioxide and silicates form the basis of the ceramic industries, to be described in a later chapter.

SUMMARY

The brief study of the nonmetals is now complete. In addition to the special points of chemical and industrial interest, general principles may be observed as shown by this group of elements. The following may be written in the way of recapitulation.

In physical characteristics these nonmetals vary greatly, as a contrast between carbon and nitrogen will show. In certain chemical features also they are in strong contrast. Carbon is sluggish, while chlorine and phosphorus show intense activity, although of different kinds. Nevertheless, in the structure of their compounds there are definite regularities. The following summary will show this.

Two types of compounds are apparent, those which the nonmetals form with hydrogen, and those which they form with oxygen. In both cases they develop acids, and acids invariably lead to salts.

THE HYDROGEN TYPE

Chemical name	Acid name	Typical salt
Hydrogen fluoride, HF	Hydrofluoric acid	NaF
Hydrogen chloride, HCl	Hydrochloric acid	NaCl
Hydrogen bromide, HBr	Hydrobromic acid	NaBr
Hydrogen iodide, HI	Hydriodic acid	NaI
Hydrogen sulphide, H_2S	Hydrosulphuric acid	ZnS

THE OXYGEN TYPE

Nitrogen and sulphur form two oxides of this type, and each of these acts further in the normal manner.

The oxide, with water forms the acid, real or theoretical		Typical salt
$CO_2 + H_2O \rightarrow H_2CO_3$	Carbonic acid	Na_2CO_3, the carbonate
$SiO_2 + H_2O \rightarrow H_2SiO_3$	Silicic acid	Na_2SiO_3, the silicate
$SO_2 + H_2O \rightarrow H_2SO_3$	Sulphurous acid	Na_2SO_3, the sulphite
$SO_3 + H_2O \rightarrow H_2SO_4$	Sulphuric acid	Na_2SO_4, the sulphate
$B_2O_3 + 3H_2O \rightarrow 2H_3BO_3$	Boric acid	$Na_2B_4O_7$, the borate
$N_2O_3 + H_2O \rightarrow 2HNO_2$	Nitrous acid	$NaNO_2$, the nitrite
$N_2O_5 + H_2O \rightarrow 2HNO_3$	Nitric acid	$NaNO_3$, the nitrate
$P_2O_5 + 3H_2O \rightarrow 2H_3PO_4$	Phosphoric acid	Na_3PO_4, the phosphate

A few compounds, as carbon monoxide, CO, ammonia, NH_3, and phosphine, PH_3, do not fall within this classification.

CHAPTER X

SYMBOLS, FORMULAS, VALENCE, EQUATIONS

THE symbols, formulas and equations which are used in the study of chemistry often seem to the beginner somewhat appalling. The experience of further study soon demonstrates that they are useful adjuncts, in fact essentials for an exact appreciation of the nature of the relations and reactions. They must, however, be used as aids to the chemical thought, not pursued as an end in themselves, as though they were puzzles of a new type.

The symbols used for the chemical elements are shown in the table of the elements. They are the initial letters of the name, frequently the Latin form, and when two elements have the same initial letter, a second characteristic letter is used. But the symbol means something more than the element. It means also one unit amount of the element, that is, an atom, with the atomic weight which characterizes that element. H means one atom of hydrogen, possessing a weight of 1. O means the atom of oxygen, with its atomic weight of 16. The symbol is often used to imply also this weight expressed in grams, a matter of some convenience. $Ca + O$ under these conditions would imply 40 grams of calcium and 16 of oxygen.

The formula of a compound is made up of the symbols of the elements composing it, and expresses the kinds and numbers of the atoms in the molecule. The symbols of the metals are usually written first. These formulas are more or less self-evident, but the use of numbers may be confusing. A number written before a formula modifies all the atoms in the formula. $2H_2SO_4$ indicates the whole formula taken twice. The subscript modifies the one element only. These devices are simple and with a little care are soon mastered.

ATOMIC AND MOLECULAR WEIGHTS

Atomic weights may be conveniently defined as the weights of the atoms of the elements, compared with that of the atom of hydrogen. For convenience the unit is made 1/16 of the atomic weight of oxygen, 16, because hydrogen has a weight deviating from this to a slight extent, and reference to an even number saves many re-calculations. The definition just given, however, is open to criticism, as we cannot distinguish or weigh an atom. The definition of the atom may be stated to be the unit particle, portion or proportion of an element which enters into combinations. The first two of these expressions are really figurative. All that we really can measure is the proportion of an element going into and coming out of compounds. For most a picture of the atom as a some-what concrete unit will be useful. The atomic weight really represents the combining weight of the elements. If an element enters into compounds with more than one proportion, the smallest proportion is the one selected. The determination of atomic weights is one of the most carefully conducted operations of chemistry, and requires theoretical considerations as well as practical experimentation. The outcome of atomic weight determinations for ordinary purposes is that there is associated with every element a number, the atomic weight, which represents the mass which enters into all combinations. When we say that the atomic weight of oxygen is 16 we mean that for every unit of oxygen present in a compound a mass of oxygen represented by that number is present.

In the same manner the molecular weight of a compound may be defined as the weight of the molecule referred to the same unit. It is determined with readiness by adding up the atomic weights of the various atoms present in the molecule. The molecular weight of sulphuric acid is 98, obtained by adding up the atomic weights. $H_2 = 2$, $S = 32$, $O_4 = 64$. The atomic and molecular weights form the basis of all numerical considerations involving the composition of compounds.

In many reactions groups of elements pass from one combination to another without being modified. Nitric acid, HNO_3, forms potassium nitrate, KNO_3, and sodium nitrate, $NaNO_3$; the nitrate group, NO_3, remains intact; hence it is convenient to consider them more or less as units, and in many cases they are placed in parentheses, as $Ca(NO_3)_2$, calcium nitrate. These are called radicals. The most common are SO_4, NO_3, CO_3, PO_4, OH, NH_4, called sulphate, nitrate, carbonate, phosphate, hydroxide and ammonium respectively.

VALENCE

The formulas of certain compounds, HCl (hydrochloric acid), H_2O (water), NH_3 (ammonia), and CH_4 (methane), make it clear that the four elements, chlorine, oxygen, nitrogen and carbon have unequal combining power as measured by hydrogen. This varying combining power, as illustrated by these elements, varies from one to four. This is called the valence of the elements, and in all formulas and reactions it must be considered.

The valence of an element is its combining power (quantity, not intensity), compared with that of hydrogen. The simplest way of determining this valence is by considering the hydrogen compounds, mentioned above, when the valence is apparent at a glance. It may be determined from other combinations as well, especially from those with oxygen, which has a valence of two. From the formulas K_2O, CaO, Al_2O_3, CO_2, it may be seen that the valences of the elements combined with oxygen are respectively, 1, 2, 3, and 4, and these valences will be required to balance the total valence of the oxygen.

Radicals have definite valences, determined by the residual valence of their constituents. In the SO_4 radical, the four oxygen atoms have a valence of eight, the sulphur of six, hence two are unprovided for, and this residual valence is the valence of the group. This is confirmed by the fact that the group combines with two hydrogen atoms, forming H_2 (SO_4). When it can be measured against hydrogen, valence is always easy to determine.

In spite of its simplicity the idea of valence is sometimes difficult for the beginner to grasp. The matter will be considered only when necessary, but all formulas and equations must be written in strict conformity to its requirements.

Valence is sometimes variable. Sulphur shows a valence of four in SO_2, and of six in SO_3. Copper has a valence of one in $CuCl$, and of two in $CuCl_2$. This may seem to introduce uncertainty into the whole matter. But such is not the fact. We may say simply that when sulphur has an abundance of oxygen available it will unite with three atoms. The compound formed will be SO_3, and the valence of the sulphur will be six. When, however, there is a dearth of oxygen, sulphur will unite with only two atoms, and its valence will be four. The same reasoning applies to copper and chlorine and all similar cases.

The valence of an element is far from a numerical abstraction. It determines the combining and building up capacity of the element in a very real way. This may be shown by examples:

The valence of chlorine is one, indicated somewhat materially by the symbol, Cl^-. When another element, as hydrogen, combines with chlorine, this one valence is satisfied as indicated by the formula $Cl - H$. The chlorine atom is now incapable of any further addition.

The valence of oxygen is 2, thus represented, $O^=$, or better $-O-$. This indicates that oxygen can make two connections, as $K-O-H$, $K-O-NO_2$, and it thus becomes a link in the building up of molecules. This is especially striking in organic chemistry, for there we will meet with complexes of the greatest significance, owing their structure and their reactions to this linking by means of oxygen. The well known ether is such a compound. Its formula $(C_2H_5 - O - C_2H_5)$ is conveniently written to show this. This relation will be strongly emphasized in the later study of organic and of food chemistry. Nitrogen has a valence of 3. $N^{\equiv}$. Like oxygen it is a linking element, and the all-important proteins owe their structure to this fact.

Carbon has a valence of 4. $C^{\equiv}$. The possibility that the carbon atom can be linked to four different atoms or groups of atoms is at the basis of the whole subject of organic chemistry, and makes possible the phenomena of plant and animal existence. It might not be too much to say that this fact ranks along with the action of gravity and the activity of oxygen as one of the fundamental features of the world as we know it.

EQUATIONS

Equations have already been used as necessity has demanded, and to make the ideas of the subject clearer. Two forms of expression are used:

$$NaCl + KNO_3 = NaNO_3 + KCl, \text{ and}$$
$$NaCl + KNO_3 \rightarrow NaNO_3 + KCl$$

The latter is often the more convenient, as it indicates more than mere equality, and by reversal of the arrow it can be made to indicate the opposite reaction.

$$NaCl + KNO_3 \leftarrow NaNO_3 + KCl$$

Further when both arrows are used, it indicates that the reaction is reversible, that is, may go in either direction, according to conditions.

$$NaCl + KNO_3 \rightleftarrows NaNO_3 + KCl$$

In equations there must be a numerical balance of all the atoms. In using an equation to express a reaction it must first of all indicate the facts, the valences must be properly considered and the equation must balance. These equations are of great value for checking up reactions, for explaining them, and for suggesting new ideas. For example, the equation

$$Zn + H_2SO_4 \rightarrow ZnSO_4 + 2H$$
$$\text{Zinc + sulphuric acid} \rightarrow \text{zinc sulphate + hydrogen}$$

represents a common reaction between a metal and an

acid. If instead of the metal zinc we apply its oxide it is easy to see what becomes of the additional oxygen.

$$ZnO + H_2SO_4 \rightarrow ZnSO_4 + H_2O$$
Zinc oxide + sulphuric acid → zinc sulphate + water

Or if zinc chloride is used, the reaction is easy to follow;

$$ZnCl_2 + H_2SO_4 \rightarrow ZnSO_4 + 2\ HCl$$
Zinc chloride + sulphuric acid → zinc sulphate + hydrogen chloride

These equations are lacking in that they indicate nothing concerning the energy transformations. This information is sometimes supplied thus:

$$2\ H + O = H_2O + 68,000 \text{ calories}$$
$$H + I = HI - 6,000 \text{ calories}$$

These equations indicate that in the formation of water from its elements 68,000 calories of heat are developed, while in the second case the union of hydrogen and iodine absorb heat. The amounts applied are the atomic weights called for by the symbols, respectively 2 and 16 grams in the first, forming 18 grams of water. In the second equation 1 gram of hydrogen and 127 grams of iodine unite to form 128 grams of hydriodic acid.

Further, these equations do not indicate that the reactions must necessarily take place. If the reaction does take place it does so in accordance with the given equation, but it is not a mathematical necessity.

CALCULATIONS

The simpler calculations of chemistry are based upon atomic weights, formulas, and equations. If we rewrite one of the above equations, introducing the atomic and molecular weights, some of the numerical relations may be made clear.

$$\underbrace{\underset{65,\ 16}{Zn\ O}} + \underbrace{\underset{2\times1,\ 32,\ 4\times16}{H_2\ S\ O_4}} \rightarrow \underbrace{\underset{65,\ 32,\ 4\times16}{Zn\ S\ O_4}} + \underbrace{\underset{2,\ 16}{H_2\ O}}$$
$$81 \qquad\qquad 98 \qquad\qquad\qquad 161 \qquad\qquad 18$$

Zinc oxide is thus seen to be 65/81 zinc, and 16/81 oxygen, and calculations may be made accordingly. Should the question arise how much zinc sulphate could be formed from a given amount of zinc oxide or sulphuric acid, we need only consider the above values in a proportion.

$$\frac{ZnO}{ZnSO_4} = \frac{81}{161} = \frac{\text{known amount zinc oxide}}{\text{unknown amount zinc sulphate}}$$

or

$$\frac{H_2SO_4}{ZnSO_4} = \frac{98}{161} = \frac{\text{known amount of sulphuric acid}}{\text{unknown amount of zinc sulphate}}$$

This method lends itself to all possible combinations and is at the basis of all the calculations of analysis and manufacturing.

NOMENCLATURE

Although the system of nomenclature used in chemistry is far from ideal it is simple and serviceable enough. For ordinary purposes the following principles apply.

Compounds containing two elements are given names ending in "ide," as sodium chloride, NaCl; calcium oxide, CaO. A metal is uniformly mentioned first. In case of nonmetals the element which seems to be of the greater interest is mentioned first. There are exceptions to this rule for "binaries" in such substances as sodium hydroxide, Na (OH); ammonium chloride, (NH_4) Cl; sodium cyanide, Na (CN); but in each of these the group in parenthesis may be looked upon as a unit, acting as though it were a single element. The names are sometimes reversed, so that we hear "chloride of sodium" and "oxide of calcium." But there is no other change.

When there is more than one combination of the same elements numbers are often used, as carbon monoxide CO, and carbon dioxide CO_2. Sulphur dioxide SO_2, and sulphur trioxide SO_3, nitrogen trioxide N_2O_3, and nitrogen pentoxide N_2O_5. Other ways of differentiating are also used, which often have no recommendation except custom. However, a name like hydrogen peroxide, H_2O_2, is suggestive as implying that this compound contains more oxygen than the usual oxide of hydrogen, water. So also a name like silver suboxide suggests that the compound contains less than the normal amount of oxygen. In general a suffix, "ous," indicates less, and "ic" more of the element considered secondary in the compound, as, for example, in the cases of cuprous and cupric chloride, CuCl and $CuCl_2$.

Acids are named in respect to their containing oxygen or lacking oxygen. In the former case they are classed as oxy-acids, HNO_3, and in the latter as hydro-acids, HCl. The oxy-acids are named after the nonmetal present, the ending of the name indicating the relative amount of oxygen. The name ending in "ic" is used for the most important acid, as sulphuric H_2SO_4, nitric HNO_3, carbonic H_2CO_3. The salts from them are called by names ending in "ate," as sulphate, nitrate, carbonate. The modifications of this for other cases are best shown by a table.

The common acid, $HClO_3$, chloric acid; its salt, $KClO_3$, potassium chlorate.

With more oxygen, $HClO_4$, perchloric acid; its salt, $KClO_4$, potassium perchlorate.

With less oxygen, $HClO_2$, chlorous acid; its salt, $KClO_2$, potassium chlorite.

With still less oxygen, $HClO$, hypochlorous acid, its salt, $KClO$, potassium hypochlorite.

Like the names of the first group, these are sometimes reversed, so that we may say chlorate of potassium. Names like "chlorate of potash" are unscientific, but are usually readily understood.

The hydro-acids are simply named, hydrochloric, hydrobromic acid, and so on, according to the nonmetal contained in them. Their salts, as $NaCl$, fall into the first group and are named after the manner of sodium chloride.

Many substances like ammonia NH_3, and methane CH_4, have specific names which are used to the exclusion of any names based upon their composition. They apply usually to familiar substances and cause little trouble.

CHAPTER XI

CHEMICAL REACTIONS

IF any progress has been made by the reader in the understanding of the characteristics of the elements and their compounds so far discussed, the nature of chemical reactions must to a certain extent now be familiar to him. The first conception may not be an easy one, but after the first comprehension progress should be rapid. Chemical reactions vary less than might be supposed at first glance, and it is the purpose of this chapter to classify and analyze them.

The simple reactions which come under the scope of inorganic chemistry may be placed in one of four classes.

(A) Union of elements and compounds.

$$S + O_2 \rightarrow SO_2; \quad SO_3 + H_2O \rightarrow H_2SO_4$$

(B) Decomposition into elements or simpler compounds, the reverse of A.

$$HgO \rightarrow Hg + O; \quad H_2CO_3 \rightarrow CO_2 + H_2O$$

(C) Withdrawal of one constituent from a compound through its greater affinity for another. This reaction often takes the form of the replacement in a compound of one element by another element of similar nature.

$$Ca + H_2O \rightarrow CaO + H_2; \quad Zn + H_2SO_4 \rightarrow ZnSO_4 + H_2$$

(D) Ionic reactions among acids, bases and salts, including double decomposition and neutralization.

(A) CHEMICAL UNION

Union among elements and compounds is a familiar experience in the laboratory, and a few experiments would make the idea clearer than much explanation. Some cases of union are familiar, such as combustion, a reaction in which the element burning unites with oxygen to form the respective oxide. Corrosion of metals is another illustration. Metals unite with oxygen or sulphur to form simple compounds, as zinc oxide, or zinc sulphide. A union may be so rapid that we call it a combustion, or only moderately rapid, so that it requires some minutes perhaps, or again so slow that in short periods of time its action is imperceptible, as in the tarnishing of metals.

The essential features of such a union are that the elements cease to exist as free elements; they are merged into a new substance with a set of properties differing from those of its constituents. The compounds contain the elements, but in a chemical sense, not as a bottle contains a liquid, or sirup contains sugar. The element is not usually apparent in its compound. Unless some special tests are applied, neither carbon nor oxygen is noticeable in their compound, carbon dioxide. Hydrogen, a gas, uniting with oxygen, a gas, forms the liquid, water. This may be further illustrated by the union of copper and sulphur. Both these elements have definite and easily recognizable characteristics. When they are heated together an action is apparent as the mass of material glows brightly. A new substance will be noted, black and brittle, essentially different from the elements applied, yet evidently made up of these elements. The union of simple compounds to form more complex compounds is of somewhat similar nature. The constituents, as in the case of elements, are merged into the new substance and lose their own characteristic properties. The union of water with oxides of metals and nonmetals represents the most characteristic phase of this. The union of sulphur trioxide and water, $H_2O + SO_3 \rightarrow H_2SO_4$, is an example of this.

The convenient signs by which a chemical union, in fact any chemical change, may be recognized are: the development of heat, although in some cases heat is absorbed; the appearance of a new set of properties; the fact that proportions involved are absolutely definite. When these facts are noted, we may be certain that the change which has taken place is of a chemical nature.

All chemical changes are theoretically reversible and we can hardly conceive of such reversion being impossible. It is true, if ordinary conditions favor a reaction in one direction, the conditions must ordinarily be altered materially to favor the opposite. Hence in most simple discussions one phase of a reaction is likely to be all that demands our attention.

(B) DECOMPOSITION INTO ELEMENTS AND SIMPLER COMPOUNDS

This is the opposite of the reaction of union. Naturally another set of compounds is ordinarily to be discussed in cases of decomposition. For union we select our illustrations from active elements like phosphorus and magnesium. For decomposition mercuric oxide and nitrogen compounds, both unstable, offer good illustrations.

$$HgO \rightarrow Hg + O; \quad NH_4NO_2 \rightarrow 2H_2O + N_2$$

The above statement applies in great measure to the decomposition of compounds into simpler compounds. For union we can refer to the often mentioned formation of sulphuric acid, $SO_3 + H_2O \rightarrow H_2SO_4$. For the opposite action we select an unstable compound like carbonic acid, $H_2CO_3 \rightarrow CO_2 + H_2O$.

(C) The Withdrawal of One Constituent from a Compound

Several reactions of this type have already been referred to. When water is treated with calcium, the affinity of the calcium for the oxygen is so great that it extracts the oxygen from the water, combining with it, and the hydrogen is left free. Copper oxide when heated with carbon or hydrogen loses its oxygen to the carbon and the copper is left in uncombined form.

$$H_2O + Ca \rightarrow CaO + H_2$$
$$CuO + H_2 \rightarrow H_2O + Cu$$

Replacement. An interesting case of replacement is that of the action of one of the more active metals with an acid. The metal replaces the hydrogen, and the latter is freed. This is the regular method of preparing hydrogen.

$$Zn + H_2SO_4 \rightarrow ZnSO_4 + H_2$$

Again a more active metal replaces a less active metal from its salt when in solution.

$$Zn + CuSO_4 \rightarrow ZnSO_4 + Cu$$

(D) Ionic Reactions Among Acids, Bases, and Salts

These are of such a special type that they will require special treatment later (Chapter XIII).

Catalysts (Catalyzers)

The topic of chemical reaction would be incomplete without a reference to *catalysts*. These are substances which accelerate a reaction which might otherwise ultimately be completed, but at a slower rate. At the end the catalyst is found to be unaltered. So striking is the difference in speed of reaction at times that the catalyst seems actually to cause the change to take place. The reason for the action of catalysts is often not clear, but several types are fairly well understood. Many catalysts include elements which have a variable valence. It is possible, and in some cases certain, that these elements take up an additional amount of oxygen from the air, for example, thus passing to a compound of higher oxygen content. They then lose this oxygen to some other substance, dropping to the lower valence. This may be repeated indefinitely. Oxides of cobalt, manganese, cerium, and nitrogen are in this group.

Another group of catalysts is supposed to act through the formation of intermediate compounds, which are again decomposed and the catalyst is left in its original state. Such a supposition is plausible enough, but can be verified in few cases.

Still another catalyst is the metallic, often called the contact catalyst. Palladium and platinum are especially efficient. These act in the case of gases particularly. It is supposed that they absorb the gases by a process called occlusion. The gases are thus brought into such intimate contact within the minute spaces of the metal that they come within the sphere of their natural chemical attraction.

Water is an important catalyst. In fact it acts more

often than we ordinarily suspect. Chlorine is said to bleach, but the presence of water is essential. The substances called enzymes, active in the digestive juices, are catalysts. This carries us into other chapters of our subject, but they should be mentioned in this connection. A small amount of the enzyme brings about the change in a large amount of food. Ferments, too, are similar in their catalytic action, but since they are living organisms, explanation of an altogether different type is possible.

"Negative catalysts" is a term applied to substances which retard the rate of action of other substances. They may actually have a retarding effect, or in a sense nullify the action of positive catalysts. The name "negative" explains itself. They do not compare in importance with the catalysts of the type mentioned above.

Equilibrium of Chemical Reactions

The general idea of equilibrium in a physical sense will be illustrated from the case of a bottle partially filled with ammonia water. We will first imagine the stopper of the bottle to be in place. Ammonia gas escapes from the water into the space above. Presently this space becomes saturated, and ammonia passes back into the water at as rapid a rate as it leaves it. We now have a state of equilibrium, the rate of action in one direction balanced by the rate in the opposite direction. There are abundant proofs that this condition is not one of rest. It is simply balanced action.

If now the stopper of the bottle is removed, the ammonia gas in the space above the water will escape into the air, and its amount in that space diminishes. The equilibrium is now disturbed, and more ammonia escapes from the water in an attempt to fill up the space, but from the space the gas will continuously pass into the air. In this manner the ammonia will finally all pass from the water. If, on the other hand, more ammonia gas were forced into the bottle, the equilibrium would be disturbed in the other direction and the gas would pass into the water to the limit of its capacity. This simple physical example is cited to make clear the same idea applied to chemical reactions. Reactions of the double decomposition type are of such a nature that equilibrium is the first condition, and, unless there is some disturbance of this equilibrium, there is no progress in the chemical reactions. If we mix solutions of sodium chloride and potassium nitrate, we might readily assume that there would be formed two new substances, sodium nitrate and potassium chloride. Then, if we begin with the latter two, they will react to form the first two. The following two equations have the same meaning.

$$KCl + NaNO_3 \rightleftarrows NaCl + KNO_3$$
$$NaCl + KNO_3 \rightleftarrows NaNO_3 + KCl$$

The result is an equilibrium. The equilibrium will remain, and all four substances will be present unless we find some means of disturbing it, by pushing it in one direction or the other. There are two simple devices, akin to the ammonia water device, of removing one of the products from the reaction.

One of these devices is to so select our substances that one of the products is a gas, or can readily be converted into a gas, which will then escape from the solution. The reaction between calcium chloride and sulphuric acid is such a case, $CaCl_2 + H_2SO_4 \rightarrow CaSO_4 + 2HCl \uparrow$ (a gas).

The hydrochloric acid formed escapes from the mixture on account of its gaseous condition and has no further action. The reaction cannot reverse; the arrow pointing upward indicates the escape of the gas.

The other device is the selection of substances so that one of the products is insoluble in the water present, hence it is just as truly removed from the reaction as though it were a gas. The insoluble substance precipitates and its escape would be indicated in an equation by an arrow pointing downward.

$$CaCl_2 + NaCO_3 \rightarrow 2NaCl + CaCO_3 \downarrow \text{ (an insoluble solid)}$$

Simple as this matter is, it is an essential consideration in the progress of chemical reactions. Some important industrial methods, like the Solvay soda process and the Haber ammonia process, have become possible by the full appreciation of the conditions of equilibrium.

CHAPTER XII

THE LAWS OF MOLECULES AND ATOMS—SOLUTIONS

IT is evident that gases resemble each other fairly closely. A more exact study reveals the fact that in certain physical considerations all gases are quite alike. They obey the same laws, and, it will be seen presently, have the same physical composition. The gas laws concern pressure, temperature, and diffusibility.

The Law of Pressure—Boyle's Law

Gases are made up of molecules moving rapidly through the empty spaces lying between them. The molecule is small in comparison with the spaces in which it moves. The expansion and contraction of a gas does not involve the molecules proper, but only the spaces between them. When pressure is applied to a gas, the distance between the molecules is diminished, while it increases when the pressure is relieved. This diminution or increase of volume is perfectly regular, depending directly upon the change in pressure, and is the same for all gases, whatever their nature. This fact is expressed formally by the law: other conditions remaining constant, the volume of all gases varies inversely as the pressure. This is expressed also by the formula

$$\frac{P}{P'} = \frac{V'}{V}$$

Pressure is measured conveniently on the basis of the column of mercury, 760 mm., or 30 inches high, which balances the weight of a column of air of indefinite height at sea level. This unit of pressure is one atmosphere, or 760 mm., and is expressed in English units as 15 pounds to the square inch. Under ordinary conditions, near sea level, the pressure may be ordinarily assumed to be one atmosphere, or 760 mm. A given volume of any gas will just double its volume if this pressure is cut down one-half, or it will contract to half volume if the pressure upon it is increased to double.

THE LAW OF TEMPERATURES—CHARLES'S LAW

The addition of heat to a gas increases its molecular activity and the gas expands. Withdrawing heat, that is cooling, diminishes its molecular activity and the gas contracts. It is found that the amount of expansion and contraction for all gases is directly proportional to the changes of temperature. The law may be stated formally as follows: all gases expand or contract equally, in direct proportion to the increase or diminution of the absolute temperature. Formula:

$$\frac{V}{V'} = \frac{abs.\ T}{abs.\ T'}$$

This increase or diminution is 1/273 of the volume of the gas, starting at 0° C. for every degree warmed or cooled. In order to make comparisons we must use a scale for temperature measurement which has an actual meaning, for the ordinary scales are arbitrary, starting at a zero point determined solely by convenience. The absolute zero is at a point 273° below that of the centigrade scale, and it is determined as follows: When a gas which is at 0° C. is cooled 1° C., its contraction is 1/273 of its volume. Cooled 10°, the contraction is 10/273 of its volume. Hence, cooled to —273°, the contraction is 273/273. Its volume is now zero. As contraction is due to decrease of molecular motion, the seeming contraction to zero indicates a cessation of all molecular motion. The point at which this condition exists, —273° C., is therefore a real starting point of molecular motion, that is, of temperature. On the absolute scale, then, 0° C. equals 273° Abs., and room temperature, 21° C., is 294° Abs. Temperature comparisons for volume changes must be made on this absolute scale, which is obtained by adding 273 to the temperature on the centigrade scale.

THE LAW OF DIFFUSION—GRAHAM'S LAW

Gases diffuse into space at unequal rates, but according to the same law. It can easily be seen that a heavy gas will diffuse slowly and a light gas rapidly. Hydrogen, with a molecular weight of two (there are two atoms in the molecule), will diffuse more rapidly than oxygen, molecular weight thirty-two. It will, however, diffuse only four times as readily, instead of sixteen times, as might be expected. Gases then diffuse in the inverse ratio of the square roots of their densities.

To these three laws involving the gases, *Avogadro's hypothesis* may be added and our conception of the molecules and their motion will be reasonably complete. This hypothesis is that, in equal volumes of all gases under similar conditions, the number of molecules is the same. This is not capable of absolute proof, but it is supported by much evidence both physical and chemical. As an example of the latter is this fact: When hydrogen and chlorine unite, exactly one volume of hydrogen unites with one volume of chlorine, and they form together two volumes of hydrochloric acid. There could not be this equality, assuming our chemical theory to be sound, unless the numbers of molecules were the same in each of the three gases. The reaction requires an equal number of molecules per c. c. for each substance.

The equality of the numbers of molecules in equal volumes of gases under similar conditions makes it possible to use a simple device, called the *gram-molecular volume*, in dealing with them We take the molecular weight in grams for all gases, for hydrogen, 2 g. (the molecule of hydrogen contains two atoms) for oxygen, 32, for carbon dioxide, CO_2, 44g. These weights indicate equal numbers of molecules. Upon trial, it is found that 2g. of hydrogen occupy 22.4 liters. So also it is found that 32 g. of oxygen and 44 g. of carbon dioxide occupy 22.4 liters. Experiment further shows that the gram-molecular weight of all other gases occupies this same volume, a fact which must follow also from theoretical considerations. The practical convenience of this agreement is that it makes it an easy matter to establish the relation between molecular weights of gases and their actual weights. To find the molecular weight of a gas it is only necessary to find the weight of 22.4 liters of the gas in grams. The number thus found is the molecular weight. On the other hand, given the molecular weight of a gas, it tells us at once how many grams there are in the gram-molecular volume, 22.4 liters. From this the weight of any desired volume may be calculated.

Now all our laws and hypotheses conform to the facts

of mechanics. The pressure of all gases must be equal, for pressure is made up of the individual momentum of all the molecules. Those molecules which lack in speed compensate for this by the greater weight of the molecule so that the momentum of all is equalized.

LAWS INVOLVING THE ATOM

The preceding discussion has been one of physics, very intimately associated, however, with chemical discussions. Certain chemical regularities also are observed and these are expressed in laws. These principles have led to the development of the atomic theory. We will assume the latter as fully accepted, and show how it conforms to these laws.

a. Matter is indestructible, and the underlying atoms ordinarily do not change. They may unite with other atoms, and may separate from them, but their existence as atoms is always maintained.

b. The law of constancy of composition must follow from the constant nature of the atom. The molecule of the compound cannot vary, for it is always built up from the same number of unvarying atoms.

c. The law of multiple proportions is illustrated by the following pairs of compounds, H_2O and H_2O_2, CO and CO_2, SO_2, and SO_3. These compounds, involving the same elements, must be made up in such simple ways, for the atom is the building unit. Carbon united with oxygen may form carbon monoxide, CO, or carbon dioxide CO_2, perhaps other similar compounds, but there can be no variation in proportions, except by simple whole numbers.

Assuming the atomic structure and the atomic weights,

these and other laws involving the atom seem self-evident. Historically the development was in the reverse direction. These laws and truths led to the atomic theory.

SOLUTIONS

Solution is generally assumed to be the merging of a substance in a liquid, so that the two form a homogeneous mixture, one that is altogether clear and even throughout. Gases mingle with other gases, they are absorbed by solids, and solids mix evenly as in the alloys. These are all properly solutions, but our chief interest centers in solutions in liquids, and especially in solutions in water.

The *solvent action of water* varies *in respect to gases*. Oxygen and nitrogen (air) dissolve so little that the ordinary observer must have his attention called to the fact of their solubility. One thousand cubic centimeters of water absorb about 20–30 cubic centimeters of air, of which one-third is oxygen. This is a small amount, yet enough to provide water-breathing animals with oxygen, and to supply enough oxygen for the purification of waters not too highly polluted. Another class of gases includes carbon dioxide, hydrogen sulphide, and chlorine. Water dissolves about equal volumes of each of these, so that the presence of the gases is noticeable by taste, color, and odor. These solutions can even be used for laboratory reagents, but they are very dilute. The volume of the gas, equal to that of the water, represents only a small fraction, about 1/100, of its weight. A third class of gases is represented by ammonia and hydrochloric acid, which are so soluble that in their solutions the water is usually overlooked. One volume of water dissolves several hundred volumes of these gases, from 25–40 per cent by weight, and these solutions show very marked chemical properties.

The solvent action of water on liquids.—There are rather few common inorganic liquids. The three acids, sulphuric, nitric, and phosphoric, are soluble in all proportions. Among organic liquids, of which there are many, the solubility is usually determined by the presence of the hydroxyl group (OH). Alcohols and organic acids, as acetic and lactic, contain this group and are therefore likely to be soluble. Mineral and vegetable oils are insoluble.

The greatest interest attaches to the *solvent action of water on solids.* The matter is usually looked upon from the other side, namely the solubility of solids in water. Their solubility varies considerably, from that of quartz, which is considered to be absolutely insoluble, to that of sodium iodide, which dissolves in less than its own weight of water.

It is well known that when water is heated, it will, in most cases, dissolve an increased amount of any soluble solid. For any given temperature there is a limit however, and when a hot saturated solution cools, the solid in part separates out. This operation is frequently used in the handling and purification of soluble solids. As a part of the solid under consideration separates out, the impurities, if not too abundant, are likely to remain in solution.

The general effect of heat is the increase of molecular activity. The solution of a solid involves greater molecular activity, so that it is but natural that the effect of heat is to increase the solvent action of water upon solids. For the same reason heat diminishes the solvent action of water upon gases. To dissolve a solid we heat our solvent, to dissolve a gas we cool it; in both cases we strive to attain the liquid state.

Solids dissolved in water exert some influence on the physical properties of the water. It no longer boils so easily, nor does it freeze so easily. The most interesting feature of these facts is that their influence is a regular one, depending upon the actual number of molecules of the solid present, and not upon its individual nature. Therefore, amounts of solids which show equal numbers of molecules will have the same influence. To obtain molecular equality we need only to apply the molecular weights of different substances in grams, obtained by adding together the atomic weights of the constituent elements. Such weights must contain equal numbers of molecules. Osmotic pressure is the pressure which a solid exhibits in distributing itself through a solvent, and resembles the diffusive power of gases as they distribute themselves through space. In all these respects the solid distributed through a solvent resembles a gas, its conduct being determined by the number of molecules present, rather than by the chemical nature of the molecules.

Supersaturation. When solutions saturated at high temperatures are cooled, we may expect the solute (the substance dissolved) to crystallize out as its solubility becomes lessened at the lower temperature. With care, however, in many cases, the substance may be prevented from separating out, although it is present in amounts above the solubility limit. This is, however, not a condition of equilibrium, and if a crystal of the solute is introduced the excess crystallizes out with great rapidity.

CHAPTER XIII

ACIDS, BASES, AND SALTS. THE IONIC THEORY

NO classes of substances are of greater importance than these three—acids, bases, and salts. They have been referred to repeatedly and now must be discussed more fully.

Acids invariably contain hydrogen, and under favorable conditions this hydrogen is replaceable by a metal. In such cases salts are formed. Acids may be solids, as boric acid; liquids, as sulphuric acid; or gases, as hydrochloric acid. In the popular mind acids are associated with the liquid condition, and when used in this condition in solution in water, their reactions are most typical and their characteristics most evident.

They have a strong sour taste, and are readily detected by certain colored substances called indicators. Of these litmus is the most common. This last is colored red by acids, it is turned blue by bases, and is not affected by the typical salts. Other indicators show other color changes, but, except for a greater delicacy of action, they have virtually the same application.

As was stated in a previous chapter, acids fall into two classes. First, those of the type of hydrochloric acid, HCl. These are the hydro-acids. HCl, HBr, HI and H_2S are the chief members of this group. The acids of the other group contain oxygen and are uniformly built up on the plan of sulphuric acid, namely a nonmetallic oxide united with water.

Sulphuric acid, $H_2SO_4 = SO_3 + H_2O$
Sulphurous acid, $H_2SO_3 = SO_2 + H_2O$
Nitric acid, $2HNO_3 = N_2O_5 + H_2O$
Nitrous acid, $2HNO_2 = N_2O_3 + H_2O$
Carbonic acid, $H_2CO_3 = CO_2 + H_2O$
Phosphoric acid, $2H_3PO_4 = P_2O_5 + 3H_2O$

It is convenient to refer to these compounds as acids, although their true acid nature asserts itself only when they are dissolved in water.

Acids vary greatly in strength. Hydrochloric, nitric, and sulphuric are among the strongest, while carbonic acid is exceedingly weak. They vary in stability. Phosphoric acid is decomposed with great difficulty, while carbonic acid separates into its constituents as rapidly as it is formed.

Bases are formed by the union of the oxides of the metals with water. In cases of the more active metals the union is readily accomplished, in others it must be brought about indirectly. Typical are:

$$Na_2O + H_2O \rightarrow 2NaOH$$
$$CaO + H_2O \rightarrow Ca(OH)_2$$

The bases are thus hydroxides and in their reactions the hydroxyl group—OH, is likely to remain intact, passing unchanged from one combination to another. Bases are the complements of acids. They are derived from the metals, the acids from the nonmetals. Bases yield the hydroxyl group, acids yield hydrogen, which together form water, characteristic by-product of their interaction. Bases turn litmus blue, while acids turn it red. The active bases are corrosive like the active acids, but, when the two unite, they lose their characteristic properties, and the resulting salts are neutral. Bases are solids and only the more active are soluble in water.

Salts are formed by the interaction of bases and acids; water is formed in every case as the by-product. Salts are usually crystalline substances. Some have a simple salty taste, but many vary from this. Lead salts are sweet, aluminum salts are astringent. Salts are colored only when they contain certain metals or acids. When made up of bases and acids of equal activity, they are neutral substances, as Na_2SO_4, sodium sulphate. If the base is an active one, and the acid weak, the properties of the base predominate, as shown by their turning litmus blue. If however, the acid is an active one and the base weak, the acid characteristics predominate, and such salts turn litmus red. Sodium carbonate, Na_2CO_3, and ferrous sulphate, $FeSO_4$, are such salts. The acids, nitric acid, HNO_3, sulphuric acid, H_2SO_4, and phosphoric acid, H_3PO_4, differ in the amount of the characteristic acid hydrogen which they contain. This shows itself in the possibilities developed when this hydrogen is replaced by a metal. Let sodium be selected for the metal. In the case of nitric acid, the salt formed by replacing the hydrogen by the sodium is sodium nitrate, $NaNO_3$, and there is no other salt possible. When, however, sulphuric acid is the acid in question we may form $NaHSO_4$, sodium hydrogen sulphate, and Na_2SO_4, sodium sulphate, the normal salt. The salts which still contain acid hydrogen are called acid salts, and have the properties of both acid and salt. For this reason they often have unique value.

Salts are formed most simply by the reaction called neutralization, the union between a base and an acid. These reactions proceed with rapidity and completeness.

The base supplies the metallic part, the acid the nonmetallic part. The by-product is water, the hydroxyl group coming from the base, the hydrogen from the acid. Equations showing neutralization differ only in the numbers of groups applied. In all cases the number of hydroxyl groups of the base must balance the number of hydrogens of the acid. For instance:

$$NaOH + HCl \rightarrow NaCl + HOH$$
$$Ca(OH)_2 + H_2SO_4 \rightarrow CaSO_4 + 2HOH$$

The simplicity of this reaction between the two most characteristic types of compounds is perhaps due to the formation of water. This illustrates along with other relations the fact that the greater portion of inorganic reactions are in a "water system."

Although neutralization is the simplest way of forming a salt, salts are formed in general whenever a metal replaces the hydrogen of an acid directly or indirectly. Salts may also be considered independently from the acids from which they are derived. It is evident that they must be made up of a metallic residue and a nonmetallic residue. Such salts as FeI_2, ferrous iodide, and FeS, ferrous sulphide, are made up simply of the metal and the nonmetal, and they are prepared by the simple union of these. Salts containing oxygen are more complex, but their composition may readily be appreciated.

Calcium carbonate, $CaCO_3 = CaO + CO_2$
Calcium sulphate, $CaSO_4 = CaO + SO_3$
Sodium sulphite, $Na_2SO_3 = Na_2O + SO_2$
Lead nitrate, $Pb(NO_3)_2 = PbO + N_2O_5$
Calcium silicate, $CaSiO_3 = CaO + SiO_2$

It is not always possible to put together these constituents in order to prepare salts, but the borates and silicates, especially in glass making, are thus prepared. In decomposing salts at high temperatures this aspect of their structure is of prime importance, and they usually decompose in accordance with this idea of their composition.

As acids and bases represent the typical active compounds of inorganic chemistry, so salts represent the end products of many chemical reactions. If we imagine an active base, as sodium hydroxide, somehow formed in the course of nature, its affinities are such that it would unite with the first substance of acid nature with which it came in contact. The product would be a salt. So also any active nonmetallic substance would sooner or later form an acid, by union with oxygen and water. This acid then would combine with the first substance of basic nature with which it came in contact. Such a course of events takes place in the case of the so-called sulphur found in coal. The sulphur is acutally in the form of iron sulphide, FeS_2, which upon burning, or uniting with air, yields sulphur dioxide, SO_2. This unites gradually with more oxygen to form sulphur trioxide, SO_3, which in its turn forms sulphuric acid, H_2SO_4. This acid soon unites with basic substances, especially calcium and magnesium compounds, and forms salts, sulphates, in which form it is likely to remain indefinitely. The great mass of the earth's crust is composed of compounds of the order of salts, in which the affinities of the elements and compounds have spent themselves. Active substances like free sulphur and boric acid are found occasionally, but they have been formed under unusual conditions and have been protected by chance from the normal reactions to which they are subject.

Molar Solutions

In discussing chemical reactions, it is evident that the units of all reactions are atoms and molecules. If we combine calcium oxide, CaO, and sulphuric acid, H_2SO_4, one molecule of each is needed. We cannot of course pick out one molecule, but if we take the molecular weight of each, in grams, respectively 56 grams and 98 grams, we will have equivalent amounts, representing the same number of molecules for each. This is the principle of molar solutions. Molar solutions are made by dissolving the gram-molecular weight of any substance in one liter of water. Any given amount of such a solution will correspond exactly to the same amount of any other molar solution.

Normal Solutions

Molar solutions are only partially satisfactory. One molecule of sulphuric acid, H_2SO_4, will require two molecules of sodium hydroxide, NaOH, to neutralize it, and phosphoric acid, H_3PO_4, containing three hydrogen atoms, requires three molecules of sodium hydroxide. It is a convenient expedient, therefore, to reduce all solutions to the simplest possible equivalent. If molar sulphuric acid is diluted to half strength, it will now just balance the molar sodium hydroxide solution. So phosphoric acid, H_3PO_4, must be reduced to one-third strength. Calcium hydroxide, $Ca(OH)_2$, must be reduced to one-half strength, and so on. Such solutions, reduced to an absolute equivalence, are called normal solutions, and form the basis of all fine chemical work involving solutions.

It will not be difficult to appreciate that normal solutions may be too concentrated. Normal sodium hydroxide contains 40 grams in one liter. Normal sulphuric acid, 49 grams. Hence normal solutions are usually diluted and used as half normal, fifth, tenth, or twentieth normal, to suit the convenience of the operator. The exact relationship between different solutions of course still continues to apply.

IONIZATION

The reactions which involve solutions of acids, bases, and salts take place with a degree of readiness and completeness which differentiate them from all others. Sodium has a striking affinity for chlorine, and their compound, sodium chloride (salt), NaCl, is exceedingly stable and can be decomposed only with great difficulty. But if a solution of sodium chloride is treated with one of silver nitrate, the chlorine is found to combine with the silver instantly.

Potassium hydroxide reacts at once and completely with an acid, and also with many salts. Instances of reactions of these types can be found in great numbers. All such reactions are explained with great clearness by the assumption of the ionic hypothesis. Briefly stated this is as follows.

When acids, bases, and salts are dissolved in water, they dissociate into their constituent groups, hydrogen or metallic on the one hand, and hydroxyl or nonmetallic on the other. These groups are distinguished from other groups or atoms by carrying a positive or a negative charge of electricity and are called ions. Being dissociated as soon as placed in solution, they are ready to react as soon as they meet with other groups with which reaction is possible. This dissociation into different groups is called ionization.

I. Ionization applies to acids, bases, and salts only. Even then only the stronger acids and bases are ionized to any considerable degree, and the lack of ionization of the weaker bases and acids gives rise to various phenomena, especially to an important action called hydrolysis. It is safe to assume that all salts ionize.

II. The substances must be in solution in water. This is readily illustrated by dissolving hydrochloric acid gas in benzene. It then fails to respond to the tests which are usually applied to acids. Other reagents probably ionize substances dissolved in them, but compared with water their importance is insignificant.

III. Dissociation and decomposition must not be confused. In the case of dissociation the parts into which a compound separates retain a definite relation to the original. They preserve their identity and are capable of reuniting as soon as the conditions causing their separation are removed or reversed. In decomposition the connection between the compounds and the products of the separation is lost. A comparison of two nitrogen compounds will illustrate this. If we heat ammonium nitrite, NH_4NO_2, it decomposes into water and nitrogen, $NH_4NO_2 \rightarrow 2H_2O + 2N$, and only elaborate roundabout methods will serve to unite them to form the original substance. This is decomposition. When however ammonium hydroxide, NH_4OH, is gently heated, the separation into its parts may be reversed by mere cooling of the residual water, $NH_4OH \rightleftarrows NH_3 + HOH$. This is a dissociation. In the process of separation into ions we have a case of dissociation. $Na\,Cl \rightleftarrows Na^+ + Cl^-$. If more water is added, the dissociation is increased. If water is allowed to evaporate, the ions reunite to form the original salt. The degree of ionization may be increased or decreased by simply varying the amount of water present.

IV. The ions are groups, composed of one or more atoms, which preserve their individuality through many reactions. They are positively or negatively charged as will be shown in the sequel, and it is these charges which differentiate them from the original atom or atoms. In any complete compound, the number of positive charges upon the positive ions must equal the number of negative charges upon the negative ions. The sum total then of the charges for any molecule is zero, the charges balancing each other when the molecules are reformed. SO_4 is a common negative ion, but without its charges it cannot exist. If we discharge it electrically, by bringing it in contact with the positive pole of a battery, it at once decomposes into sulphur trioxide and oxygen, $SO_3 + O$. The groups which form ions are readily learned from a consideration of acids, bases and salts. The positively charged ions are hydrogen and the metals. The negatively charged ions are either hydroxyl or the nonmetallic groups.

The list of ions is not a long one.

Positive ions, H^+ and typical metals, Na^+, Ca^{++}, Al^{+++}.

Negative ions, $(OH)^-$ and the acid groups the chief of which are: Cl^-, Br^-, I^-, NO_2^-; $SO_3^=$, $SO_4^=$, $CO_3^=$, $PO_4^{\equiv}$.

Various elements or groups carry more than one charge, either positive or negative, according to their valence. The total number of positive charges balances the total number of negative charges. Acids, bases, and salts are called ionogens, a name indicating that they are capable of producing ions when dissolved in water. In the industries they are called electrolytes. The connotation of this term is that their solutions in water carry the electric current, and that in the end they can be electrolyzed—which we shall explain later.

The peculiar properties of acids and bases are due to the reactive hydrogen and hydroxyl ions respectively. Hence their strength is determined by the amount of ionization which takes place when they are dissolved in water. A strong acid or base is one that is highly dissociated, a weak acid or base is only slightly dissociated. The conductivity for electricity is also determined by the number of ions present. The values found for strength of acids and bases, and that found for their conductivity are found to be the same.

In accordance with this ionization hypothesis, acids, bases, and salts may be defined again in new terms. Acids are compounds which yield positive hydrogen ions when dissolved in water. This statement carries all that is essential. A positive ion requires a negative ion to balance it, and this negative ion can be composed only of a non-metallic group. Bases are compounds which, when dissolved in water, yield negative hydroxyl ions: the other ion is perforce positive and must be composed of a metal. A salt yields positive metal ions, and negative nonmetal ions.

Water itself is very little ionized. In comparison with the more active bases, acids, and salts its ionization may be considered negligible. But when very weak bases and acids come into consideration, the very slight ionization of water must be considered.

The evidence of the ionization hypothesis is drawn from various considerations based upon physical measurements of solutions. Solutions containing ionogens show abnormal characteristics in respect to their freezing points, boiling points, and osmotic pressure. Solutions of sodium chloride, NaCl, for example, show an effect which would be due not to the presence of one molecule, but of two. This is to be attributed to the fact that in aqueous solution this salt yields, not one molecule of NaCl, but two units, namely, Na^+ and Cl^-. Electrical measurements are in agreement with this. There are indications of ionization outside the field of these delicate measurements. The ready reactivity of ionogens is such an illustration. Solutions of ionogens conduct electricity, for the current is carried by the ions, and electrolysis is another illustration. The colors of salts in solution often show ionization. Copper sulphate by itself is white, copper chloride is yellow, copper bromide is olive colored, yet, when they are in solution, they all show the blue color of the common copper ion.

Ionic reactions, although very common, do not, of course, include the entire range of chemical reactions. Combustion and other similar combinations are outside their province. This is true of many combinations and decompositions accomplished at high temperatures, where the presence of water is out of the question. The use of the terms, "in a wet way" and "in a dry way," now obsolete, emphasized a distinction between the two classes of reactions.

ELECTROLYSIS

Electrolysis is one of the fascinating chapters of chemistry. Its details are explained with ease by means of the ionic hypothesis. This assumes that when an ionogen (acid, base, or salt) is dissolved in water, it is dissociated into ions, certain of the ions carrying positive, and others negative charges. So far, the electric current has not come into the discussion. Let us place two poles of a battery into a solution of an ionogen. The negative ions of the solution will now begin to travel toward the positive pole, and the positive ions to the negative pole. This conduct has given origin to the name ion, which means to move or to travel. When the ions have arrived at the corresponding pole, the positive charge of the pole and the negative charge of the ions neutralize each other and the ion ceases to exist as such. The same happens at the negative pole. Hence at these two poles we have released atoms or groups of atoms, no longer in the ionic form. This will be best understood by following specific illustrations.

A. We take a solution of copper chloride, Cu^{++} and $2Cl^-$, and introduce the poles of a battery. The copper ion is drawn to the negative pole and its charge is neutralized. The Cu^{++} ion has now become ordinary copper, Cu, and is deposited on the pole. So the Cl^- ion is converted into chlorine, Cl, and escapes as the familiar gas.

Electrolysis is supposed to be the separation of a compound into its parts by means of electricity. It will be seen that the separation was already effected by the ionization, and that the current merely attracts and discharges the ions previously present.

B. To illustrate another phase of electrolysis we select sodium chloride, $Na^+ + Cl^-$. When the current is passed and the respective ions attracted to the opposite poles, their charges are neutralized and the chlorine ions become atoms, that is, molecules, and the gas escapes. At the negative pole in like manner molecular sodium is formed. Sodium, however, is so active that it at once decomposes the water present.

$Na + HOH \rightarrow NaOH + H$. Hydrogen escapes and the sodium hydroxide remains in solution. The original action is the same as with the copper chloride solution, but a secondary reaction takes place on account of the activity of the sodium. The chlorine escapes as before.

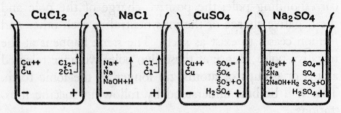

SCHEMATIC REPRESENTATION OF ELECTROLYSIS

C. Copper sulphate shows another form of secondary reaction. The electrolysis develops Cu, the metal, which is deposited, and SO_4, a hypothetical group, which can exist only as part of a compound or as an ion. It then must break down into substances capable of existence by themselves. Such are SO_3 and O. Hence at the positive pole oxygen will be evolved, and the residual sulphur trioxide will form sulphuric acid with the water present.

D. Sodium sulphate, Na_2SO_4, illustrates the most complicated case. As the result of electrolysis we should have Na_2, sodium, and SO_4, sulphate. The former, however, reacting with water yields sodium hydroxide and hydrogen, $NaOH + H$, the latter, hydrogen sulphate (sulphuric acid) and oxygen, $H_2SO_4 + O$.

These four cases represent essentially all the ordinary complications of electrolysis. On account of the response of acids, bases and salts to the action of electricity, the term electrolyte has some justification.

A recent revision of the interpretations of ionization and the structure and action of acids and bases (by Brönsted) has not been presented. For an elementary presentation the interpretations given above seem to the author more serviceable.

The applications of the principles of electro-chemistry to batteries, electroplating and similar problems will be discussed more advantageously under the head of the metals.

CHAPTER XIV

THE METALS, OR BASE-FORMING ELEMENTS

THE rough classification of all the elements into two groups, metals and nonmetals, is based upon essential differences in both physical and chemical respects. Metals as a class, considering the well-known metals, are opaque solids, heavy, malleable—that is, they can be flattened out under the blows of a hammer—good conductors of heat and electricity, mostly of a silver color (gold and copper are exceptional), and possessing a shine which is called the luster. The nonmetals on the other hand are not predominantly in any one of the three physical states. They vary much in weight, are brittle, nonconductors, have a variety of colors, and no marked luster. The chemical differences are even more pronounced. The metals form bases, the nonmetals acids. In salts the metal is positive, the nonmetal negative. Some metals have less pronounced characteristics, and a number of elements are doubtful, but in the main the classification is logical and useful.

The popular impression as to what constitutes a metal is correct as far as it goes, but it includes in its range only one type of metals, those which are in ordinary use. In this group are platinum, gold, silver, mercury, copper, lead, tin, nickel, iron, zinc and aluminum. These metals are of such low chemical activity that when they are once obtained free, they are permanent enough to serve many purposes. These purposes are mainly based upon the physical properties of these metals, such as tensile strength, ductility, malleability, toughness, great weight, conductivity for electricity, color, and luster. To this group we are now ready to add another group of metals, sodium, potassium, calcium, magnesium, and several others. These differ mainly in two respects. They are light, only one being as heavy even as aluminum, and they are so active chemically that they are obtained free with great difficulty, and readily revert to compounds. It is therefore natural that they are unfamiliar in their free state, and not available for practical purposes. Their usefulness lies in their compounds, in contrast to the metals of the other group, which like copper, iron, and zinc serve more uses in the form of the actual metal.

The "light" metals are those included in the first column of the table "electrochemical series." The term may be taken to connote approximately three features, low specific gravity, ready combustibility, and such high chemical activity that they are known and used chiefly in the form of their compounds. "Heavy" metals are heavy (exception aluminum), less active, and usable in the form of metals. The designation of light and heavy metals is a very suggestive one, although the demarcation of properties is not absolutely sharp.

Aluminum on account of its lightness, abundance and color has been a great asset, while its chemical activity has not been a serious disadvantage. We are now becoming familiar with the fact that magnesium, one of the "light" metals, is now being produced for special purposes. The advantages of its abundance and lightness counterbalance any limitations due to high chemical activity. The eyes of the chemical world are even now turning to beryllium of the same group, with reference to possible availability and usefulness.

THE ELECTROCHEMICAL SERIES

Barring the points of difference just discussed, the metals may be said to be strikingly alike in their chemical properties. This resemblance applies to the nature of their affinities, which are of the same general nature, but vary in degree, from the highly reactive potassium, to inactive gold, which forms compounds only with difficulty. If the intensity of the affinities among all the metals is compared, they may be arranged in order, the most active first, the least active last. This list is called the electrochemical series, and may be used in many ways as the index of the chemical properties of the metals.

THE ELECTROCHEMICAL SERIES

A	B	C
Lithium	Aluminum	Hydrogen
Potassium	Manganese	Copper
Calcium	Zinc	Arsenic
Sodium	Chromium	Antimony
Magnesium	Iron	Mercury
	Cobalt	Silver
	Nickel	Platinum
	Tin	Gold
	Lead	

Each metal of this list has a greater tendency to go into combination than any following it, and a lesser tendency than any preceding it. If, therefore, we introduce zinc into a solution of copper sulphate, the zinc will go into solution, forming zinc sulphate, and the copper will be deposited.

The arrangement of the metals in groups shown by the three columns is suggestive. The first group includes the light metals, already discussed. The second group includes the more active heavy metals. The third group includes those which are less active. Hydrogen, which in acids stands for the metals of salts, marks the division between the more and less active groups. The more active will directly replace hydrogen from acids, the less active will do so only indirectly. A practical outcome of this relation to hydrogen is that in nature only the metals of the last group are found free. The others occur only in their compounds.

We may summarize. In the electrochemical list we have a complete arrangement of the metals in respect to the intensity of their affinity. These may be roughly divided into three groups represented by the three columns: A, the most active, known and used mostly in the form of compounds, ending with magnesium; B, the more active of the common metals, ending with lead; C, the less active of the common metals, the last three being known as the noble metals on account of their low chemical activity.

OCCURRENCE OF THE METALS

The study of the earth's crust impresses us with the preponderance of two nonmetals, oxygen and silicon; and of six metals, aluminum, iron, calcium, magnesium, sodium, and potassium. All the other metals are present in insignificant amounts compared with the whole mass of the earth. When we look for them in ordinary rock they are difficult to find. It is only through concentrations of scattered masses, and through concentrations of concentrations, that such metals as lead, copper and zinc are found in amounts sufficient to be useful. Fortunately there are such concentrations, and men seek them and utilize them with the greatest eagerness.

The more active metals are found in nature only in compounds in two general states. The first of these is as a constituent of the primary rock of the earth, in the form of more or less complex silicates. They are in these forms in stable combination and are practically unavailable to men; an example is potassium in granite rock. The second set of compounds represent decomposition products of the first, formed through endless years of weathering and other agencies, and subsequent concentration in forms which are ordinarily of great usefulness. Common salt, NaCl, and the German potash deposits, KCl, are of this order, while the vast quantities of potassium compounds tied up in the mineral feldspar are altogether useless in the present state of the chemical industries. The ocean represents a concentration of compounds of sodium and other metals, while the many salt deposits of the land represent a still further concentration, with an increased advantage to men.

The metals of the active group are useful mainly in the form of compounds. Sodium, potassium, calcium, and magnesium form many such compounds which are applied in various ways. In the study of these metals, then, the elements play a minor rôle. Compounds of metals are in the form of oxides, hydroxides, and the salts, of which the most important are carbonates, chlorides, sulphates and nitrates. Some other salts also come into consideration, like the phosphates of sodium and calcium.

The less active metals occur in somewhat different forms

in nature. Aluminum and iron are abundant in the form of silicates, in primary rock, but the useful compounds of these and other metals are found in secondary formations and concentrations. Among these utilizable forms are the oxides, as iron oxide, Fe_2O_3; the hydroxides, as limonite, iron hydroxide, $Fe_4O_3(OH)_6$; the carbonates, as zinc carbonate, $ZnCO_3$; and the sulphides, as lead sulphide, PbS. Chlorides and sulphates do occur, but in lesser abundance. The least active metals mentioned near the end of the electrochemical list occur in the free state. The chief in this group are copper, bismuth, platinum, and gold.

EXTRACTION OF THE METALS

As these elements are of use chiefly in the free form, as metals, the extraction from their ores is a most important chemical consideration. This will be described in a later chapter on metallurgy. It may here be outlined most briefly. The extraction of the metals takes three main forms. The first is treatment of the oxide, and this includes hydroxide and carbonate, for upon heating, these are converted into the oxide. The oxide is simply heated with carbon, which combines with the oxygen, and the metal is left free.

$$2CuO + C \rightarrow 2Cu + CO_2$$

$$\left. \begin{array}{l} Cu(OH)_2 \\ CuCO_3 \end{array} \right\} \text{ heated} \rightarrow CuO + \left\{ \begin{array}{l} H_2O \\ CO_2 \end{array} \right.$$

When an ore is in the form of sulphide it must first be converted into the oxide by "roasting," that is, heating in a current of air. The sulphur is thus disposed of and the metal oxide is now ready for reduction by means of carbon.

$$ZnS + 3O \rightarrow ZnO + SO_2$$
$$ZnO + C \rightarrow Zn + CO$$

The third type of ores includes those which contain the metal in the free form. The metal may simply be melted out. But in the case of gold and platinum the metal is so thinly scattered that various devices must be applied. Some of these devices are of chemical nature, as conversion of the gold into chlorides and cyanides and washing out the soluble salts, from which the gold is readily recovered. They may also be physical, as the process of amalgamation, that is, solution in mercury, or separating the heavy particles of gold from the lighter particles of rock by flushing with water.

CHAPTER XV

THE ALKALI METALS

THE whole class of metals will be considered in four groups, departing somewhat from the usual classification. The first group will consist of the alkali metals, to be treated in this chapter. The next will include metals of the calcium group (Chap. XVI). Our third group will include the more active heavy metals, down to hydrogen (Chap. XVII), and the last group the less active metals (Chap. XVIII). The numerical balance is by no means maintained by this classification, but the chemical ideas are better developed thereby.

The alkali metals include five closely related metals.

	ATOMIC WEIGHT
Cesium, Cs	133
Rubidium, Rb	85.5
Potassium, K	39.1
Sodium, Na	23
Lithium, Li	7

The first point in their relationship is the difference in their atomic weights. Among similar elements the difference between the lower atomic weights is always found to be 16; and this is the difference found between the weights of the lighter metals in the list above. The next difference is about 45, as in the chlorine group, and this applies to the other two intervals among the alkali metals.

In the case of the chlorine group, the more active and characteristically nonmetallic element is that with the lower atomic weight. Among the metals the reverse is true, and cesium, with the highest atomic weight, is the most active. These five metals are remarkably alike. They have the same valence, 1; they occur in similar manner, as silicates in primary rock, or in secondary salt deposits; they are active, oxidizing spontaneously in the air, so that they must be kept under an oil free from oxygen. They burn when heated and decompose water readily. Their hydroxides are very soluble and strongly basic, and their compounds are in the main stable and soluble. They impart characteristic colors to the Bunsen flame, and give simple lines in the spectroscope. These properties are all markedly different from those of other metals.

After the resemblances among these metals have been established, our attention is attracted to their differences. These are in degree, and not in kind. For example, potassium decomposes water with energy sufficient to cause the liberated hydrogen to ignite. Sodium when it decomposes water causes the ignition of the liberated hydrogen only under favorable conditions. The flame colors and the spectra are characteristic for each metal, so that, if the compound is pure, the metal may readily be recognized. By other tests it is very difficult to distinguish between them, for they are so similar that they respond in the same manner to the tests applied.

In studying the compounds of the various metals, the reader is in danger of being overcome by the demands on his attention of a multiplicity of seemingly disconnected descriptions. It may be helpful for him, therefore, to perceive the logical order possible in the formation and discussion of these compounds. The order to be followed here is this:

After the study of the metal itself is completed, we turn to the compounds. That compound which is formed most naturally is the oxide. The discussion will be illustrated by equations, using sodium and calcium as types. $Na_2 + O \rightarrow Na_2O$; $Ca + O \rightarrow CaO$.

The next logical step is the union of the oxide with water, $Na_2O + H_2O \rightarrow 2NaOH$; $CaO + H_2O \rightarrow Ca(OH)_2$, with the formation of the hydroxide, the base.

The natural reaction of a base is to form a salt with an acid. Four acids come into consideration more than others, and the salts thus formed are often of definite interest.

Carbonate: $2NaOH + H_2CO_3 \rightarrow Na_2CO_3 + 2H_2O$
$Ca(OH)_2 + H_2CO_3 \rightarrow Ca_2CO_3 + 2H_2O$
Chloride: $NaOH + HCl \rightarrow NaCl + H_2O$
$Ca(OH)_2 + 2HCl \rightarrow CaCl_2 + 2H_2O$
Nitrate: $NaOH + HNO_3 \rightarrow NaNO_3 + H_2O$
$Ca(OH)_2 + 2HNO_3 \rightarrow Ca(NO_3)_2 + 2H_2O$
Sulphate: $2NaOH + H_2SO_4 \rightarrow Na_2SO_4 + 2H_2O$
$Ca(OH)_2 + H_2SO_4 \rightarrow CaSO_4 + 2H_2O$

In the case of the more abundant metals many of these compounds are likely to possess some practical interest, and that interest should be mentioned, even with the result that facts are multiplied. The chemical principles involving their usefulness will be brought out as far as possible. In some cases compounds outside this list will require attention.

SODIUM

Sodium is the leading metal of the alkali group. It exceeds potassium in this respect mainly because it is more available. The natural concentrations of sodium compounds are so much greater than those of potassium that the industries turn to the former wherever possible. Plants require potassium, and sodium cannot therefore be substituted in fertilizers. Otherwise it is convenient to turn to sodium for all applications of an alkali metal.

Sodium is a bright white metal; on account of its chemical activity it tarnishes instantly on exposure to air, hence its luster is unfamiliar. It is lighter than water and so soft that it can be molded easily. Chemically, it is characterized by a great affinity for oxygen, so that it must be kept under oil; it oxidizes spontaneously, burns readily, and decomposes water with the liberation of hydrogen. In general, sodium unites readily with nonmetals, especially the halogens. Heated sodium, introduced into a cylinder of chlorine, burns freely, forming sodium chloride, common salt. When sodium or any of its compounds comes in contact with a Bunsen flame, the flame is colored yellow, a definite characteristic of the metal. (Sodium lights.)

Sodium oxide, Na_2O, is now available commercially. To a casual reader this may seem a matter of little moment. Nevertheless the preparation of that compound has in the past been impossible. Its achievement now marks an advance in the chemical industries.

Sodium Hydroxide, NaOH. This is the typical base of chemistry, as sulphuric acid is the typical acid. It is a white, that is, colorless, solid, exceedingly soluble in water. Its solutions have a characteristic slippery feel. Chemically it is characterized by strong basic reactions. It neutralizes acids with great readiness. It is so powerful a base that it will extract from the atmosphere and will combine with the exceedingly weak carbonic acid, formed by the union of carbon dioxide with water. Its greatest use is in the making of soap. It is used for removing fatty material from textiles, for mercerizing cotton, and wherever an active base is needed for furthering chemical reactions and neutralizing acids. In purely scientific operations it is used in endless ways, depending in the main on its strongly basic properties.

Sodium Carbonate, Na_2CO_3. Sodium carbonate is made and used in vast quantities. As the dry salt it is called soda ash and is much used in the industries. Its use depends on three principles. It carries the carbonate group, and hence is used in water softening to convert soluble calcium compounds into insoluble calcium carbonate. It is a mildly alkaline substance. The active sodium base is only partly neutralized by the weak carbonic acid, so that it has cleansing properties in respect to fatty substances. It is used in laundries and in cleansing powders, and is known to be mildly corrosive. Finally it is a convenient raw material for making most of the other sodium compounds which the industries demand. Illustrations, sodium hydroxide and glass.

$$Na_2CO_3 + Ca(OH)_2 \rightarrow 2NaOH + CaCO_3$$
$$Na_2CO_3 + SiO_2 \rightarrow Na_2SiO_3 \text{ (Water glass)} + CO_2$$

In the household it is known as sal soda, or washing soda, and is applied in the form of its crystallized salt, $Na_2CO_3 \cdot 10H_2O$. This form is more conveniently handled. Its use depends upon the second of the principles mentioned above.

Sodium Hydrogen Carbonate, $NaHCO_3$. This salt is the common baking soda. Its formula indicates that it is carbonic acid, H_2CO_3, with one hydrogen atom replaced by sodium, in contrast to sodium carbonate, Na_2CO_3, in which both hydrogen atoms are replaced. Another way of considering it is as carbonic acid added to sodium carbonate.

$$Na_2CO_3 + H_2CO_3 \rightarrow 2NaHCO_3$$

This last aspect has resulted in the name sodium bicarbonate, it being considered as sodium with a double portion of carbonate. Because of this double portion of acid, the strongly basic properties of the sodium are pretty well neutralized, and the salt is a mild, nearly neutral substance, suitable for use in foods, where it serves as a source of carbon dioxide for leavening, and is of service in neutralizing acids which may be undesirable.

Baking powders are used in large quantities to supply a gas for the purpose of lightening dough and batter Air is often beaten into dough, and steam is at times the leavening agent, but the most convenient gas is carbon dioxide, CO_2, and a convenient source is baking soda. In order to liberate the carbon dioxide the sodium of the soda must be replaced by hydrogen. Any acid will supply this hydrogen, but few acids are tolerable in connection with foods.

$$NaHCO_3 + H(Ac) \rightarrow H_2CO_3 + Na(Ac)$$
$$\downarrow$$
$$CO_2 + H_2O$$

The most familiar substances used are tartaric acid and its acid salt cream of tartar. Another source of hydrogen is calcium or sodium hydrogen phosphate, which is more readily available than the cream of tartar. These substances are mixed in the dry form, and enough starch added to keep them from interacting until they are used. The residue which these powders leave in the food is considerable. One pound of cream of tartar baking powder leaves almost three quarters of a pound of Rochelle salts. But no effect has ever been traced to this in the food. The phosphates formed in the phosphate baking powders might be considered of value, but, as in the case of other powders, no result has been clearly demonstrated.

Alum baking powders are not altogether popular; yet they are used, and the reaction involved is of interest to the chemist. Alum is used as a substitute for the more expensive phosphate and tartrate. Such baking powders are made up of aluminum sulphate and baking soda. When used, the combination momentarily forms aluminum carbonate. This is a compound of a weak base and a weak acid and it at once breaks up, yielding the carbon dioxide.

Another form of baking powder, which is interesting, but almost unheard of in this generation, is ammonium carbonate. No further ingredient is needed, as the heat of the oven decomposes it into carbon dioxide, ammonia, and water. $(NH_4)_2CO_3 \rightarrow 2NH_3 + H_2O + CO_2$. There is no residue.

Sodium Nitrate, NaNO₃. This salt, because of its relation to nitric acid, is one of the most important raw materials of chemistry. Its occurrence in nature in such large quantities as those found in South America is a matter of surprise, because soluble compounds of nitrogen are seldom abundant. These deposits have been until recently the chief sources of sodium and potassium nitrates as well as of nitric acid. The production of synthetic sodium nitrate has now been successfully developed, and this is one of the great achievements of modern chemistry. Besides being the raw material for nitric acid, sodium nitrate is valuable as a fertilizer on account of its nitrogen content.

Sodium Chloride, NaCl. Common salt is in a group with water and sulphuric acid as being the substances which count for most in the chemical world. Its interest lies in its form of occurrence, accumulated in such vast amounts in the sea, in its use in the food of men and animals, and in its being the source of all the sodium compounds and the chlorine which men use.

As the solid rocks of the earth's crust disintegrate their physical breakdown is followed by chemical decomposition; and compounds of sodium, potassium, calcium, and magnesium pass into solution. Potassium compounds are to some extent retained by the soil and later taken up by plants, and calcium and magnesium carbonate too are probably deposited. But considerable amounts of all four reach the sea and are accumulated there. Of these four sodium is predominant and it has, for reasons which are not clear, taken the form of sodium chloride or common salt. It is safe to say that the salts of the sea are the final products formed under natural conditions after all possible changes of these compounds have worked themselves out. The sea contains about 3.5 per cent salts, of which about four-fifths is common salt.

The amount of salt in the sea, when considered from the standpoint of human interests, is enormous. When compared with the great mass of the earth's crust, it is less imposing, as it comprises only about 0.3 per cent of the whole. Sea water varies somewhat, especially in land-locked seas, where there is an influx of fresh water or unusual evaporation. The waters of the Black Sea and of the Baltic Sea are much less salt than those of the ocean, whereas the Red Sea contains an excess of salt.

Salt contents of various waters are:

Atlantic Ocean	3.5 per cent	
Indian Ocean	3.6 "	
Red Sea	5.0 "	and above
Mediterranean Sea	3.9 "	
Baltic Sea	1.2 "	and less
Black Sea	1.8-2.2 "	
Lake Erie	.001 "	
Mississippi River	.002 "	

The accumulation of salts is not confined to the ocean. Salt lakes are, similarly, reservoirs of accumulating salts. There are many of these in Asia and Africa. But the three best known are the following:

Dead Sea	23 per cent salts	
Caspian Sea	1.3 " "	
Great Salt Lake	19 " "	

In these lakes and many others, sodium chloride predominates, but in some of our western lakes, as well as in many in Africa, sodium carbonate is the final form of the sodium. The alkali deposits which are common in arid regions have an origin similar to that of common salt.

When some arm of the sea has been shut off from the main body of water, and in course of time the water has evaporated, salt deposits are formed. Such deposits should contain all the salts of the sea. However, this is exceptional, as the less abundant salts either escape deposition or are dissolved away later. These deposits, therefore, are made up mainly of common salt.

Salt is obtained from its natural sources in several ways. Sea water and the waters of the Great Salt Lake are evaporated for the salt. But the greater portion comes from subterraneous deposits, like those in New York and Louisiana. Salt is actually mined in some of these, but the more common method of obtaining it is by forcing fresh water down to the deposits. After it has become saturated the brine is pumped up and evaporated. The process is simple, but there is opportunity for much ingenuity in the economical application of the fuel used for evaporation and the machinery used for handling.

The uses of salt are for food, not alone for kitchen and table use, but also in preparation of such foods as butter and in curing meats. Cattle consume much salt in their food. Salt is the source of most of the sodium compounds used, as also of chlorine and hydrochloric acid. It is applied in silver extraction in the process by which the silver sulphide is first converted to silver chloride, and much is consumed for the purpose of refrigeration.

The list of sodium salts of lesser importance than those already mentioned is a long one. Sodium is such a typical metal that it forms salts with all the acids, strong or weak. The salt is the form in which many elements and groups of elements are applied, and sodium is the most convenient metal for making salts. Among such compounds the following may be mentioned. Sodium sulphite, Na_2SO_3, used for bleaching, as an "antichlor" to remove excess of chlorine, and in photography. Sodium thiosulphate, $Na_2S_2O_3$, the "hypo" of the photographers, has somewhat similar uses. Sodium nitrite, $NaNO_2$, is the source of nitrous acid in the preparation of dyestuffs. Sodium phosphate, Na_2HPO_4, is applied in enamels, textiles, and in medicine. Borax, $Na_2B_4O_7$, or sodium borate, is used in glazing, brazing, and as a cleansing agent. Sodium silicate, $Na_2Si_2O_5$, water glass, is interesting because it is a form of glass, which, on account of its freedom from metals of the next group, is soluble in water. It is used as a preservative, and an adhesive, and is mixed with textiles to make them fireproof.

SOAP

The chemist considers the amount of sulphuric acid manufactured as the index of industrial progress. He might also claim that from the sociological standpoint the chemical industry of greatest significance is the manufacture of soap. Soap-making is chemically simple. Fats are salts, purely organic, with base and acid like any other salt. The plural word fats is used because there are many of them, all of the same general structure, and differing from the standpoint of soap-making in no essential way. When fat is heated with concentrated sodium hydroxide solution, the strong inorganic base combines with the organic acid to form a sodium salt, which is soap.

The cleansing action of soap carries us into a field called colloid chemistry. For our present purpose a simple explanation will give us some clue to the fat-removing qualities of soap. It is the removal of fat, either of food, or from the body, which is the great problem of cleansing. Fat is not soluble in water, it is not even wetted by water, facts which might be anticipated from its composition. But water must be the great cleansing agent, and we have in soap a substance which serves as an excellent intermediary between water and fat. Soap is made up of sodium, and the compounds of sodium are soluble and closely associated with water. The other part of soap is the fatty residue, and this end of the molecule establishes contact with the fat. The final effect is that soap water wets the fat, and upon agitation tears off parts of it and in fact emulsifies it, so that it forms tiny droplets which the water is able to wash away. This applies to many other substances as well, such as kerosene, although soap is by no means universal in its action.

Years ago, before sodium hydroxide (lye) was purchasable at every distribution point not too remote from the centers of industry, soap was made from materials available on the farm. The potassium carbonate of wood ashes was leached out and treated with lime. The potassium carbonate was thus converted into the more active potassium hydroxide, and with this the fat was heated. The action is the same as with sodium hydroxide, except that the soap in the end does not harden. Thus the old-fashioned farm soap was soft soap. This custom must be nearly in oblivion, yielding, like so many other home industries, to the more effective competition of the factory.

Concerning the general features of the chemistry of soap, there is not much more to be said. There is little difference in different soaps except in the purity of the ingredients, and in the exactness of the balance between the fat and the lye. For toilet purposes the lye should be carefully balanced. For laundry purposes an excess of lye is an advantage. Ordinary soap contains considerable quantities of water, and when the housewife lets it dry out, she simply causes it to become hard so that in its use it does not waste away so fast. There is an element of fallacy in this, because until the soap is dissolved in water it is of no use.

One complication in the use of soap appears when it is used with hard water. The latter contains small amounts of calcium and magnesium salts in solution. These salts react with the soap as follows: Sodium stearate (soap) + Calcium sulphate → Sodium sulphate + Calcium stearate. The soap is destroyed, and in its place is formed the insoluble calcium stearate, which serves no purpose as soap, and in fact adds to our troubles, as it forms a disagreeable scum. The softening of water consists simply in removing these calcium or magnesium salts.

The harmful action of hard water is avoided by the use of a new type of soap, one form of which is known commercially as "dreft." This involves special organic features and will be discussed in a later chapter.

POTASSIUM

A description of potassium is a rehearsal of that of sodium with minor modifications. The occurrence of potassium in primary rocks parallels closely that of sodium, there being little difference either in the nature of the minerals or in their amounts. However, as rock disintegrates, sodium compounds find their way to the sea, and potassium compounds are retained by the soil and enter into the constitution of plants. In the sea potassium is only about one-thirtieth as abundant as is sodium.

In the past available sources of potassium compounds, in the form of secondary deposits, have been the Stassfurt deposits in Germany and some in Alsace. With the interruption of these supplies, the dearth was strongly felt by agriculture, which consumes the greater portion used. Consequently great activity has been manifested in developing American supplies. Deposits in the Southwest have been developed and promise in course of time to supply our needs. Although sodium can replace potassium in most branches of industry, potassium is indispensable in agriculture as a fertilizer.

Potassium itself is obtained less readily than sodium, and there is no occasion for its preparation in more than small amounts. It is noticeably more active than sodium.

Compounds of potassium are very similar to those of sodium, and in all fields except agriculture and medicine are gradually being replaced by those of sodium. The compounds of potassium are all very similar to the corresponding sodium compounds; but slight differences are to be noted in respect to solubility and conduct toward the moisture of the air. All potassium compounds color a Bunsen flame violet to purple.

Potassium nitrate retains a special interest on account of its connection with black gunpowder and pyrotechnics. Black powder has yielded almost entirely to smokeless powder, and even in black powder sodium and ammonium nitrates are replacing potassium nitrate. Black gunpowder is made up of 75 parts potassium nitrate, 13 parts charcoal, and 12 parts sulphur. These ingredients are thoroughly mixed by long grinding. When ignited, the charcoal and sulphur burn with the greatest readiness, combining with the oxygen of the nitrate. The reaction is so complicated that no single equation can be used correctly. The essential result is that an abundance of highly heated gases is produced. These consist of carbon dioxide, carbon monoxide, and nitrogen, and their sudden formation and expansion cause the explosion. The solid ingredients form potassium carbonate, sulphate, and sulphide, which are blown into the air in the form of smoke.

INTERIOR OF STEEL MILL, SHOWING THREE BESSEMER CONVERTERS, ONE TILTED

POURING STEEL INTO A LADLE—OPEN-HEARTH FURNACE

It is this smoke, or solid residue, which has done so much to discredit the use of black powder in warfare. The modern smokeless powders are made up essentially of cellulose nitrate, $C_6H_7O_2(NO_3)_3$, whose ingredients all pass off in the gaseous form, and so produce no smoke.

The explosion of gunpowder is perhaps more correctly termed a rapid combustion. This was initiated in the earliest firearms by igniting the charge through a touch-hole by means of any convenient torch. The flintlock was an advance, in that a spark was produced by the flint and steel as occasion required. The percussion cap was a greater step in advance. In this a highly unstable substance, mercury fulminate, was exploded by the blow of the hammer, and the heat of its decomposition set the powder on fire. The modern cartridge simply includes the cap in the cartridge in a much more convenient form. This ignition is different from the detonation used in firing the so-called high explosives.

SUMMARY

In making a survey of the uses of compounds of the various metals, these general principles may be observed. First, the salts are often used for their properties as a whole. Sodium carbonate and borax are useful in cleansing because they have certain desirable properties. The same is true of glass and lead pigments. Second, many salts are applied simply for the metal which they contain. Sodium salts used in glass-making lose all but the sodium oxide in the fusion. Any potassium compound will serve as a fertilizer, as it is the potassium which is efficient regardless of the rest of the molecule. Copper sulphate and silver nitrate are simply convenient sources of these metals. Third, many salts are used solely for their acid constituent, and the metal is used simply as a means of holding the acid in a convenient form. The metals which are likely to be used for such purposes are sodium, potassium, calcium and magnesium, and of these sodium is the most generally useful. Illustrations are: baking soda, $NaHCO_3$, used for the carbon dioxide to be obtained from it; potassium nitrate and chlorate, used for the oxygen content; sodium sulphite, for the sulphur dioxide, which is a bleacher and an antiseptic; bleaching powder is a convenient form of handling and applying chlorine. The uses of chemical substances run into endless channels, so varied that it is almost impossible to follow them. The principles outlined above, however, are simple and outstanding.

Other metals of the sodium group are *cesium, rubidium* and *lithium*. Their properties are the typical properties of the group.

These metals are called the alkali metals. The name alkali is associated with the active hydroxides and carbonates of these metals, but it has been further extended to include the whole aspect of these metals in a broad way. The striking characteristics of this group may be thus summarized. In the metallic form they are so active that they oxidize spontaneously when exposed to the air, burn readily, and decompose water. Their hydroxides are soluble and exceedingly active, uniting even with the weakest acids. Their carbonates are soluble and mildly alkaline, and the salts as a class are well defined, stable and soluble. Their compounds impart a characteristic color to the Bunsen flame, and in the spectroscope show simple lines.

In a previous chapter, under nitrogen, mention was made of the ammonium compounds, as closely resembling those of sodium. Ammonium (NH_4), this peculiar combination of nitrogen and hydrogen, acts in its compounds in all respects like a metal of the sodium group. Its hydroxide is an active base, although much behind sodium hydroxide. Its salts are soluble and altogether comparable with those of sodium. The chief ammonium compounds are: the hydroxide, ammonia water, useful for cleansing; ammonium carbonate, mentioned before in connection with baking powders; ammonium chloride, used in batteries and as a flux; ammonium sulphate, the convenient form for applying ammonia as a fertilizer. All these compounds dissociate readily into ammonia and the constituent acid.

CHAPTER XVI

THE METALS OF THE CALCIUM GROUP

THE metals of the calcium group parallel those of the sodium group very closely, as is shown by the following comparison:

SODIUM METALS	ATOMIC WEIGHT	CALCIUM METALS	ATOMIC WEIGHT
Cesium	133	Barium	137.4
Rubidium	85.5	Strontium	87.6
Potassium	39.1	Calcium	40
Sodium	23	Magnesium	24.3
Lithium	7	Beryllium (Glucinum)	9.1

Magnesium and calcium are preëminent in this group as are sodium and potassium in the other. The four metals just named, along with iron and aluminum, are the common metals of the earth's surface, and they form the material environment of living organisms. The first four are found in the sea, the repository of much of the material leached out of the solid rock; but iron and aluminum, perhaps because they are so likely to form insoluble compounds, are not found there. If life originated in sea water, it is but natural that the four metals found in that medium should be congenial to living organisms, and normal to their existence; and, by the same token, all other metals, except in traces, would be abnormal and not compatible with their best development.

Calcium and magnesium are found in nature in strikingly parallel forms, both as silicates and in the secondary formations from them. They occur as individual carbonates, and as dolomite, a combined carbonate, of which entire mountain ranges are composed. They are both found as sulphates, calcium sulphate insoluble, magnesium sulphate soluble, the former known as gypsum and alabaster, the latter as Epsom salts.

In the metallic form calcium is interesting, but not practically important. Its properties are what one might expect from a member of the group following the sodium group. It is heavier and harder than sodium, oxidizes readily, burns, and takes the oxygen from water; but in all these reactions its activity is less than that of sodium. Magnesium digresses still further from sodium. It is reasonably permanent in the air, decomposes water slowly, even when the water is heated. But when ignited in steam it combines with the oxygen with some degree of violence. As magnesium is very light, only two-thirds as heavy as aluminum, it has come to be applied to the making of automobile parts. To a chemist who has known magnesium only as an active substance in the laboratory, it might seem that its activity is too great for ordinary uses. But the same is to a certain extent true of aluminum; yet it has been used for many years without any reports of disaster.

Calcium

Calcium oxide, CaO, is the compound known as quicklime. Its great importance is due to the fact that it is so easily obtained from calcium carbonate, limestone, and when obtained is a substance of distinct chemical reactivity. Before the electrolytic methods were developed, this substance was at the basis of the alkali and soap industry, much as sulphuric acid is at the basis of the acid industry.

Calcium oxide, or lime, is made by heating the carbonate in limekilns. Lime is used very little as the oxide, but is usually converted into the hydroxide by the addition of water, with which it unites with the evolution of considerable heat. This reaction is typical of the more active metallic oxides. The base formed, the hydroxide, possesses the active properties which are usually associated with lime. Lime is now being placed upon the market in the form of calcium hydroxide, because of the greater convenience and serviceability of that form.

Aside from the relation to basic substances, lime has two uses worthy of attention. One is the use in mortar. Its mixture with sand and water sets and then gradually hardens. The causes are not absolutely clear, but are probably associated with the slight, yet definite solubility of the hydroxide, and of the carbonate formed upon absorption of carbon dioxide from the air. A substance of limited solubility may dissolve and settle out again, with the result that it binds together any particles with which it comes in contact. Old-fashioned mortar has been superseded almost entirely by Portland cement.

Another use of lime is agricultural. As organic matter in the soil decays, there is danger of an accumulation of slightly acid material. Lime neutralizes this as fast as it is formed, and its use for this purpose is steadily increasing. Finely ground calcium carbonate is also used, but its action is much slower than that of the more active and soluble calcium hydroxide.

The word lime is often used colloquially for any compound of calcium which may be present in water or in soil. The interest in all these cases is in the calcium, and hence the misuse of the word causes little confusion.

Calcium carbonate, CaCO₃, for a number of reasons, is one of the most interesting substances in nature. One reason has already been mentioned, that it is a common substance which is easily converted into an active reagent, lime.

$$CaCO_3 \xrightarrow{\text{heat}} CaO + CO_2$$

Another reason is its usefulness in a general way as the source of calcium compounds and of carbon dioxide, both very valuable. It is an abundant mineral, and, on account of its varying solubility under different conditions, results in many mineralogical and geological phenomena. Finally it is associated in a very interesting manner with many forms of animal life, seashell, coral.

Calcium carbonate is only slightly soluble in water, 13 parts in one million. But when an excess of carbon dioxide is dissolved in the water, there is formed a much more soluble acid salt. Consequently such waters dissolve limestone rock and in course of time form subterranean passages and caves which are of great extent and interest. Again this soluble combination is easily broken up, so that the normal carbonate is redeposited, with the formation of stalagmites and stalactites, and cementing of fragments of limestone and other rocks into solid masses. The presence of the acid carbonate is the cause of the hardness of many natural waters, with the consequent inconveniences connected not alone with the destruction of soap, but also with the deposition of boiler scale, when the water is used for generating steam. For when waters containing this acid salt are heated, the acid salt is decomposed and the calcium carbonate is deposited as a crust. When waters contain a considerable amount of this, it must first be removed to render them usable in boilers. The destruction of soap by hard waters, already discussed, is also a serious waste and nuisance; yet the softening of public water supplies is practiced to only a limited extent.

Certain animal organisms store up calcium carbonate in their shells. When the animal dies, this carbonate is for the most part permanently stored away in deposits of one kind or another, and in the end often forms solid rock. The coquina rock of Florida illustrates nicely the transition from shells to permanent limestone rock. In the same fragment shells may be seen and again the calcium carbonate so altered that it has lost all resemblance to its constituent shells. In these and other limestone deposits, the carbon dioxide of the atmosphere is being gradually stored away, and permanently withdrawn from the use of plants and animals. The supply is constantly being renewed by the combustion of coal and from subterranean sources. Unless the renewal equals the loss, it is conceivable that in the remote future living organisms will fail to find enough carbon dioxide to serve as the raw material for building up their tissue.

It is not desirable to describe other calcium compounds in too great detail. They are second only to sodium compounds in practical importance and a very brief statement concerning those of chief value will be sufficient. Almost all of them represent industries not alone of scientific chemical interest, but of very great practical importance, involving many large manufacturing establishments.

Calcium chloride, CaCl₂, has a striking affinity for water, tending to absorb it to pass over to the crystalline form, $CaCl_2.6H_2O$. It is hence much used to dry gases and organic liquids. It is used to lay the dust on unpaved roads; it keeps them moist through its attraction for water. *Calcium sulphate* occurs in abundance as gypsum and alabaster, $CaSO_4.2H_2O$. Upon careful heating it loses part of its water, forming plaster of Paris. When this dehydrated compound is mixed with water, it recombines with the water and in doing so sets in the familiar manner. *Calcium phosphate* is the chief mineral constituent of bones, and in the form of a mineral is the source of the phosphate used in fertilizers. The natural rock is heated with sulphuric acid to render it somewhat soluble, and thus available for plants. Bleaching powder, $CaOCl_2$, involves calcium only as a means of holding the chlorine in a convenient form. Calcium carbide, CaC_2, is made as a source for acetylene, C_2H_2, as also for the purpose of fixing nitrogen in the cyanamide ($CaCN_2$) process. Calcium sulphite, $CaSO_3$, or its acid salt, is used in the disintegration of wood for the making of paper pulp. Finally, glass is a silicate of calcium and sodium, so important that it will receive special discussion in another place.

MAGNESIUM

Industrially, magnesium has begun to take a place by the side of aluminum. Being only two-thirds as heavy as aluminum, it has obvious advantages in the making of such articles as automobile parts. Though in small masses, wire or powder, magnesium is very combustible, the kindling temperature is so high that large masses are not likely to become ignited. The supply of magnesium is inexhaustible, a fact giving reassurance when we consider the possible exhaustion in course of time of deposits of less abundant metals. When magnesium burns, the light is rich in actinic rays. Hence its use for "flashlight" photography.

Magnesium oxide is used medicinally for the neutralization of acids. Such a use is not a purely isolated one. It is based upon the position of magnesium in the whole series of metals. A base (for metallic oxides are practically bases) derived from a metal preceding magnesium would be too active for medicinal use. One from a metal following would not be harmless. Magnesium in several respects has special uses because it is last of the more active metals, not too active, yet active enough to accomplish what zinc and other metals following cannot do.

CHAPTER XVII

THE MORE ACTIVE HEAVY METALS

THE more active heavy metals are the typical metals of the industries. They are reasonably abundant, they are so low in chemical activity that they endure the vicissitudes of ordinary use, and they possess the physical properties which are desired. They are:

Aluminum	*Chromium*	*Nickel*
Manganese	*Iron*	*Tin*
Zinc	*Cobalt*	*Lead*

(Copper, from the next group, should be included as being one of the typical metals of the industries.)

Manganese and cobalt have no application as pure metals. The former is necessary in steel making; the latter gives color to such substances as glass, and forms blue pigments. Chromium is one of the ingredients of some forms of steel, and chromium-plated articles are now familiar.

All these metals are too active to be found free in nature in amounts which are more than curiosities. They occur mostly in combination with oxygen or sulphur, and are extracted from their ores in the regular way.

ALUMINUM

Aluminum has some resemblance to the more active metals, and requires special treatment for its extraction. It is obtained by the electrolysis of the oxide dissolved in the fused fluoride. Obtaining the oxide in sufficiently pure form is the chief difficulty of the process. The advantage of aluminum over other metals for ordinary uses lies in part in its light weight, in part in its handsome appearance. Its specific gravity is 2.7, which is as high as that of stone. Aluminum seems light, however, in competition with iron and copper, which are about three times as heavy. The light color of aluminum is not marred by the formation of the oxide on its surface, for the latter is colorless and transparent, thus altering the appearance very little. When aluminum was first introduced into the household, there were fears expressed that its high chemical activity would result in its dissolving in the acid juices of the foods. With ordinary care aluminum cooking utensils have proved to be reasonably serviceable.

The high affinity of metallic aluminum for oxygen is made use of in the Goldschmidt method of welding. The finely divided metal is mixed with iron oxide. When this mixture is fired, the aluminum combines with the oxygen of the iron oxide with such great development of heat that the resulting iron is melted, and can be caused to weld together the parts of metal with which it comes in contact.

ZINC

Some of the chief uses of zinc are based upon its position in the electrochemical series. It is one of the more active of the ordinary metals, and hence is used as an active metal in chemical laboratories, especially for the purpose of liberating hydrogen from acids. Its use in batteries depends upon this fact, as also its application in galvanizing iron. The use of the more active metal zinc in protecting iron, a less active metal, may seem paradoxical, but it acts as follows. Iron rusts on account of its affinity for oxygen in presence of water. When iron rusts to a small extent, the rust spots formed act as nuclei for the rapid increase of the corrosion, and the rusting now proceeds much more rapidly. When the iron is coated with zinc, all initial oxidation affects the zinc, and rust nuclei are not established. Zinc is frequently used much as an ordinary metal as it has desirable physical properties and is not very rapidly affected by water. Much is used in alloying copper to form brass.

IRON

Iron is first among the metals on account of its abundance and general usefulness. There are so many phases in the composition and uses of commercial iron that in the great field of industrial chemistry it forms a division of its own. Comparison is often made between the value of common iron and the precious metal gold. When iron is developed into some of its most refined products, like the small parts of watches, its value, weight for weight, is fabulously greater than that of either gold or platinum.

Iron occurs in large quantities as a minor constituent scattered throughout most rocks. In addition to these scattered masses, iron compounds form a number of abundant minerals. First comes hematite, iron oxide, Fe_2O_3, so called from its blood-red color. Even specimens which do not seem red show this color when finely pulverized, as when rubbed on a rough porcelain surface. Magnetite, Fe_3O_4, is attracted by a magnet and is a valuable ore. Masses of this which have become magnetic due to their location in the earth are called lodestones. Siderite, $FeCO_3$, and limonite, bog iron ore, $Fe_4O_3(OH)_6$, are less abundant. Iron pyrites, FeS_2, is a handsome mineral of metallic appearance resembling gold. It is valuable as a source of sulphur compounds, but the difficulty of removing all traces of sulphur limits its use as a source of iron.

The extraction of iron from its oxide is in theory simple enough. The ore is heated to a high temperature with carbon and the oxygen is thus removed. $Fe_2O_3 + 3C \rightarrow 2Fe + 3CO$. There are, however, features, economic and chemical, which greatly complicate the operation. In spite of all difficulties iron is produced on a huge scale at a low price. There follows an analysis of some of the details.

A. Pure iron is not sufficiently fusible to handle in a modern blast furnace. The iron is therefore combined with a certain amount of carbon and silicon, and the resulting metal, cast iron, is comparatively easily melted. It is cast, when made, into the so-called "pigs," or else is made directly into steel.

B. Carbon is introduced into the blast furnaces to serve a number of purposes. It supplies the fuel needed to give the required temperature; it unites with the oxygen of the ore; and it supplies the carbon for the compound mentioned in A. At the end of a number of chemical changes, much of the carbon finally emerges in the form of carbon monoxide, CO, still possessing considerable fuel value. This is utilized by being burned in great stoves filled with a checker work of fire brick, until these bricks are very hot. The air which is then fed into the furnace is preheated by passing over this checker work, and the heat of the carbon monoxide is thus utilized. This carbon monoxide is also utilized for fuel either by being burned under the boilers or in gas engines.

C. Mixed with the ore there is considerable earthy material not sufficiently fusible to melt and run out of the furnace. Therefore limestone is added to the ore and coke, in order to supply calcium oxide to make a readily fusible slag. This slag is occasionally run off from the top of the molten iron, and forms a considerable amount of by-product. This slag is used in various ways as a rock material for filling or ballasting and is in some places by chemical manipulation worked over into useful products, glass or cement. An important function of this slag is the protection of the molten iron from the action of the oxygen of the air blast.

D. The air blast gives the name to the blast furnace. In order to attain the necessary temperature, a blast of air must be blown in upon the fuel. Such a volume of air naturally has a serious cooling effect. By preheating the air by means of the stoves mentioned above, the cooling effect of the air is considerably diminished and the necessary high temperature more easily attained.

As was previously stated, the product of the blast furnace is not pure iron, but a compound with carbon and silicon. This has many uses, but for some purposes must be modified by the removal of these foreign substances. The different properties of the various compounds and mixtures, and the formation of these make up the great study of iron and steel.

We will consider only a few phases of this complex subject. When we have the compound called cast iron, we have the following conditions and properties. Cast or pig iron contains as much as 5 per cent of carbon.

It is fusible in foundry furnaces and can be thus used for making castings, a rapid way of shaping iron; it is hard, but brittle; it is not forgeable or weldable; only in masses will it endure a strain.

On the other hand, when practically all the carbon and silicon are removed, the following properties are found in the resulting wrought iron. It is no longer easily fusible; it is comparatively soft, but very tough, of high tensile strength, and no longer brittle; it can be forged and welded.

These properties of cast iron and wrought iron are seen to be supplementary to a striking degree, and the two forms of iron are used in accordance with these properties.

Wrought iron is seldom made now, as steel serves most of its purposes. It was made by adding oxygen to molten pig iron until the carbon which gave the characteristic properties was burned out. The wrought iron was then taken out and rolled, forged, and shaped, casting being no longer possible.

Steel is a form of iron intermediate between cast iron and wrought iron, possessing various degrees of composition intermediate between them, and showing such combinations of properties that it has become the leading form of iron. Steel was made years ago by adding the right amount of carbon to wrought iron, but the method was slow and the product irregular. Yet wonderful results were attained.

It was the invention of the Bessemer process which revolutionized the steel industry. Bessemer argued that a quick way to make steel would be to blow air through molten pig iron until just the right amount of carbon was burnt out. His supposition has proved to be a correct solution of the problem, and steel can thus be made with great rapidity. The molten iron is placed in egg-shaped "converters" and air is blown through for the proper length of time. The product is modified at the end by the addition of manganese, carbon, and silicon, so that the proper proportions are attained.

The following is a summary of the properties of steel. It must be remembered that steel includes all gradations from the carbon-free wrought iron on the one hand to a high carbon steel on the other.

Steel is more fusible than wrought iron. Fusion, or melting, is a convenient way of handling the metal. Steel is harder than wrought iron, it can be forged, and is very strong. According to its carbon content, it is harder and more brittle, or softer and more malleable, all gradations being prepared for the great variety of uses.

The open-hearth process of steel making depends upon the successful development of very high temperatures and control of the operation throughout. The choice of raw material for this method is capable of wide variation. If iron low in carbon is used, pig iron, supplying more carbon, may be added. If the carbon is too high, iron ores (Fe_2O_3) may be added to supply oxygen to burn out this carbon. Before the metal is cast, it is possible to make check tests, assuring the proper carbon content of the product.

In a superficial discussion of steel, its composition may be said to be an iron containing a certain proportion of carbon. But steel as now made and used is a very complicated and variable substance. In making various steels, silicon, manganese, nickel, vanadium, chromium, tungsten, molybdenum, titanium, and uranium are used. The properties of steel are determined by the nature and proportions of these constituents and their relations to each other.

As the years pass, many iron articles outlive their usefulness. Hence the not insignificant "scrap iron" industry for reintroducing this metal into the industries. The great disadvantage of iron is its tendency to "rust." Startling statements are made as to the large amount of iron which must be produced each year as an offset to this rusting. The protection of iron, one way or another, is naturally one of the great problems of the industry.

The compounds of iron present one point of interest, not peculiar to iron, but most conspicuous with this metal. Iron forms two classes of compounds, in that it combines with oxygen and other negative groups in two proportions. Such compounds are:

Ferrous oxide, FeO Ferric oxide, Fe_2O_3
Ferrous hydroxide, $Fe(OH)_2$ Ferric hydroxide, $Fe(OH)_3$
Ferrous chloride, $FeCl_2$ Ferric chloride, $FeCl_3$
Ferrous sulphate, $FeSO_4$ Ferric sulphate, $Fe_2(SO_4)_3$

In ferrous compounds the iron functions with a valence of two, in the ferric, of three. Ferrous compounds are usually white or pale green in color while ferric are yellow, brown, or red. It is therefore easy to recognize them. Ferrous compounds remain ferrous in the usual transformations of chemistry, and the ferric remain ferric, unless a definite change, called oxidation or reduction, transfers them from one class to the other. In nature this is seen often when the ferrous compound of a grayish clay or rock, upon exposure to the air, gradually oxidizes. There is then formed the ferric compound with the characteristic red or yellow color, so conspicuous in some of our soils.

TIN

Tin is found mainly as tinstone, SnO_2, and is extracted in the usual way. It is a handsome metal and as it is fairly well down in the electrochemical list, it is not readily attacked by oxygen or other reagents. It is therefore rather permanent and is used as a protective coating for iron. Sheet tin is iron thus coated, and the making of this constitutes its great use. Pure tin, called block tin, to distinguish it from the tin-coated sheets of iron, is often used in special apparatus, where an inactive metal is needed. Tin has a low melting point, and therefore, mixed with lead, is valuable for solder.

LEAD

Lead is more abundant than tin and is used in a greater variety of ways. It is less active in some respects, but with some substances, water and carbon dioxide for example, it does corrode. As lead is used much for water service, and it is so poisonous, this question of corrosion is an important one. A redeeming feature in the use of lead is that the ordinary impurities of water often cause the formation of an insoluble coating on the inside of the pipe, so that the water has no further action. Lead is a silvery white metal, and the general impression of its dull color is due to the coating of oxide formed on its surface. The uses of lead depend in part on its physical properties. It is heavy, and therefore used for weights, shot and such purposes. It is soft and easily handled, so used for pipes. It has a low melting point, for which reason it is used in solder. Other uses are based in part on its chemical properties. Its low chemical activity and the insolubility of its compounds make it useful for such purposes as tanks, chambers, and pipes in acid factories, as the acids corrode it only slowly.

Useful compounds of lead are many. White lead is the commonest of the solids mixed with linseed oil for the making of paint. It is a basic carbonate, that is, partly lead hydroxide, and partly lead carbonate. The virtues of white lead are its clear white appearance combined with opaqueness, so that a thin layer spread over a surface conceals what lies beneath. Red lead, Pb_3O_4, has a fine red color and is used in paints for that reason. Lead is a constituent of other pigments, as chrome yellow, $PbCrO_4$.

CHAPTER XVIII

THE LESS ACTIVE METALS

THIS list includes copper, arsenic, antimony, mercury, silver, platinum, and gold. Within the group there is considerable variation of activity. The chemical activity and compounds of copper are of distinct importance, while gold and platinum are so inactive that their compounds are few and unimportant. From the standpoint of the chemist, copper is the most interesting of the group.

COPPER

Copper has much in common with the last metals of the previous group. Yet in the matter of occurrence in nature there is a marked deviation, for copper occurs as the free metal in great abundance. The Lake Superior mines, yielding free copper, are famous, although the greater proportion of all the copper mined comes from the sulphide. The advantages of copper over other metals are in part apparent, and in part require technical knowledge to appreciate. It is handsome, and even if not permanent in the air, it may be cleaned easily, and its beauty restored. When used for such purposes as roofing, it corrodes only superficially, with the formation of the beautiful green basic sulphate, an appearance which is welcomed. Copper alone and in the form of brass lends itself to the making of delicate parts, as, for example, electrical apparatus. Cooking utensils on a small and large scale, for home and factory use, are often made of copper and are very permanent. Its high conductivity for electricity makes it the most used of the metals for this purpose. Among its alloys are brass, bronze, German silver, gun metal, and the alloys of gold, silver, and nickel used in coinage. Alloys consume more than half the amount of copper produced.

In addition to the uses of copper just enumerated, its properties suggest relations between chemistry and electricity to which we must give careful consideration. The chief point at issue is that copper is the lowest of the more available metals in the electrochemical list; it is the least active, that is, it tends least of all of them to go into combination. This, as will be seen, is closely related to the development and application of electricity.

The relation between heat and chemical changes runs through all our discussion of chemical phenomena. We also make frequent mention of the relation of electricity and chemical change, and the properties of copper invite a discussion of this topic.

ELECTROPLATING

It will be desirable to recall the simpler details of electrolysis. If we dissolve copper chloride in water, the salt is ionized into its positive and negative ions, Cu^{++} and $2Cl^-$. If now we introduce the electrodes from a battery into this solution, the positive copper will be attracted to the negative electrode, and the negative ion to the positive electrode. As the ions arrive at the respective electrodes, the charges upon them will be neutralized and the copper and chlorine left in the form of elements. The copper will deposit and the chlorine escape. With slight modification this operation can be converted into one of copper plating.

For the latter operation the object to be plated with copper is suspended in the solution as the negative electrode, and a plate of copper of considerable amount made the positive electrode. As the current passes, the copper is deposited in the usual manner on the negative pole, that is, on the object to be plated. The negative chlorine ion travels to the positive pole, but instead of being discharged combines with the positively charged copper, to form copper chloride which replenishes the solution. From the solution the copper continues to be deposited on the negative pole, and from the positive pole—the

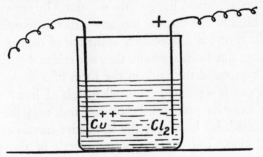

DIAGRAM ILLUSTRATING ELECTROLYSIS OF SALTS, ELECTROPLATING AND ELECTRO-REFINING

In every case the ions are attracted to the poles of opposite charge.

plate of copper—the copper continuously passes into solution. The final result is that the copper passes from the plate of copper forming the positive electrode, to the object to be plated, forming the negative electrode. Except in details the plating of other metals is the same.

ELECTRO-REFINING

Another application of these ideas is that of electro-refining, applied especially to copper. Again we take a solution of copper chloride. A thin sheet of copper, simply to serve as a foundation, is made the negative pole, while the heavy bar of copper which is to be refined is made the positive pole. As the current passes, the salt in solution is electrolyzed and copper is deposited upon the negative pole, while the chlorine ion collected at the positive pole attacks the copper there and causes it to go into solution. Now comes the differentiation between copper and the other metals, which are the impurities to be eradicated. As the chlorine attacks the positive pole, only copper and the more active metals above copper in the electrochemical list go into solution. In presence of a metal high in the list, the less active metals remain in the metallic form; and inasmuch as the bar of copper is disintegrating, due to its solution, they are released and deposit at the bottom of the tank in the form of a sludge. Thus the copper is separated from all metals of lesser activity. At the negative pole, on the other hand, only the copper is deposited, for here only the less active metals can leave the solution. But the less active metals of the positive pole never went into the solution; consequently the copper alone can deposit and the more active metals are left in the solution in the form of chlorides.

ELECTRIC BATTERIES

Another application of this relative activity of the metal is the primary cell. We are now turning the matter about and converting chemical energy into electrical energy. The Daniell cell will illustrate our point. This consists of a dilute solution of sulphuric acid, in which are suspended a plate of zinc, high in the electrochemical list and a plate of copper, low in the list. They are connected outside the solution with a wire to establish electrical connection. On account of its high solution tension (activity) the zinc tends to go into solution, that is, to form zinc sulphate. But in zinc sulphate, ionized as it is, the zinc ions must take on a positive charge; and to accomplish this the zinc plate must take on a negative charge, much as a boat is driven south when a diver leaps from it to the north. The hydrogen of the acid is now left unprovided for and is liberated at the copper plate. While in solution the hydrogen ions are positively charged, and to come out of solution the hydrogen must lose its charge, which is given up to the copper plate, which thus acquires the positive charge. Thus the zinc plate is continuously charged negatively, and the copper plate positively. A current is established when the circuit is completed.

Another case is the secondary or storage battery. This consists, with many mechanical refinements, of two plates which, when the battery is charged, consist, the one of lead, and the other of lead peroxide; that is, one plate contains no negative group in combination with the lead, the other a double portion. Work comes from inequality of conditions. The steam engine has high pressure within the boilers, low pressure without. Water power represents the same thing and the work is done by the equalization of these unequal conditions. When the battery is discharged, both plates become equalized in that they both consist of lead sulphate. The mechanism of the discharge is as follows:

The two plates, one lead, Pb, the other lead peroxide, PbO_2, are immersed in dilute sulphuric acid. The surplus oxygen of the peroxide takes up hydrogen from one molecule of the sulphuric acid forming water. But in this combination the hydrogen is, so to speak, un-ionized; that is, it loses its charge, which is passed over to the plate, which thus becomes positively charged. This leaves the sulphate of the acid unprovided for and it combines with the lead of the other plate. In doing so it is un-ionized in its turn, so that this plate receives a negative charge. The first plate then is continuously receiving positive charges from the hydrogen, the other is continuously receiving negative charges from the sulphate, and this means the passage of a current. The residual lead oxide is promptly converted into lead sulphate according to the simple chemical reaction, $PbO + H_2SO_4 \rightarrow PbSO_4 + H_2O$. Both plates are now in the form of lead sulphate and the battery is discharged.

To recharge the battery the first of the plates mentioned above is connected with the positive pole of a source of electricity, and the other plate is connected with the negative pole. When a current is passed the positive pole attracts negative ions in the regular way from the sulphuric acid present, and the positive, $PbSO_4$, plate becomes $Pb(SO_4)_2$. This compound cannot persist and decomposes into $PbO_2 + 2SO_3$; the former represents the form of the plate in the charged battery, the latter unites with water to form sulphuric acid, $SO_3 + H_2O \rightarrow H_2SO_4$. At the negative pole the hydrogen ions of the sulphuric acid are attracted, and upon reaching it remove the negative SO_4 ions from the plate, forming sulphuric acid and leaving the plate in the form of lead. The battery now stands, PbO_2, lead peroxide on the one hand and, Pb, lead on the other, the state of inequality necessary for work. The solution of sulphuric acid is now more concentrated, as all the SO_4 ions are in the solution as H_2SO_4,

It is well known that the readiest way to tell whether a battery is charged or not is by the amount of acid present in the solution.

ARSENIC AND ANTIMONY

These metals are interesting in that they are brittle and show some of the properties of the nonmetals. The greatest interest of arsenic outside of its purely scientific interest lies in the poisonous nature of its compounds and to some extent in their medicinal value. They are used as insecticides for spraying foliage to kill leaf-eating insects. Paris green and lead arsenate are the forms applied. Their frequent application in this respect gives rise to some concern as to whether the arsenic thus scattered around will presently be a menace to men and cattle. It seems likely that this will not be the case, as it will probably be dissipated beyond the point of danger. The menace, however, must never be forgotten. Antimony is used to give hardness to lead alloys. Its sulphides are used to some extent in the match industry and for giving certain qualities to rubber.

MERCURY

Mercury is remarkable for its liquid state, and also for the fact that its compounds are easily decomposed. The decomposition of mercuric oxide by heating and the consequent discovery of oxygen is a classic in the study of science. The liquid state of mercury is the reason of its great usefulness in physical apparatus. The use in thermometers, in barometers, and in apparatus for the handling of gases is of the highest importance. This fact is also at the basis of its use in the recovery of gold and silver. As solvent for these metals it simplifies their extraction, and 40 per cent of the mercury mined is used in this way.

Mercury compounds are very poisonous. They are therefore used as antiseptics and disinfectants, the most valuable being mercuric chloride, "corrosive sublimate." Mercury has some application in medicine as, for example, calomel, mercurous chloride. Mercuric sulphide as ordinarily prepared in the laboratory is of an uninteresting black color, but when prepared in a special manner it forms the brilliant vermilion of commerce; and the preparation of this pigment constitutes one of the great uses of mercury. When thus used, as is the case in the use of copper as a fungicide, the metal is permanently lost. Fulminating mercury is used to "fire" the various explosives.

SILVER

Silver has three main fields of interest—ornamental ware, coinage, and photography. The last of these is of the greatest chemical importance, but the chemist cannot neglect the other two altogether. Silver is found as silver sulphide, and if the ore were pure it would be an exceedingly simple matter to extract it. But silver ores are very lean. An ore producing twenty ounces of silver to the ton might be valuable enough to work; yet it would have a silver content of less than one-tenth of one per cent. To recover this a large amount of useless material must be handled. The methods of extraction lie beyond the scope of this work.

For coinage and plate, silver is usually alloyed with copper (7½ per cent for the sterling silver plate of commerce). The beauty of silver lies in its permanence and whiteness. It is the whitest of the metals and does not corrode except in the presence of sulphur or sulphur compounds. It is then easily cleaned. The high reflecting power leads to the making of mirrors by the coating of glass with silver. A solution of silver nitrate in ammonia is virtually silver oxide, Ag_2O. When heated with substances like grape sugar, or formaldehyde, the latter extracts this oxygen in such a way that the silver is deposited in the smooth, even layer which constitutes the mirror.

THE CHEMISTRY OF PHOTOGRAPHY

Silver compounds are not the only substances which respond to the chemical stimulus of light. Compounds of iron (blue prints), mercury and other metals are changed by the action of light. The whole process of plant growth is the great illustration. But silver compounds are the most sensitive and the most used. Silver further is readily thrown out of its compounds in the form of an opaque powder, so that it is easily made into an image. The light which is most effective is the portion of the spectrum at the violet end and beyond. Light weak in these rays is ineffective, as is illustrated by the red light of the dark room. Flaming arc, mercury, and magnesium light are rich in these rays and may be used for photography in the absence of sunlight.

The camera and its use come under the head of physics. The lens serves to throw upon the plate the exact image of that which is to be photographed. Our chemical story begins then with the projection upon a plate of an image, that is, light of varying degrees of intensity. The plate is made up of a film of gelatine, filled with silver bromide.

The silver bromide is acted on in proportion to the intensity of the light which falls upon it, although an inspection of the plate reveals no change. It is likely that there is formed a limited amount of silver subbromide. This operation is the exposure and the image is called the latent image. It is an image only in its possibilities. If this exposed plate is now immersed in a solution which has a reducing action, it will take from the silver the bromine with which it is combined, in proportion to the amount of the action of the light, and there will be deposited a corresponding amount of silver, in finely divided form, very black and opaque. We now have a real image, but dark where the object was light, and light where the object was dark, so that it is called a negative. Much of the original silver bromide is still unchanged, and this must be removed, or in course of time it would change under the influence of light and blacken the whole. The removal of this residual bromide is called fixing and is accomplished by immersing the plate for a while in a solution of sodium thiosulphate ("hypo"), which changes the silver bromide into a soluble compound, to be later washed out. When dried, the plate is ready for printing.

Printing on the whole is accomplished according to one of two methods, the printing out and the developing. In the former the paper is covered with silver chloride which blackens under the influence of light, due to the formation of mixed oxygen compounds. The paper is put in the sunlight under a negative and printed until done. Such prints are toned, that is, immersed in gold and other solutions, so that new compounds are formed with more pleasing colors. These prints must be fixed as are the plates by the removal of any silver compounds not acted on. The developing papers are similar to the plates, only not nearly so sensitive. There is first formed the latent image, which must be developed and fixed like a plate. The great advantage of this process is that artificial light is quite adequate to make the impressions, whereas the printing out papers need sunlight. There are, of course, endless refinements and details, a full discussion of which does not come within the scope of this volume. The above are the main features.

THE PLATINUM METALS

There are six metals of the platinum group. Of these platinum is the most abundant and the most useful. These metals fall into two groups, those with atomic weights about 106, ruthenium, rhodium, and palladium, and specific gravity about twelve; and the other set, osmium, iridium, and platinum, with atomic weight about 200, and specific gravity about twenty-two. They all have a high melting point and low chemical activity. The uses of platinum are of two types, one being for crucibles, as the metal does not melt readily and is stable to most reagents. But many a crucible has been ruined because the operator assumed that platinum was absolutely inactive. The other use depends on the high value of platinum as a catalyst. This applies especially to the contact process for the manufacture of sulphuric acid. As platinum is of unique value for chemical manipulations, its use for jewelry is frowned upon by chemists, who find satisfaction in calling attention to the fact that the beauty of platinum was not appreciated when it was comparatively cheap.

Gold

Gold naturally attracts much attention. Its great beauty, rarity, and durability result in a high estimate of its value. It is the least active metal on the list and is attacked by only a few reagents, particularly chlorine and mixtures which yield chlorine, like aqua regia, a mixture of nitric and hydrochloric acids. The compounds of gold are of minor importance. The obtaining of gold from its ores is a fine illustration of the importance of engineering as compared with pure chemistry. Some gold ores yield only a tenth of an ounce of gold to a ton of ore. To make this extraction profitable is not a simple matter. Gold extraction is partly mechanical, especially with the help of the solvent action of mercury, and in part chemical, the gold being put into solution by the action of chlorine or of sodium cyanide. This last process has done much toward making lean ores available, as it enables large quantities of ore to be handled at low cost.

Courtesy, Bethlehem Steel Company

A BESSEMER CONVERTER DURING A "BLOW"

Courtesy, Bethlehem Steel Company

HUGE COKE OVENS DISCHARGING BYPRODUCTS

CHAPTER XIX

CLASSIFICATION OF THE ELEMENTS

IF THE study of chemistry were mere acquaintance with a large number of isolated facts, and knowledge of a number of disconnected elements, and of reactions which varied with every set of substances which came together, the whole would be a hopelessly confused mass of information which would lead us nowhere. Our subject would not be a science and would be unworthy of the high esteem in which it is held. But this, of course, is not the case. Chemistry is not disconnected. The veriest beginner will find general principles at once, and if he appreciates an action for one substance, will look for a similar action in the next. Our subject is an orderly one, and even if there is some danger that many facts will stand out by themselves, the general order of the subject should be looked for conscientiously.

The first conception of the elements is that they are the absolutely distinct chemical units from which compounds are derived. If we begin with different elements we obtain different compounds, and from the same compound we must always come back to the same element. We assume that the element, that is, the atom of the element, never changes. The atom is constant through all our manipulations, and no matter how much we build up and tear down we must come back to the original. The ninety-odd elements might indicate ninety different lines of experience, each element a law unto itself. But

a very cursory glimpse at chemistry shows that the different elements, although always absolutely distinct and
unchanging, are not laws unto themselves; but that they
are strikingly similar, and react in a similar manner to
a remarkable degree. The similarity of the elements is
shown most promptly by the metals, which form a group
with striking physical and chemical resemblance. Among
the nonmetals the members of the halogen group are very
much alike. They are so regular in their properties that,
given the characteristics of one, those of the others may
be anticipated. Of more striking value than the qualitative resemblance is the numerical relation of their atomic
weights. This regularity is conveniently shown by the
following table:

THE HALOGEN GROUP		THE SODIUM GROUP		THE CALCIUM GROUP	
	Atomic weight		Atomic weight		Atomic weight
Fluorine	19	Sodium	23	Magnesium	24.3
Chlorine	35.5	Potassium	39.1	Calcium	40
Bromine	80	Rubidium	85.5	Strontium	87.6
Iodine	127	Cesium	133	Barium	137.4

The increase of atomic weights is the same in all these
groups. The difference is sixteen between the first two
and about forty-five between the others. These differences
occur so frequently that they may be considered regular.

Facts like these are bound to lead to speculation as to
their cause. What is this relationship between the different
elements? It is altogether evident that the elements are
not absolutely independent.

Early in the nineteenth century, there was much interest
manifested in Prout's hypothesis. At that time, the atomic

weights of the elements, referred to hydrogen, seemed to be whole numbers, and Prout's hypothesis assumed that the different elements were made up of hydrogen as the constructive unit. Later work showed discrepancies, and it remained for recent investigations to establish the structure of the atom as based upon "protons," hydrogen units, and electrons. This new conception, founded upon experience, and not merely an ingenious speculation, is discussed more fully later.

A rough classification of the elements into the metals and the nonmetals has been in constant use in these pages. So also a further classification into such groups as the halogen group, the sodium group, and the calcium group.

So far as they go these groups are most useful and much of our work is based upon them. But the periodic classification now to be described comprehends all the elements in one complete system. This was published in 1869 by Mendeléeff and Lothar Meyer independently. It is so valuable and satisfactory that it has been universally adopted and remains the cornerstone of all broad conceptions of the elements and their relations. It may be stated thus: The elements are written down in the order of their atomic weights. These are values which have been determined with the greatest accuracy, and on the whole are reliable. It will then be noticed (leaving hydrogen and the rare gases out of consideration for the present) that after the first seven have been considered, the eighth, sodium, is very similar to lithium, the first one considered; the ninth is similar to the second, and so on, until we come to the fifteenth, potassium, which again resembles the first, and this repetition of resemblances continues, when certain modifications and omissions are made, right on through the whole list of elements. Because the properties thus repeat themselves in regular periods, this classification is called the periodic classification. The periodic table follows. Atomic weights are given above; atomic numbers are below, enclosed.

Group	o	I	II	III	IV	V	VI	VII	VIII		
Typical Compounds to H	None	NaCl Na$_2$O	MgCl$_2$ MgO	AlCl$_3$ Al$_2$O$_3$	CH$_4$ CO$_2$	PH$_3$ P$_2$O$_5$	SH$_2$ SO$_3$	ClH Cl$_2$O			
Valence to H		1	2	3	4	3	2	1			
Valence to O		1	2	3	4	5	6	7			
		H 1 (1)									
1st Short Series	He 4 (2)	Li 7 (3)	Be 9 (4)	B 11 (5)	C 12 (6)	N 14 (7)	O 16 (8)	F 19 (9)			
2nd Short Series	Ne 20 (10)	Na 23 (11)	Mg 24 (12)	Al 27 (13)	Si 28 (14)	P 31 (15)	S 32 (16)	Cl 35.5 (17)			
Long Series	A 40 (18)	K 39.1 (19)	Ca 40 (20)	Sc 45 (21)	Ti 48 (22)	V 51 (23)	Cr 52 (24)	Mn 55 (25)	Fe 56 (26)	Co 59 (27)	Ni 58.7 (28)
		Cu 63.6 (29)	Zn 65.4 (30)	Ga 70 (31)	Ge 72.6 (32)	As 75 (33)	Se 79 (34)	Br 80 (35)			
Long Series	Kr 84 (36)	Rb 85.4 (37)	Sr 87.6 (38)	Y 89 (39)	Zr 91 (40)	Cb 93 (41)	Mo 96 (42)	Ma 98 (43)	Ru 102 (44)	Rh 103 (45)	Pd 107 (46)
		Ag 108 (47)	Cd 112 (48)	In 115 (49)	Sn 119 (50)	Sb 122 (51)	Te 127.5 (52)	I 126.9 (53)			
Long Series	Xe 131 (54)	Cs 133 (55)	Ba 137.4 (56)	La 139 (57)	Hf 178.6 (72)	Ta 181.5 (73)	W 184 (74)	Re 186 (75)	Os 190 (76)	Ir 193 (77)	Pt 195 (78)
		Au 197 (79)	Hg 201 (80)	Tl 204 (81)	Pb 207 (82)	Bi 209 (83)	Po 210 (84)	(85)			
	Rn 222 (86)	(87)	Ra 226 (88)	Ac 229? (89)	Th 232 (90)	Pa 231 (91)	U 238 (92)				

The trans-uranic elements:

Np 237 (93)	Pu 239 (94)	Am? (95)	Cm? (96)

The elements 58 to 71 are conveniently omitted, as their relationship to one another and to the remaining elements is not clear. Their omission does not lessen the value of the rest, and the classification has been of preëminent usefulness as a summary of what was known before, and as an inspiration for the research of the future.

Considering the table, the following facts stand out:

A. The elements, considered from the standpoint of their atomic weights, and arranged in that order, are comprehended in one complete scheme, showing a periodic recurrence of properties.

B. Of the series thus established the first and second each include seven elements comprising the short series. The third and fourth short series are needed to form together the long series. The regular variation and periodicity applies in some measure to these two short series, but the full rounding of the period does not come until the end of the long series. At the middle portion of the long series occur groups of three elements strikingly alike —an exception to the usual variation.

C. The atomic weights increase from element to element by small increments. Owing to the periodicity, the atomic weights of similar elements differ in a regular way. At first the increment is sixteen, but after the third short series, following only those elements which are on the right or left of each column, the increment is about forty-five. From fluorine to chlorine the increment is sixteen, the weights being respectively 19 and 35.5, whereas bromine and iodine show increments of about forty-five. The eighth column shows a different principle, in that similar elements vary little in their atomic weights.

D. The variation in valence is regular. Since valences are variable, and frequently are higher in respect to oxygen than to hydrogen, the higher is usually assumed to be the true expression of valence. In the classification the valence of the elements in the different columns is found to increase from one to four when considered with respect to hydrogen, and then to drop back to one, whereas the valence toward oxygen increases steadily up to seven. The valence of the eighth group should perhaps be left outside of this brief consideration, but it is interesting to observe that the only elements, osmium and ruthenium, which do have a valence of eight, fall into this group.

E. The common and active metals have low atomic weights and fall into the first part of the table. Iron, fifty-six, has the highest weight of the abundant elements.

F. When this table was first proposed there were vacancies in the places now occupied by scandium, gallium, and germanium as well as by others. Mendeléeff predicted the discovery of elements which would fulfill the conditions required by these three positions, and he outlined in detail the properties of such elements and their compounds. The elements thus predicted were discovered in the course of the next decade and confirmed Mendeléeff's predictions to a remarkable degree. The table can then anticipate and suggest future discoveries, both of unknown elements, as well as of the properties that any missing elements would possess. It is also a check on facts already supposed to be known. For example, the atomic weight of beryllium was corrected from 13.5 to 9, as a result of its fitting in a place in the second column suggested by the value 9, while for the value 13.5 there was no vacancy.

G. Inasmuch as metals as a class have lower valences than the nonmetals, the metals are more likely to be found in the first columns, and the nonmetals in the later columns. Further, in any given group, or column, the more metallic element has a higher atomic weight and the more characteristic nonmetal the lower. Potassium is more characteristically metallic than sodium; so on the other hand chlorine is more characteristically nonmetallic than bromine. Therefore the metals, in case of doubt, are near the lower portion of the columns, as the nonmetals are near the upper portion. Combining these two principles a diagonal may be drawn across the table from a point above beryllium to a point below iodine. The metals on the whole will be found below this line, the nonmetals above, and the doubtful elements near it. (Omitting Column VIII.)

H. When argon, the first of the rare gases of the atmosphere, was discovered in 1894, no place was found for it in the table as then accepted. It was finally placed in a column preceding the first, the so-called zero column. Thus the way was opened for the investigations which presently resulted in the discoveries of the other rare gases. This column was in the end filled out as completely as were the others. The complete lack of chemical activity falls in with the suggestion that their valence is zero.

I. The periodic arrangement causes the elements to fall into groups, which are represented by the columns. After the second short series, the elements of the first half of the next long series are written to the left, those from the second half to the right. The true groups are made up of the metals directly under each other, so that there are in each column two related groups. In each group the properties vary with great regularity as we advance in the atomic weight. We thus have a number of groups, in each of which the properties as a whole, and their variation within the group, are determined according to very definite principles.

J. The discrepancies of the classification. The use of the double series after the second, and the grouping of certain elements, not otherwise fitting in, in the eighth column, and the location of the inert gases in the zero column, are no longer looked upon as irregularities. These arrangements fit in admirably, now that they are better appreciated, and instead of detracting from the good order of the whole, they have aided much in their suggestiveness. But the inversion of the order of atomic weights for tellurium and iodine still stands as a striking exception. Nevertheless, no confusion comes from accepting this exception, and it is the part of wisdom to adopt the usefulness of the rest and leave the explanation of the doubtful features to the future. The same fact is to be observed in the case of argon and potassium. There were reasons for placing argon after fluorine, assuming a weight of 20, instead of 40. This would have avoided this discrepancy. When, however, argon was finally placed before potassium in the zero column, this position was soon justified by the discovery of the other members of the group.

There is a group of metals, called the rare earths, with a valence of three and having atomic weights of from 140 to 180, which have not been satisfactorily placed.

There is no place for hydrogen in this scheme. Hydrogen is seemingly unique; we may tentatively assume that it occupies a place by itself, or we may look to its proper placing in the course of time.

Many modifications of the plan as here given have been proposed. The main principle of the periodic classification is retained in all of them.

ATOMIC NUMBERS

Since 1913 another light has been thrown upon this question of the periodic arrangement by the study of X-ray spectra of the elements. These are obtained by photographing a diffracted X-ray beam which had impinged upon the element, much as the usual spectrum is obtained and photographed. From the study of these spectra, it is seen that the elements fall into a regular order near to that of the periodic classification, and from this order they receive a number called the atomic number. The numbers run from 1 for hydrogen to 92 for uranium. From a consideration of these new ideas, the following facts stand out.

The general ideas of the periodic classification are confirmed. The anomalies noted in the three cases, argon and potassium, cobalt and nickel, tellurium and iodine, disappear, as the atomic number calls for the accepted arrangement based upon chemical properties. It would seem, then, that the atomic weight only approximately determines the position of an element: that the exact position is determined by other factors, suggested by these X-ray spectra. The total number of elements was determined by the atomic number of uranium as 92. This seemed to set a limit to the possibilities, and gave the search for new elements some guidance, a fact which will be of especial value in the study of the confused chapter of the rare earth metals.

CHAPTER XX

CONCLUSIONS FROM THE STUDY OF THE RADIOACTIVE ELEMENTS

THE discovery of the radioactive elements has resulted in a great stimulation to investigators, with respect not alone to the facts concerning these substances, but lately even more to the significance of these interesting phenomena; and their investigations have led to valuable conceptions as to the nature of the atom and the influences involving chemical action. These studies to a great extent carry us away from the field of ordinary chemical observation and it is to the physicist that we must look for experiences and assistance in interpretations.

RADIOACTIVITY

Radium was discovered by the Curies in 1898. It is the most striking of the radioactive elements. It is a metal of the calcium group, resembling barium most closely in its chemical characteristics. Its atomic weight is very high, as are also the weights of thorium and uranium, the other conspicuously radioactive elements. The outstanding feature of radium is that it is spontaneously giving forth energy. This output of energy is manifested by its giving out light and heat, and rays which affect the photographic plate, render gases conductors of electricity and have pronounced physiological effects. The amount of energy thus emitted was soon shown to be very great.

All attempts to explain this phenomenon on the basis

of previous conceptions failed, and soon an entirely new and unexpected explanation was forthcoming. It is now well known that the radium atom is disintegrating and in this process emanates both material particles and energy. As this atom loses material, atoms of lesser atomic weight are formed; these in turn similarly disintegrate. The process continues until a stable atom is formed, presumably that of lead. It must be remembered that the amounts involved are always small, and the changes must be followed by physical means, not by the material observations of the chemical laboratory.

The emanations from radium are of three kinds. The alpha rays are particles of positively charged helium units (not helium atoms). The beta rays are negative electrons, the unit of negative electricity, $1/1845$ of the mass of the hydrogen atom. The gamma rays are akin to the X-rays. They are not particles, and although of great importance in physical considerations, will not be considered further for our purpose.

The atom is to be compared to the solar system in that it is made up of a comparatively compact mass, the nucleus, which is surrounded by distant electrons, as though by planets. The compact mass is made up of hydrogen units, equal in number to the atomic weight. These hydrogen units are of two types, the protons and the neutrons. The protons are the hydrogen atoms lacking an electron, and the lacking electrons are the constituents of the outer shells, the planetary electrons. Hence the number of protons and planetary electrons is the same, and the number of these is the atomic number of the element. The protons, for loss of the negative electron, are positive. The remaining hydrogen units are combinations in some manner of protons and electrons, and are advanta_{geously} called neutrons. They are internally neutralized, as the positive protons are balanced by an equal number of negative electrons.

This may be restated in other words:

Every atom contains a number of hydrogen units corresponding to the atomic weight; these are all in the nucleus. Also an equal number of electrons, either in the nucleus or the planetary system without. The distribution is as follows:

In the nucleus there are two types of hydrogen units, (a) the protons, hydrogen units lacking a negative electron; therefore they are positive. The number of these is the atomic number of the element. (b) The remaining hydrogen units are the neutrons. The neutron is composed in some manner of a positive proton and a negative electron, and is therefore neutral. (c) In the planetary system, or the so-called shells, are the electrons, equal in number to the protons. The atomic number is conveniently referred to these rather than to the protons.

The atom as a whole is neutral. Even at the risk of some repetition this will be illustrated by a reference to the element Aluminum: Atomic weight 27, atomic number 13. In the nucleus, 13 protons, positive; and 14 neutrons, neutral. In the planetary system, 13 electrons, negative.

The nucleus, $14 + 13$, determines the atomic weight of the aluminum atoms. The number of the electrons, 13, the atomic number, and their arrangement, as will be seen, determine the chemical properties of each of the elements.

The following diagrams will bring out these points for elements 2 (hydrogen is not included) to 14. Further illustrations are repetitions of these, with an increasing number of shells.

In these diagrams, the protons are indicated by the sign $+$. Their number in each atom is the same as that of the planetary electrons, which determines the atomic number of the element.

The neutrons are indicated by the sign $\pm$. The number of neutrons plus the number of protons is the atomic weight of the element.

The shells of the planetary system are represented by the imaginary cubes, as shown by the dotted lines. They are spoken of as of different levels. K is the first level, that of the two electrons of helium, which are not included in a cube. L is the first imaginary cube, the corners of which are progressively occupied by electrons (e). M is the second imaginary cube, the corners of which, successively occupied by the increasing number of electrons, repeat the configuration of the shell L.

The detailed description of the sequence of atoms is as follows:

Hydrogen, atomic number 1, is a law unto itself.

Helium, atomic number 2, includes two neutrons and two protons in the nucleus. The two planetary electrons are at energy level K, marked *ee* in the diagram.

Lithium, number 3, includes four neutrons and three protons in the nucleus. Of its three planetary electrons, two are, as in all cases, at energy level K. The third electron is at a greater distance, taking one of the eight positions of the imaginary cube (octet at energy level L). This one electron and its position give to lithium its valence and other chemical properties.

Beryllium, number 4, includes five neutrons and four

ATOMIC STRUCTURE OF ELEMENTS
FIRST SERIES

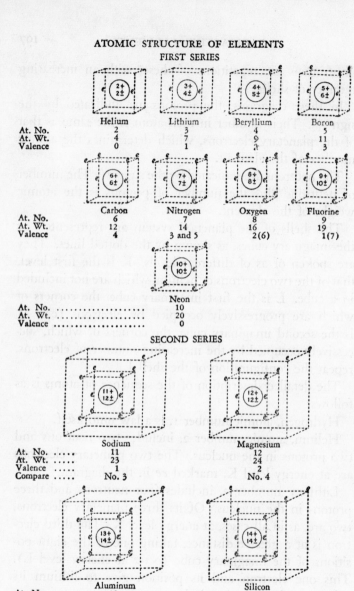

	Helium	Lithium	Beryllium	Boron
At. No.	2	3	4	5
At. Wt.	4	7	9	11
Valence	0	1	2	3

	Carbon	Nitrogen	Oxygen	Fluorine
At. No.	6	7	8	9
At. Wt.	12	14	16	19
Valence	4	3 and 5	2(6)	1(7)

	Neon
At. No.	10
At. Wt.	20
Valence	0

SECOND SERIES

	Sodium	Magnesium
At. No.	11	12
At. Wt.	23	24
Valence	1	2
Compare	No. 3	No. 4

	Aluminum	Silicon
At. No.	13	14
At. Wt.	27	28
Valence	3	4
Compare	No. 5	No. 6

protons in the nucleus. There are now four planetary electrons. The fourth of these takes up a second of the eight possible positions of the octet. Its valence is therefore two, and it is the first member of the second (calcium-magnesium) group of metals.

This building up continues with the elements following in the proper order. The elements numbered 5, 6, 7, 8 and 9 successively add an electron to the imaginary cube. With number 10 the octet is complete and the element, neon, on account of this completeness, is incapable of any chemical activity. The shell L is thus completed.

Neon is in a sense the final element of the first series, as the shell L is now complete. Neon is also the introductory element of the second series, inasmuch as added electrons must now take positions in a newly developed shell M.

In order to provide for the added electron which the next element, sodium, supplies, it is necessary to establish a new imaginary cube (octet) shell M, the second cube. The new electron takes a position corresponding to the position of the electron of lithium, and therefore the characteristics of lithium are repeated. The element following, magnesium, repeats the configuration and characteristics of beryllium. This then continues throughout the entire range of the elements. Each time, after the completion of an octet, a new one is established, the shells being designated as indicated.

The conception just outlined offers a reasonable and usable explanation for a number of highly important phenomena.

(a) The main features of the periodic table are now brought into a clear picture, by which there may be visualized atomic weight, atomic number and periodicity.

(*b*) The valence, at least in part, is determined by the number of electrons in the incomplete octets. When a metal forms a polar, *i. e.,* ionizable, compound, an electron (or several) passes over to the nonmetallic element. By the loss of a negative electron the metal becomes positively, by the gain of this electron the nonmetal becomes negatively charged. The number of electrons involved in this case measures the valence. For elements like nitrogen and phosphorus, the valence is five when the element offers electrons in forming compounds, and three when it accepts them in the three vacant places. For nonpolar, *i. e.,* nonionizing compounds the union is explained by the sharing of pairs of electrons, as, for example, water, H:Ö:H, the final effect being a completed octet about the oxygen nucleus. So methane is formed from carbon, ·Ċ·, which shares four pairs of electrons, the remaining four being supplied by the hydrogen atoms, H. The final

form is
$$\text{H:}\overset{\text{H}}{\underset{\text{H}}{\text{C}}}\text{:H.}$$
This plan with proper variations is so well worked out that it carries the usefulness of valence interpretations well beyond its former limits.

(*c*) The inert elements have only completed octets, and thus can neither yield electrons nor accept them. They are therefore incapable of forming compounds. This conclusion has been challenged, and if it is presently shown that compounds can be formed, the above interpretation of the complete octets must be modified.

(*d*) Isotopes are readily explained on this assumption. Let us refer to two isotopes of chlorine, those of atomic weight 35, and those of atomic weight 37. In the first case there are in the nucleus 17 protons and 18 neutrons. There are, therefore, 17 electrons left for the outer shells, for K, L, and M respectively 2, 8, and 7. In the second case, isotope of weight 37, the interpretation is as follows. It contains 17 protons and 20 neutrons in the nucleus. Therefore 17 electrons, the same number as before, are left for a similar distribution in the shells, namely, 2, 8, and 7. Thus two atoms, with different atomic weights, possess similar outside electron configuration. With similar electron configuration they possess the same chemical properties, that is, they are the same element.

(e) The interpretation of the phenomena of radioactivity is fundamentally associated with the conception outlined above. The elements with high atomic weights, radium, 226, thorium, 232, uranium, 238, are evidently very complex structures, with a large number of octet shells. These are spontaneously disintegrating, throwing off clusters of protons and neutrons, in the form of helium units, the alpha rays, and also the electrons of the beta rays. Hence these atoms are simplifying, and we have a well-established series of intermediate products until the stable lead is reached, with an atomic weight of 20 to 30 less than the mother substance. Radium itself is a temporary element, being formed from uranium, and it is in turn disintegrating. In the lives of these disintegrating radioactive substances, the period of existence is of variable length, and is measured conveniently by the half life period.

(f) *Artificial Disintegration, Induced Radioactivity and Transmutation of Elements.* When the first chapter on radioactive phenomena was completed, the conclusion was drawn that all these effects were absolutely outside of human control. This conclusion is no longer accepted and much experimentation has been carried on with respect to changes which could be attained artificially. It was apparent that the ordinary methods of chemical attack would be fruitless. Results however were obtained by altogether new means, namely by the "bombardment" of the substance under investigation by means suggested by radioactive experiences. This bombardment is by protons, neutrons, and alpha particles, especially when their velocity is accelerated by high potential electricity.

Four results may now be attributed to these artificial influences. They are (1) that the composition of the atom can be altered. Atoms may change by loss (or gain) of material, the alpha particle (helium) or an electron, with two results. If the shell conformation persists the element would possess the same properties, namely form an isotope. If the shell conformation is altered, a new element would be formed. Hence the possibility of the (2) transmutation of elements, very different from the ideas of transmutation of the alchemists. The third point (3) is the fascinating question of transuranium elements, that is, elements which, if they ever did exist, were so complex that they have broken down in course of time. Bombardment of uranium with neutrons has been found to produce four new elements with atomic number greater than 92, namely numbers 93, 94, 95 and 96. All these have a short existence, their half life ranging from a few minutes to three days.

A fourth point (4) is induced radioactivity. This is illustrated by sodium. The sodium of sodium chloride, properly bombarded, developed a radioactivity of half life of fifteen hours, on the whole comparable with that of radium.

These transformations are, of course, mainly of scientific interest. The amounts involved are minute and chemical identification still meager. Their radiation, to be sure, may be of even greater use than now, as is suggested by the possible therapeutic use of radioactive sodium.

The foregoing interpretation of the relation of the protons and electrons in forming the neutrons is not finally accepted. Until the matter is more clearly understood, it may be taken as a logical and constructive assumption, tending definitely to simplify the conception of the nucleus. Other possible constituents of the atom have not been included in the discussion. They do not threaten to make a fundamental alteration in the picture. The contributions of the "Bohr atom" have not been disregarded, although not specifically mentioned. This entire subject is too extensive to include every point in a brief summary.

The energy developed in these disintegrations is very great, so that fantastic hopes are often raised with respect to its utilization, at present very doubtful. The following comparison may aid comprehension of this new type of energy.

The chemical energy residing in one gram of carbon when converted into heat energy by the process of combustion is represented by about 8,000 heat units. Each of these heat units converted into work is represented by 45,000 gram centimeters. The one gram of carbon therefore possesses mechanical energy measured by the vast number of 340,000,000 units. Sub-atomic energy (intra-atomic energy) is very great, and when translated into ordinary chemical energy has been estimated to be about 300,000 times as great, that is, one gram of radium in disintegrating gives about 300,000 times the amount of energy that could be obtained by the combustion of one gram of carbon. All these numbers multiplied together, therefore, show a very large mechanical equivalent. The experiences in the recent atomic disintegrations, in which a portion of matter is converted into energy, have led to much higher estimates of this equivalent, probably eight to ten times as great.

CHAPTER XXI

ORGANIC CHEMISTRY

THE subject of organic chemistry involves such a large phase of general chemistry that it is expedient to study it by itself and at considerable length. Moreover there are special reasons in addition for emphasizing this special study. The subject matter involves few elements, primarily carbon, secondarily hydrogen, oxygen and nitrogen in the main; and the number of combinations among these surpasses that of any other combination of elements. Although the reactions will be found to be of the old order, the principles of the structure of the compounds are distinctive. Finally the subject matter is concerned to a great extent with the products of living organisms. The connection last mentioned accounts for the name, organic chemistry, a name which was soon found to be too exclusive, but which has since been retained for its associations and convenience.

In presenting the subject of organic chemistry, the author desires to emphasize the main features which lend it its especial fascination. The subject covers a field that is coordinated as a whole, and in the development of which a logical order is maintained. To this theoretical progression and unity is added the application of its principles to two lines of human interest, the study of the material and processes of living organisms, and the contact with countless material interests of daily life as well as of more remote manufacturing processes. These applications will be touched on in some measure, either in this chapter, or in the chapter on industrial organic chemistry, which follows. In anticipation these interests may be briefly summarized.

From a practical standpoint the subject matter of organic chemistry might be considered as mainly included in two groups, one consisting of natural and the other of artificial products. In the former are all the substances formed by animal or vegetable organisms or those derived from them in simple ways, while in the latter are the products formed by the more elaborate manufacturing processes, proceeding from such raw materials as coal tar. The first group includes the rather complex compounds associated with the chemistry of living things, namely, biochemistry; the constituents of foods; the products obtained by fermentation processes; the substances involved in the extensive fat and oil industries; the essential oils, including perfumes and flavors; many medicinal preparations; and, lastly, the textiles, which may include cotton, silk, wool, leather, and rubber. The artificial group concerns itself with such substances as are obtained from the destructive distillation products of wood and coal, most conspicuous among which are the much discussed coal-tar products, particularly the dyes. Synthetic textiles and plastics are now conspicuous. Explosives, photographic chemicals and synthetic drugs are included in this group. Petroleum forms an additional group by itself.

The essential need in the study of this subject is the appreciation of its unity. This unity is expressed in the cumbrous but very suggestive working definition: "Organic Chemistry is the study of the hydrocarbons and their derivatives." To this bare statement should be added two points. (*a*) The hydrocarbons, though many in number, are readily comprehended in two classes, in each of which the individuals are related in an orderly manner. (*b*) The derivatives further are in every case related to the parent hydrocarbon according to a simple principle presently to be outlined, and as a corollary, bear an orderly relation to each other.

Our study then must be comprehended under two main heads: the nature and relationship of the hydrocarbons; and the relation to these of the derivatives and the properties of these derivatives. The treatment of the latter will be by far the more extensive.

A hydrocarbon is a compound composed of carbon and hydrogen only. Carbon is outstanding in its power to build up complex molecules, one atom adding itself to another to an extent unknown for other elements. The valences not applied for linking the carbon atoms together are filled out with hydrogen. Typical illustrations are methane, CH_4; ethane, C_2H_6; benzene, C_6H_6. There are about two thousand such combinations, a number which may seem appalling at the very beginning. We may, however, simplify by saying that all these hydrocarbons fall into two main groups, the paraffin group and the benzene group.

The hydrocarbons of both groups have many points of resemblance. They are all combustible, and not very reactive, light, insoluble in water, being composed of only carbon and hydrogen.

Nevertheless they may be definitely differentiated into two groups by two features, the amount of hydrogen present in proportion to the carbon, and their chemical reactivity. The first of these features is illustrated by the comparison between two typical members, hexane, C_6H_{14}, of the first group, and benzene, C_6H_6, of the second group. Hexane contains all the hydrogen which is mathematically possible, benzene contains very much less. The second feature is this: members of the first group respond very little to the action of chemical reagents, especially the two chief acids, sulphuric and nitric acids. Hence these hydrocarbons have received the name "paraffin," meaning of low chemical activity. The members of the second group, on the other hand, while not showing any reactivity comparable with that of the inorganic bases, do act with the above mentioned acids, and to this fact owe their industrial usefulness. These are the coal-tar hydrocarbons, the basis of the much discussed coal-tar products.

There follows immediately Part I, a discussion of the paraffin hydrocarbons. In Part II are treated the benzene hydrocarbons.

PART I

THE FIRST GROUP OF THE HYDROCARBONS, THE PARAFFINS

The hydrocarbons which are found to belong to this group contain varying amounts of carbon and corresponding amounts of hydrogen. We would naturally consider these in the order of their carbon content, and in doing so find that they may be arranged in a regular series. Thus arranged, their carbon and hydrogen content, it will be noted, increases regularly. It will be profitable to consider a table showing names, formulas, and properties of these hydrocarbons.

THE PARAFFIN HYDROCARBONS

Formula of hydrocarbon	Boiling point, C.	Specific gravity	Melting point, C.
$C\ H_4$	gas	....	..
$C_2\ H_6$	gas	....	..
$C_3\ H_8$	gas	....	..
$C_4\ H_{10}$	$1°$	....	..
$C_5\ H_{12}$	$36°$	0.628	..
$C_6\ H_{14}$	$69°$	0.658	..
$C_7\ H_{16}$	$98°$	0.684	..
$C_8\ H_{18}$	$125°$	0.708	..
$C_9\ H_{20}$	$149°$	0.718	..
$C_{10}H_{22}$	$173°$	0.730	..
$C_{11}H_{24}$	$195°$	0.741	..
$C_{12}H_{26}$	$214°$	0.751	..
$C_{13}H_{28}$	$234°$	0.757	..
$C_{14}H_{30}$	$253°$	0.764	$5°$
$C_{15}H_{32}$	$270°$	0.769	$10°$
$C_{16}H_{34}$	$287°$	0.773	$20°$
$C_{17}H_{36}$	$303°$	0.778	$23°$
$C_{18}H_{38}$	$317°$	0.784	$28°$

A study of this table will establish the appreciation of the nature of a "series." As the relation of hydrocarbons and the derivatives is a cardinal point of organic chemistry, so is a second the fact that the hydrocarbons and their corresponding derivatives invariably fall into series, showing a regular progression of physical properties based upon the progressive complexity of their structure. The first of the series is a light gas, and as we move along, the tendency to become a liquid is greater. The higher members of the series are liquids, but very volatile. Then come less volatile liquids, and finally solids. The specific gravity increases regularly, and other properties which can be measured vary similarly.

In those respects in which the paraffin hydrocarbons do not vary with the regularity just emphasized, they are remarkably alike. They are insoluble in water, combustible, and are not readily reacted upon by acids and other substances. It is only lately that the great progress of industrial chemistry has resulted in the formation of derivatives directly from the sluggish paraffins. Heretofore, chemistry has depended upon some form of natural product for such compounds.

Before the derivatives of the paraffins are taken up, it will be desirable to touch upon a chapter of applied organic chemistry which to this day of gas engines is of such vital interest, namely petroleum and its products. Crude petroleum (and for this discussion natural gas may be included) is in the main a naturally occurring mixture of the different members of the paraffin series. The great value of petroleum lies primarily in its combustibility; but the various phases of the industry are determined by the varying physical properties of the different members of the series. The first members are gases, and for some purposes gas is an ideal fuel. Next comes the mixture of members which we may call gasoline, a liquid, easily transported and handled, yet so readily converted to a gas, when wanted in that state, that it is altogether suitable for use in a gas engine. The next group is represented by kerosene, too little volatile for ordinary gas engines, but which by means of certain expedients (the wick is one of them) may be converted into a gas and burned for light and heat. Another higher group is represented by the lubricating oils, possessing physical properties suitable for such purposes. Finally we have paraffin, made up of solid members, useful just because they are solids. Some years ago, before the uses of petroleum products were so definitely concentrated in the above groups, there were various intermediate groups, for example, between gasoline and kerosene, not quite suitable for either, hence put to the humble use of cleaning liquids. Another group was called burning oils, being a residue not suited to other needs.

The whole tendency now is to concentrate into groups which have the greatest value, and particularly gasoline. The major portion of petroleum refining is the mechanical separation of a mixture of many individual hydrocarbons into convenient parts, no one part being a pure substance, but made up of neighboring members of the series, nearly enough alike to serve the same purpose. The most highly esteemed is gasoline, which, interestingly enough, in the early days of oil refining was a drug on the market. Now the great demand for this commodity has led refiners to include neighbors of the series so far down in the list that their tendency to become gaseous is appreciably less than that of the gasoline of some years ago. This has been rendered possible by the increasing mechanical perfection of the automobile engine. Now that men have enjoyed the gratification of two great human aspirations, the automobile and the flying machine, it is unlikely that they will allow the exhaustion of the petroleum supply in the future to put an end to these pleasures and conveniences.

In what direction they will turn successfully for a motor fuel it is not yet possible to say. Alcohol, being obtained from the fermentation of vegetable products, can always be supplied, perhaps in limited amounts, if it fills the need satisfactorily. Coal-tar hydrocarbons, obtained from the coke-making operations, may help somewhat, but the amount obtainable does not promise to be adequate.

Certain bituminous shales, upon destructive distillation, yield hydrocarbons and promise somewhat for the future.

Synthetic processes, namely the building up of desired liquid hydrocarbons from simpler gaseous hydrocarbons, will no doubt receive serious consideration. An operation of great promise, the Bergius process, may be said to be established, awaiting only the day when diminishing petroleum supplies necessitate its use. The Bergius process consists in the addition of hydrogen to the compounds in soft coal, so as to convert them into usable hydrocarbons.

Economy in the use of our present resources is desirable. This applies to more efficient recovery from the oil wells, for about one-half of the oil is left behind. It applies to greater production of the valuable gasoline constituent. It applies to better engine design, in which respect antiknock substances are influential. The restriction of the use of petroleum to automobiles, and the application of radically different means of developing energy are, however, topics outside the scope of the chemist.

Derivatives of the Paraffins

To the two cardinal points mentioned above, there may be added a third: namely, the derivatives of the hydrocarbons are formed theoretically and in some measure actually by the replacement of one or more hydrogen atoms of the hydrocarbon by other elements or simple groups. Three groups, $- Cl$, $- OH$, $- NH_2$, will come into consideration more than others. These groups each possess a valence of one, and therefore can replace monovalent hydrogen in a simple manner atom by atom. To compounds involving these three groups the greater number of the interesting derivatives of the paraffin series is related—not, to be sure, always in the simplest forms, but with study the relationships will become apparent.

We cannot go very far in the study of organic compounds without the use of open, or graphic formulas. The formula CH_4 has a certain numerical meaning; but if it is written $C{\equiv}^{-H}_{-H}{}^{-H}_{-H}$ it more graphically represents the structure of the molecule. If now we drop one hydrogen atom and in its place put a chlorine atom, the graphic formula of the new compound, $C{\equiv}^{-Cl}_{-H}{}^{-H}_{-H}$, makes this relation more apparent. So also, $C{\equiv}^{-OH}_{-H}{}^{-H}_{-H}$ and $C{\equiv}^{-NH_2}_{-H}{}^{-H}_{-H}$. The open formulas are often more helpful than the more compact form-

SIMPLE DERIVATIVES OF THE PARAFFIN HYDROCARBONS

Original hydrocarbon	Halogen derivative	Hydroxyl derivative	Amino derivative	Double halogen derivative
$C H_4$ methane	CH_3Cl methyl chloride	CH_3OH methyl alcohol	CH_3NH_2 methyl amine	CH_2Cl_2 dichloro methane
C_2H_6 ethane	C_2H_5Cl ethyl chloride	C_2H_5OH ethyl alcohol	$C_2H_5NH_2$ ethyl amine	$C_2H_4Cl_2$ dichloro ethane
C_3H_8 propane	C_3H_7Cl propyl chloride	C_3H_7OH propyl alcohol	$C_3H_7NH_2$ propyl amine	$C_3H_6Cl_2$ dichloro propane
C_4H_{10} butane	C_4H_9Cl butyl chloride	C_4H_9OH butyl alcohol	$C_4H_9NH_2$ butyl amine	$C_4H_8Cl_2$ dichloro butane
C_5H_{12} pentane	$C_5H_{11}Cl$ pentyl chloride	$C_5H_{11}OH$ pentyl alcohol (amyl alcohol)	$C_5H_{11}NH_2$ pentyl amine	$C_5H_{10}Cl_2$ dichloro pentane

—and so on, through the whole list of hydrocarbons.

ulas in perceiving at a glance the possibilities of organic development.

In the table on page 213 compact formulas only are shown and for the moment must serve our purpose. In later paragraphs the graphic formulas are used, as essential for bringing out the structure of the compounds.

The partial list of derivatives found in the preceding table suggests the scope of the subject when continued throughout the whole list of hydrocarbons.

This table includes only the simplest and most direct compounds. Each set of derivatives represents a series, directly comparable with the original hydrocarbon series and, like that series, showing regular progression in physical properties.

As a corollary to the third cardinal point mentioned above, namely the manner of formation of derivatives by the introduction of certain groups, there follows naturally the principle that when one group is present it may by proper manipulation be replaced by one of the other groups. When this principle is borne in mind relations such as $CH_3Cl \rightleftarrows CH_3OH \rightleftarrows CH_3NH_2$ are simply logical relations, making no demands upon mere memory efforts. This interchange of groups is one of the most useful of organic reactions. It enables us to pass from one type of compound to another, more or less at will, since it may be possible to select a derivative of the same order in one of the other groups, and then to pass over, so to speak, to the one we wish. For example, $C_2H_6 \rightarrow C_2H_4 (OH)_2$ cannot be accomplished directly, $C_2H_6 \rightarrow C_2H_4Cl_2 \rightarrow C_2H_4 (OH)_2$ can be accomplished, and thus indirectly we have gained our end. Without this device the practical possibilities of organic chemistry would have many limitations, for after all, organic compounds are not conspicuously reactive, and combinations must be effected by whatever favoring conditions we can apply.

HALOGEN DERIVATIVES

a. The chlorine, or more generally, the halogen, derivatives may be considered briefly as a whole. We have a long list of compounds, for we have several principles of variation, namely, by introducing any of the halogens, chlorine, bromine, or iodine. Typical compounds are CH_3Cl, CH_3Br, CH_3I.

b. Several hydrogen atoms may be replaced by any halogen. The four compounds of methane and chlorine all have practical applications. These are CH_3Cl, CH_2Cl_2, $CHCl_3$, CCl_4, called formally, monochloromethane, dichloromethane, tri- and tetra-chloromethane. Common names are, methyl chloride, methylene chloride, chloroform, and carbon tetrachloride (carboneum). The first and second of these are used as refrigerants, as they may easily be reduced to volatile liquids. Chloroform is well known. Carbon tetrachloride approaches being unique because it is a noncombustible organic substance, and therefore useful for a fire-extinguisher and a safe domestic solvent.

c. The derivative may be obtained from any one of the series of hydrocarbons. Illustrations are: CH_3Cl, C_2H_5Cl, C_3H_7Cl, C_4H_9Cl.

The following table is introduced to illustrate the relation of physical properties to structure. Its details need not engage the reader's attention further. The main theme should be clearly noticed.

A.

	I Boiling point	II Specific gravity
CH₃Cl	$-24°$ C.	gas
CH₂Cl₂	42	1.3
CHCl₃	63	1.5
CCl₄	77	1.6

The influence of the amount of chlorine present is apparent.

B.

	I Boiling point	II Specific gravity
CH₃I	$42°$ C.	2.3
C₂H₅I	72	1.9
C₃H₇I	102	1.7
C₄H₉I	129	1.6

In Column I the higher boiling point is associated with the increase in molecular complexity. In Column II the progress of values seems to be reversed. Yet this is logical, as the lighter hydrocarbon residue is an increasing component in the compounds.

C.

	I Boiling point	II Specific gravity
C₂H₅F	$-32°$ C.	gas
C₂H₅Cl	12	0.9
C₂H₅Br	38	1.5
C₂H₅I	72	1.9

The progress here is due to the inorganic element. The regularity of progression is maintained.

This table illustrates a fourth cardinal point in organic chemistry, namely that the physical properties of compounds are not unexpected characteristics, but may be

Courtesy, *Aluminum,* Hobbs, Bruce Publishing Co.

POURING MOLTEN ALUMINUM

A NUGGET OF SOLID COPPER IN A MICHIGAN MINE

to some extent predicted from the composition. Even when not predictable, they may be readily understood when observed. In anticipation of the chapter on alcohols, it will be seen that a simple alcohol, as $C_2H_5 . OH$, would be soluble in water, as it has the water group — OH, in its molecule. Further a higher alcohol as $C_5H_{11} . OH$ would not be soluble, as the water constituent forms a lesser proportion of the whole.

OXYGEN DERIVATIVES

In the study of oxygen derivatives, easily the leading class of organic compounds, we cannot proceed very far without a use of the open formula. This will now be discussed briefly.

The open formulas for the first four hydrocarbons are:

$$H-\overset{\overset{\displaystyle -H}{|}}{\underset{\underset{\displaystyle -H}{|}}{C}}-H, \quad H-\overset{\overset{\displaystyle H}{\diagdown}}{\underset{\underset{\displaystyle H}{\diagup}}{C}}-\overset{\overset{\displaystyle /H}{}}{\underset{\underset{\displaystyle \diagdown H}{}}{C}}-H, \quad H-C-C-C-H, \text{ and } H-C-C-C-C-H$$

These formulas represent "open chain" hydrocarbons. Each carbon atom is represented with a valence of four. Such valence bonds as are not used in connecting the carbon atoms, are satisfied by hydrogen atoms. It will be noticed

$$\text{—H}$$
that the configuration $— C — H$ occurs in every formula,
$$\text{—H}$$

and the group represented by this configuration will be the main subject of the following discussions. The essential feature of this group is that it has three replaceable hydrogen atoms. The replacing of these in succession by the oxygen unit, the hydroxyl group, — OH, yields the series of compounds called the alcohols, aldehydes and acids respectively.

Another cardinal point of organic chemistry must now be noted, namely, that in these molecules, no matter how complicated, each carbon atom is a unit, acting as though no other carbon atoms were present. It will be noticed

that the configuration
$$-\overset{\displaystyle -H}{\underset{\displaystyle -H}{C}}-H$$
occurs in every formula,

and one group, represented by this configuration, will be the only one that will receive our preliminary attention.

The significant feature of this discussion is that there are three hydrogen atoms which may be successively replaced by oxygen in the form of the previously mentioned hydroxyl, —OH, group. For this study we will use ethane, C_2H_6, as its compounds are the most familiar. To emphasize the fact that we will deal with one carbon

atom only, we will use the formula
$$CH_3-\overset{\displaystyle -H}{\underset{\displaystyle -H}{C}}-H,$$
and

this should suggest three possibilities for replacing hydrogen:

$$CH_3-\overset{\displaystyle -OH}{\underset{\displaystyle -H}{C}}-H,$$
the first oxidation product, the well-

known ethyl alcohol.

$$CH_3-\overset{\displaystyle -OH}{\underset{\displaystyle -H}{C}}-OH$$
(modified by loss of water, HOH, to

$$CH_3-\overset{\displaystyle =O}{\underset{\displaystyle -H}{C}}),$$
the second oxidation product, a less well-

known compound, acetic aldehyde.

$$CH_3 - C \begin{matrix} -OH \\ -OH \\ -OH \end{matrix}$$ (modified by loss of water to

$$CH_3 - C \begin{matrix} \!\!\!/\!\!/O \\ -OH \end{matrix}),$$ the third oxidation product, the familiar acetic acid.

This relation of alcohol, aldehyde, acid is a simple and constant relation running through the entire range of oxygen compounds. We have then in these three compounds, the alcohol, the aldehyde, and the acid, the logical results obtained by the attaching of one, two, or three hydroxyl groups to one carbon atom.

$$CH_3C \begin{matrix} /OH \\ -H \\ \backslash H \end{matrix} , \quad CH_3C \begin{matrix} =O \\ \backslash H \end{matrix}, \quad CH_3.C \begin{matrix} =O \\ \backslash OH \end{matrix}$$

The alcohols. It should now be clear that any type of derivative applies to the entire range of paraffin hydrocarbons, so that the term alcohol is a general term, including as many compounds as there are hydrocarbons. A brief list is as follows:

CH_3OH, Methyl alcohol. Liquid boiling at 66° C.
C_2H_5OH, Ethyl alcohol. Liquid boiling at 78° C.
C_3H_7OH, Propyl alcohol. Liquid boiling at 97° C.
C_4H_9OH, Butyl alcohol. Liquid boiling at 117° C.
$C_5H_{11}OH$, Amyl alcohol. Liquid boiling at 137° C.
$C_{16}H_{33}OH$, Hexadecyl alcohol. Solid.
$C_{18}H_{37}OH$, Octadecyl alcohol. Solid.

As the table shows the alcohols like all other derivatives form a regular series. The fact that the hydroxyl group introduced into gaseous methane results in a liquid can hardly be explained, but it is uniformly found that the introduction of this group raises the boiling point of compounds about 100°. The first two when pure have a pleasant odor. The fourth and fifth have a peculiar odor known as the fusel oil odor. The odor of the third is intermediate between that of the second and that of the fourth. As might be expected from the presence of the hydroxyl group, the simplest alcohols are completely soluble in water. From the fourth on the solubility is slight or lacking, as the hydrocarbon residue is more influential than the water residue (— OH).

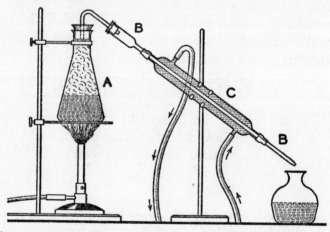

APPARATUS FOR THE DISTILLATION OF LIQUIDS, USED FREQUENTLY IN ORGANIC MANIPULATIONS

The liquid, or mixture of liquids, is boiled in A, and the vapors escaping are cooled in the tube B, which is surrounded by the water jacket C, through which a stream of cold water is passed. The condensed liquid is collected in the receiver, which is changed as the different ingredients of the mixture in A pass over.

Like most organic compounds the alcohols are readily combustible. The presence of a considerable amount of carbon is evident in the higher members as they burn with the yellow flame, while the lower alcohols burn with a non-luminous flame. Chemically we must take cognizance of two notable properties. One is that in a very mild manner they resemble the inorganic bases (compare NaOH and $C_2H_5.OH$), uniting with acids to form compounds called esters, comparable with salts in structure, possessing such special characteristics, however, that they must have a discussion of their own. The second great reaction of the alcohols may be anticipated. Being the first oxidation products, they may upon proper treatment with oxygen pass on to the second and third oxidation products, the aldehydes and the acids. The familiar example of this is the oxidation of the dilute alcohol in cider to the acid, thus forming vinegar.

Some of the individual alcohols are so important in various relations that they must be discussed in some detail. The first of these is ethyl, or grain alcohol, spirits of wine, C_2H_5OH. This alcohol is obtained, as is well known, by the fermentation of sugar, or of substances like starch, which are converted into sugar. The reaction is approximately represented by the equation, $C_6H_{12}O_6$ (upon fermenting)$\rightarrow 2CO_2 + 2C_2H_5OH$. Ethyl alcohol is now prepared to some extent from ethane. Ethyl alcohol boils at 78° C. (172° F.), and is somewhat lighter than water. The properties which find favor are its combustibility, its solvent action, and its physiological action; to which might be added a growing tendency in industry to use it as a raw material for the manufacture of other organic substances.

Methyl alcohol, CH_3OH, called wood alcohol, because it is obtained by the destructive distillation of wood, resembles ethyl alcohol very closely, but is peculiarly poisonous. Because of the resemblance, especially when pure, mistakes are frequent, and hence cases of poisoning have been common. Aside from this poisonous action, wood alcohol has properties very similar to those of ordinary alcohol. However, it should be used with care, as the action of poisons is not limited to their introduction into the stomach.

The next three alcohols, propyl, butyl and amyl alcohols are now commercial articles. They will be discussed under organic industries.

Aldehydes. We are now ready for a brief examination of the nature of the aldehydes. As in the case of all other derivatives, there is at least one for every hydrocarbon. Only one needs to be mentioned in addition to the acetic aldehyde mentioned above. That is formaldehyde

$$H.C \overset{/\!/O}{-} H,$$

derived from methane. The aldehydes hold an intermediate place between the alcohols and acids, and show a great instability, tending to gain hydrogen, thus reverting to the alcohols, or to gain oxygen, thus passing on to the acids. They unite readily with various other active substances. The molecules even tend to unite with each other, and to form more complex molecules, which may be again converted into the simple form. Such building up is called polymerization, and may involve two or more simple units. Formaldehyde acts as a disinfectant, for reasons probably connected with its high reactivity. It has the same proportionate composition as the carbohydrates, CH_2O, as compared with $C_6H_{12}O_6$, the formula for glucose. It is possible that the building up of the carbohydrates in the process of plant growth is through the polymerization of formaldehyde, which in its turn has been formed from carbon dioxide (carbonic acid). $CO_2 \rightarrow H_2CO_3 \rightarrow CH_2O \rightarrow C_6H_{12}O_6$. The alde-

hyde group $-C = O$ recurs very frequently, and is par-
$\qquad\qquad \backslash H$
ticularly important in the sugars.

Acids. The third member of the sequence is the acid.
All real organic acids contain the group $-C = O$,
$\qquad\qquad\qquad\qquad\qquad\qquad\qquad \backslash OH$
which represents the third oxygen product. As this group
may be part of all sorts of organic compounds, the number
of possible acids is very great. Our discussion now involves only the acids of the regular structure, involving
no other feature besides. Acids are obtained, as are the
other derivatives, at least one from every hydrocarbon.

THE SERIES OF FATTY ACIDS

		Boiling Point
$H CO_2H$	Formic	99°
CH_3CO_2H	Acetic	118°
$C_2H_5.CO_2H$	Propionic	141°
$C_3H_7.CO_2H$	Butyric	163°
$C_4H_9CO_2H$	Valeric	186°
$C_5H_{11}.CO_2H$	Caproic	205°
$C_{15}H_{31}CO_2H$	Palmitic	solid
$C_{17}H_{35}CO_2H$	Stearic	solid

The acid nature of these is due to the oxidized condition
of the nonmetal carbon. They are in this respect not
dissimilar to the inorganic acids. The acid groups, CO_2H,
NO_3H, SO_4H_2, PO_4H_3 are altogether comparable.

The first three of these acids are typified by the well-
known acetic acid, the acid of vinegar, which is about
4 per cent acetic acid. It is a colorless liquid of sharp
sour smell and taste, very soluble in water. Although it
is a strong acid when considered as a constituent of foods,
it is, when considered purely chemically, only about 1/100

as strong as hydrochloric acid. The group of acids containing from four to six carbon atoms are substances of an unpleasant rancid odor. In the higher acids, the peculiar acid carboxyl group, — CO_2H, is of such comparatively minor importance that these acids are insoluble, fatlike solids, with no marked odors. Yet they are real acids, for they form salts of various kinds. The salts formed with the triple alcohol glycerol as a base include the highly important group of substances called fats, while the salts which they form with sodium constitute soap.

ETHERS AND ESTERS

Inasmuch as the three types of oxygen derivatives are all that are in simple form theoretically possible, the further forms of which there are two, the ethers and the esters, must be modifications of one or more of these.

Ethers.—Ethers are modifications of the alcohols obtained by splitting off water from two alcohol molecules. $2 C_2H_5OH \rightarrow (C_2H_5)_2O + H_2O$. The hydrocarbon group of the alcohol and its relation to the oxygen are not changed. We may say that ether is an oxide while alcohol is a hydroxide. There is an ether corresponding to every alcohol, but ethyl ether is the most common and the one usually indicated by the name. The ether structure may also be considered from the following standpoint. Beginning with water, $H — O — H$, we replace one hydrogen by means of the ethyl residue and obtain $C_2H_5 — O — H$, ethyl alcohol. Replacing the second hydrogen gives us $C_2H_5 — O — C_2H_5$, or ethyl ether. The two ethyl groups are evidently held together by means of the oxygen atom. Ordinary ether is very volatile and inflammable. Its mistaken reputation in respect to explosiveness is due to the readiness with which the gas passes off, and the likelihood of its becoming ignited at a neighboring flame. Hence, before ether is handled, all neighboring lights should first be extinguished. Ether is not explosive. It is simply likely to form an explosive mixture with air. Ether is a very light liquid and only slightly soluble in water. Chemically it is rather inactive. Its chief use is as a solvent and an anæsthetic. In respect to solvent action we have in water, alcohol, and ether, an interesting group. Water is the typical inorganic liquid, and hence is the best solvent for inorganic compounds. Ether, on the other hand, represents the same relation to the organic compounds, while alcohol, partaking of the nature of each, has intermediate solvent properties.

More important than the particular characteristics of ordinary ether is the structure of its molecule, the ether structure. By this is meant the splitting of water from two alcohol groups $\begin{matrix} C_2H_5OH \\ C_2H_5OH \end{matrix}$ and the consequent formation of $\begin{matrix} C_2H_5 \\ C_2H_5 \end{matrix}\Big\rangle O$, or $C_2H_5 - O - C_2H_5$. The two hydrocarbon residues of the two alcohol molecules have become linked together by means of the oxygen. This linking must be looked at in the light of a separation, so that the two units always preserve their individuality. If the formula for ether were written $C_4H_{10}O$, we might lose sight of that fact. Written $C_2H_5 - O - C_2H_5$ we are reminded of the two facts, first that ether is obtained from ethyl alcohol, $C_2H_5OH + C_2H_5OH \rightleftarrows HOH + C_2H_5OC_2H_5$, and further of the fact that this process can be reversed, and ether reconverted into its simpler constituents. This latter process is called hydrolysis, meaning breaking apart by the addition of water. The reaction is one of the most important of both branches of chemistry. The three nutrients, the carbohydrates, the fats, the proteins, are complexes held together somewhat on this order, and in their upbuilding and utilization as foods the above linking and unlinking are processes repeated with the utmost frequency.

Esters.—Parallel with the group of organic acids, is a group of compounds the nature of which might be anticipated. These are the salts, or esters, of the organic acids, formed with the alcohols, which are bases. These esters are many in number, being made up in great variety from the various alcohols and the various acids. Ethyl acetate, $C_2H_5OCOCH_3$, is a typical member. Amyl acetate is another, $C_5H_{11}.OCOCH_3$, and is the substance which gives the banana its flavor and odor. These esters have a pleasant fruity odor, and many of the flavors of fruits are due to their presence. They are very useful solvents, and so-called banana oil is much used for this purpose. Another set of these salts is found in the waxes. These are made up of higher alcohols and acids. Beeswax is $C_{30}H_{61}.OCOC_{15}H_{31}$. Still more important are the fats, which are made up of glycerol as the base, and any one, or several, of the higher fatty acids as the acid. A typical fat is $C_3H_5(OCO.C_{17}H_{35})_3$, which might be written for the sake of simplification Gl (St)$_3$. This is glycerol stearate. The acid group may be replaced by a variety of other acids, but the most commonly occurring are stearic acid, and two others, palmitic acid, $C_{15}H_{31}.CO_2H$, and oleic acid, $C_{17}H_{33}CO_2H$. Such differences as there are in the acids appear in their esters, the fats, and it is by these differences that the fats are chiefly distinguished and their uses to some extent determined. The chief differences are two. (*a*) The position in the fatty acid series. This determines whether the molecule is a comparatively small or large one. Yet the range is not great except for butter fat, which is conspicuous for containing about six per cent of the very low fatty acids, and butter fat is readily recognized by separating out and testing these acids. (*b*) The saturated or unsaturated condition of the acid counts for even more. When the unsaturation is slight, the practical result is a liquid condition of the fat. When more marked, we have the drying oils with unique properties and special uses in making paints and varnishes.

When the fatty acid is split off by means of sodium hydroxide, and thus united to the sodium, soap is formed, $NaOCO.C_{17}H_{35}$, sodium stearate. This process of soap-making, called saponification, is represented thus:

$C_3H_5(OCO.C_{17}H_{35})_3$ the fat, $+ 3NaOH(lye) \rightarrow 3NaOCOC_{17}H_{35}$ (soap) $+ C_3H_5(OH)_3$ glycerol; or more simply thus:

$Gl(St)_3$, fat $+ 3Na\ OH \rightarrow Gl(OH)_3$, glycerol, $+ 3Na\ St$, soap

Soap is discussed also in chapters XV and XXIII.

More Complex Oxygen Compounds

The foregoing account of alcohol, aldehyde and acid should give an impression of the structure and nature of these compounds. In a previous paragraph the point was made that each carbon atom of a hydrocarbon was a unit by itself, and further that we would at the beginning confine our attention to one unit only. It is true, however, that a number of common substances are more complicated, being derivatives involving several carbon atoms. Such are glycol and glycerol among the alcohols, and the common food acids among the acids, while the carbohydrates (sugar, starch, cellulose) involve alcohol and aldehyde groups.

Glycol is a double alcohol, $CH_2OH — CH_2OH$. It is ethane in which two carbon atoms go to make up alcohol groups. *Glycerol** is a triple alcohol, $CH_2OH — CHOH — CH_2OH$ derived from propane, $CH_3 — CH_2 — CH_3$. The characteristic properties of glycerol are shown by glycol in lesser degree, namely sirupy condition, high boiling point, sweet taste. Both, as might be expected are completely soluble in water. Glycerol has certain medicinal and industrial uses, but its chief interest lies in its relation to the fats and to nitroglycerine. In each case the alcohol character of the glycerol asserts itself and it acts as a base. Other so-called polyhydroxy-alcohols exist, and the one with six carbons, *mannitol,* is very suggestive of the sugars, which are closely related. It has the same crystalline appearance and a somewhat sweet taste. All these complex alcohols are very soluble in water, as might be expected from the numerous hydroxyl groups.

COMPLEX ACIDS

Besides *acetic* acid, five other acids come into frequent discussion in connection with our foods and other ordinary substances. These acids are *oxalic, lactic, malic, tartaric,* and *citric* acids. Of these, lactic acid is usually handled as a sirupy liquid containing water, while the others are well known in crystallized form. The formula of oxalic acid is $CO_2H.CO_2H$; compare acetic acid

---

* In organic chemistry the ending "ol" is assigned to hydroxyl derivatives. As the familiar "glycerine" is such a compound, the proper name therefore is glycerol, and this name is used throughout the text, when the compound is referred to in its strict chemical relations.

$CH_3.CO_2H$, and ethane $CH_3.CH_3$. It is therefore the same as acetic acid with the hydrocarbon residue therein converted to an acid residue. Oxalic acid occurs in certain sour plants, oxalis and rhubarb. All these acids in concentrated form are poisonous owing to their chemical activity, but as we meet with them in foods they are highly diluted. Malic acid, $C_2H_3.OH.(CO_2H)_2$, and tartaric acid, $C_2H_2(OH)_2$ $(CO_2H)_2$, are closely related. They are both, as can be seen, double acids, and in addition include respectively one and two alcohol groups. In comparison with the very pronounced properties of the acid groups present, these alcohol groups are very inconspicuous. Citric acid is on the same order, but more complex, $C_3H_4.OH.(CO_2H)_3$, a triple acid with one added alcohol group. These acids are the acids respectively of fruits like the apple, the grape, and the citrus fruits. The last two are obtained commercially, and tartaric acid is used in large amounts in the preparation of baking powders. Lactic acid is the acid developed in the souring of milk; and sourness in bread also is due to this. Its formula is $CH_3CHOH.CO_2H$, namely, propionic acid, modified by the presence of an alcohol group. There are many other acids of this double or mixed nature, but these common members of the group will serve for illustrations.

CARBOHYDRATES

Carbohydrates form a chief class of complex organic compounds, including especially the sugars, starch and cellulose, so significant in the way of animal foods and plant products. The well-established name of the group is based upon their arithmetic composition, $C_6H_{12}O_3$,

$C_{12}H_{22}O_{11}$, $C_6H_{10}O_5$. The real structure of these compounds shows that the hydrogen and oxygen are not present really as water, even though water may be extracted by such powerful reagents as sulphuric acid.

Externally they differ markedly (compare sugar and cellulose), particularly in regard to solubility and crystalline appearance. But all are made up of practically the same kind of units, put together in one combination or another. We appreciate this in their classification. The first group includes the monosaccharides, formula of the chief members, $C_6H_{12}O_6$. The name implies that they are the unit substances of the entire group. The second group of the classification is that of the disaccharides, formula, $C_{12}H_{22}O_{11}$, written better for our purpose $(C_6H_{11}O_5) - O - (C_6H_{11}O_5)$; this formula shows that they are made up of two of the monosaccharide units connected by means of oxygen. Their structure is suggestive of that of the ethers. It will be noticed that the difference between a disaccharide molecule and two monosaccharide molecules is water. The disaccharide is composed of two monosaccharides, united by the splitting off of water, H_2O, and the monosaccharides can be reformed by the addition of water to the double compound thus obtained.

The third group is made up of the polysaccharides, formula $(C_6H_{10}O_5)_n$. This formula is inadequate, as the value of n is not known; but it conveniently indicates that the members of this group are made up of many monosaccharides linked together as they are in the second class, yet in a more complex manner. The addition of water under the proper influences changes a polysaccharide into its constituent monosaccharides. In nature both types of changes, from the simple to the complex and from the complex to the simple compound, are very common.

In laboratory operations and in the industries conversion of the di- and polysaccharides into their constituent monosaccharides is readily accomplished. In spite of constant efforts the reverse has practically never been achieved.

The monosaccharides. Inasmuch as the monosaccharide is the basis of all carbohydrates, we shall find that the study of this group will give us the chief information about the whole class. The most important monosaccharides are derived from hexane, the hydrocarbon of the paraffin series containing six carbon atoms. For five of these carbons one hydrogen is replaced by hydroxyl, and in the case of the sixth carbon, two hydrogens are replaced by a single oxygen. Two such combinations are found among the simple sugars.

$$CH_2.OH.CHOH.CHOH.CHOH.CHOH.CHO$$

is the formula for some of them, including the well-known dextrose or glucose.

$$CH_2OH.CHOH.CHOH.CHOH.CO.CH_2OH$$

is the formula for others, including fruit sugar or levulose.

These formulas conform to the properties of the sugars. They would naturally be solids, because of the accumulation of carbon and oxygen atoms, and their solubility and sweetness is like that of other compounds containing a number of hydroxyl groups. The hydroxyl group is attached to five of the carbon atoms. The sixth carbon attached to oxygen without hydrogen represents an aldehyde or ketone* structure, which gives the molecule the

---

* Ketones are similar to aldehydes. In the latter case the special group is attached to a terminal carbon, in the former case it is attached to an intermediate carbon. Aldehyde $CH_3.CH_2.CO.H$, Ketone $CH_3.CO.CH_3$.

reactivity needed for a substance taking part in the vital processes. This reactivity is lessened by the building up of the double and complex carbohydrates; but as they are so readily reconverted into the simple molecules, the reactivity is in the end readily available.

Many monosaccharides are known, but three are outstanding. *Glucose,* also called dextrose or grape sugar, occurs most frequently among plant products, not alone as such, but even more as a constituent of di- and polysaccharides. It is one unit in the makeup of cane sugar, milk sugar and maltose, and is the sole constituent of starch and cellulose. It is very natural then that glucose can be manufactured from starch and even from cellulose. A very high grade of glucose is now a commercial article and it has been legally accepted as a proper food. Glucose crystallizes with some difficulty, hence it is deliberately introduced or developed in candies to prevent their becoming "sugary." Glucose ferments readily with yeast, while the more complex carbohydrates as cane sugar and starch do not ferment until they have been converted into the simple sugars.

The second simple sugar is *fructose,* fruit sugar, levulose, best known as the second constituent of cane sugar. It is the unit moreover of inulin, a polysaccharide resembling starch, which is found in the tuber of the Jerusalem artichoke. This plant is now cultivated to some extent to supply fructose, which in its turn is used as a sweetener and a source of alcohol. The third simple sugar, *galactose,* is the second constituent of milk sugar.

In connection with the sugars, and other similarly complex compounds, there should be mentioned, even if not fully discussed, the fact that these substances exhibit what is called optical activity. If light of a certain kind (polarized) is passed through a solution of sugar, it is found to be affected. The plane of polarization is turned to the right or to the left. This is due to the arrangement, in space, of the various atoms around the nucleal carbon atoms. This has a very practical significance, in that it results in the formation of different sugars, glucose and galactose, which would otherwise seem to be identical. It serves also as a quick means, by help of the physical instrument called the polarimeter, of measuring different sugars.

The Disaccharides. As was indicated above, the disaccharides are double compounds, made up of the union of two monosaccharides by the process of splitting off water. Acids, enzymes, and ferments readily break down ordinary cane sugar into its constituent groups, a process usually considered undesirable, yet possessing advantages in certain cases. *Sucrose,* saccharose, or cane sugar (this includes beet sugar, for there is no chemical difference) is the most highly esteemed of all the sugars. There are several reasons for this fact. It occurs in several plants, cane, beet, maple, in such quantities that its extraction is easy. It is readily obtained in a pure and attractive form, and possesses pure sweet taste in high degree. The sugar shortage of 1918, 1919, and 1920 illustrates very plainly how dependent we have become upon this form of food. In fermentation and digestive processes this disaccharide, like the others, is converted into monosaccharide before final changes take place. Its formula is usually written, $C_{12}H_{22}O_{11}$, but would be more suggestively written, $C_6H_{11}O_5 - O - C_6H_{11}O_5$, thus showing its double structure, like that of the ethers. The hydrolysis of this, like all other disaccharides, is expressed by the equation,

$$C_6H_{11}O_5 - O - C_6H_{11}O_5 + HOH \rightarrow C_6H_{12}O_6 + C_6H_{12}O_6.$$

Milk sugar is of somewhat similar composition. It is crystalline, but not so soluble or sweet as cane sugar. It is so seldom separated from milk that we do not appreciate how much of it we consume. Milk contains five per cent milk sugar, that is, about one and one-half ounces to the quart. This means a vast amount used as food throughout the country. The third common disaccharide is *maltose,* frequently formed as an intermediate product in the fermentation industries, but at once converted into alcohol.

The Polysaccharides. Dextrin, starch, and cellulose are the three polysaccharides of the greatest moment, and each of these probably occurs in several varieties. The formula for all polysaccharides is written $(C_6H_{10}O_5)n$, meaning that they are made up of many glucose units, but the exact number of these units is unknown. It is likely that the value n is greater for starch than for dextrin, and still greater for cellulose. By treatment with enzymes and acids, these polysaccharides are caused to take on water, and to be converted into the constituent monosaccharide, usually glucose. Hence the great industry of making glucose from starch.

Dextrin is ordinarily found on the market as a transparent gum, somewhat soluble in water, possessing a slightly sweet taste, and giving a marked purple color with iodine. It is useful for such purposes as gumming postage stamps, and is an important intermediate product between starch and sugars.

Starch, the well-known polysaccharide, is insoluble in cold water, but upon heating with water swells and becomes soluble. The insoluble granules of starch, as well as the solution, give with iodine a strong blue color, so pronounced that it serves as a delicate test for both iodine and starch. Starch from different sources may be distinguished by means of the microscope, but no chemical difference has been established. Chemically considered, the most important feature of starch is its conversion by means of enzymes or acids into simple compounds. With care at least five intermediate products may be distinguished, each one undoubtedly simpler than its predecessor, when starch is converted into its constituent monosaccharide, glucose. This change occurs in the digestive process, and also in manufacturing processes wherein glucose is made for its sweetening value.

Glycogen, called animal starch, is formed and secreted in the liver, as a means of storing and later utilizing the glucose which is brought to it by the blood stream. It is reconverted into glucose as the needs of the body demand.

Inulin closely resembles starch in appearance and function in plants. It is a polysaccharide made up of fructose units. It is found in the tubers of dahlias and the Jerusalem artichoke, and both, especially the latter, are used as sources for the constituent fructose. It does not give the blue color with iodine, a test which is so conspicuous with starch.

Cellulose, best illustrated by the fiber of cotton, and as a constituent of wood, is more stable and less reactive than the previously mentioned polysaccharides, and therefore the inference is a fair one that it is more complex. Its value, of course, lies mostly in its use as a textile; but its chemical nature does count in some operations, as in the making of guncotton, collodion, rayon and other products (Chap.

XXIII). It reacts, upon proper treatment, as a regular polysaccharide, being broken down into its constituent glucose molecules. Hence the possibility of sugar from wood.

Xylose, similar to cellulose, is the corresponding constituent of corn cobs and grain hulls.

Fruit gums are in part polysaccharides based upon five carbon monosaccharides.

THE NITROGEN DERIVATIVES

The simple nitrogen derivatives are based upon ammonia, $NH_3(H - NH_2)$, as the simple oxygen derivatives are based upon water, H_2O ($H - OH$). In this respect, as in others, ammonia is comparable with water. Corresponding to the hydroxyl group, $- OH$, is the amino group $- NH_2$, and this correspondence will be apparent in several of the compounds to be discussed.

It is common knowledge that nitrogen compounds are essential to the development of plants and animals. Unfortunately the chemistry of nitrogen compounds is a difficult subject, although in a sense the structure of the oxygen compounds is repeated. In a brief work like this they may be touched on only lightly.

Four types only will be described.

A. The *amines.* In the first analysis these are compounds derived by replacing the hydrogen of the various hydrocarbons by the amino group.

$$CH_4 \rightarrow CH_3NH_2, \quad C_2H_6 \rightarrow C_2H_5NH_2, \quad C_3H_8 \rightarrow C_3H_7NH_2$$

This thought may be reversed thus. The amines are formed by replacement of the hydrogen of ammonia by the various hydrocarbon residues.

$$NH_3 \rightarrow NH_2CH_3 \rightarrow NH(CH_3)_2 \rightarrow N(CH_3)_3$$

The chief feature of these compounds after their composition is their physical and chemical resemblance to ammonia. A striking difference, which to be sure is but natural, is that the hydrocarbon residue causes these to be combustible. The same is true of the water derivatives, that is, the alcohols.

B. An organic acid may have its acid group modified by the replacement of the hydroxyl group therein by means of — NH_2, thus forming an *acid amide*. Example, acid $CH_3.CO.OH$, acid amide $CH_3CO.NH_2$. The exchange is readily effected in either direction.

C. In the hydrocarbon part of an acid, the hydrogen may be replaced by — NH_2, forming the *amino acids*. Example, $CH_3CO.OH$, the acid, and $CH_2NH_2.CO.OH$, the amino acid. The chief interest of these lies in the fact that the all-important proteins are complexes made up of amino acid units.

D. *Urea* represents the excretory product of practically all the nitrogen of the foods. The formula of urea is $CO.(NH_2)_2$, which, when compared with that of carbonic acid, $CO.(OH)_2$, shows that it is amide of that acid, in that the two hydroxyl groups of the acid are replaced by the amino group.

The analogy between the hydroxyl group and the amino group is shown in the four types of compounds mentioned above.

The amines	$CH_3.NH_2$	like $CH_3.OH$
The acid amides	$CH_3.CO.NH_2$	like $CH_3.CO.OH.$
The amino acids	$CH_2.NH_2.CO_2H$	like $CH_3.OH.CO_2H$
Urea	$CO.(NH_2)_2$	like $CO.(OH)_2.$

An analogy between water and ammonia is also found in inorganic chemistry.

Related to urea we find a number of more complicated compounds, in which list are such substances as uric acid, $C_5H_4N_4O_3$, xanthine, $C_5H_4N_4O_2$, and caffeine, $C_8H_{10}N_4O_2$. They are a few examples of a long list of substances, many of them derived from the proteins, of the greatest interest in the study of biochemistry. Important as these substances are from that standpoint, they may only be mentioned here.

In Retrospect

Because of the similarity in composition among organic compounds it is desirable to keep in mind constantly the steps in the development of the subject. The feeling that there are many compounds not very different in composition, must yield to the appreciation that there are variations which are of a regular order. Each type of compound in structure, derivation and reactions conforms to simple fundamental principles.

A review scheme of the subject developed so far may be helpful in presenting a rapid survey of the important material in Part I.

The paraffin hydrocarbons, general nature and occurrence in regular series.

Derivatives of three types, by replacement of hydrogen by halogens, oxygen (as — OH) and by nitrogen (as — NH$_2$).

Each type occurring in series based upon the original hydrocarbon series.

A. CH_3Cl B. CH_3OH C. CH_3NH_2
   C_2H_5Cl C_2H_5OH $C_2H_5NH_2$
   Etc.   etc   etc

A. Variations in halogen group by

    a. varying hydrocarbon, CH_3Cl, C_2H_5Cl, C_3H_7Cl, etc.

    b. varying number of halogen units, CH_3Cl, CH_2Cl_2, $CHCl_3$, CCl_4.

    c. different halogens involved. CH_3F, CH_3Cl, CH_3Br, CH_3I.

B. Among oxygen derivatives, three orders, which result in compounds of different natures.

    a. First order, alcohols,
$$CH_3C \overset{\displaystyle -OH}{\underset{\displaystyle -H}{-H}}$$

    b. Second order, aldehydes,
$$CH_3C \overset{\displaystyle -OH}{\underset{\displaystyle -H}{-OH}}, \text{ actually } CH_3C \overset{\displaystyle =O}{-H}$$

    c. Third order, acids,
$$CH_3C \overset{\displaystyle -OH,}{\underset{\displaystyle -OH}{-OH}} \text{ actually } CH_3C \overset{\displaystyle /\!\!/O}{-OH}:$$

Corollaries.

    Ethers, union of two alcohol groups $CH_3\overset{H_2}{C} - O - \overset{H_2}{C} - CH_3$, more compactly $C_2H_5 - O - C_2H_5$.

    Esters, union of acid and alcohol groups.
$$CH_3C \overset{/\!\!/O}{-} O - C_2H_5$$

    Duplication of types, double alcohols, and double acids, and alcohol acids.

    Examples, glycol, $CH_2OH - CH_2OH$,

        Oxalic acid, $CO_2H - CO_2H$

        Lactic acid, $CH_3 - CHOH. - CO_2H$.

    A special group of mixed type is that of the carbohydrates, alcohol aldehydes, forming three groups, mono-, di-, and polysaccharides.

C. Among nitrogen derivatives.

    a. Nature of simple type, $CH_3 - NH_2$

    b. Combination of nitrogen and oxygen derivatives.

        Acid amides, $CH_3C \overset{=O}{-} NH_2$ from $CH_3C \overset{=O}{-} OH$

        Amino acids, $CH_2NH_2CO_2H$ from $CH_3.CO_2H$

    Types under *b* related to proteins.

THE UNSATURATED OPEN CHAIN COMPOUNDS

A conspicuous feature of all the paraffin hydrocarbons and their derivatives so far discussed is that they are saturated, that is, all the affinities of the carbon nucleus are satisfied. No modification in these compounds can be made without first eliminating some atom or group of atoms already present. Methane, CH_4, can form a derivative only after the loss of one or more hydrogen atoms, the places of which atoms are then filled with the new group. The chlorine derivatives illustrate this, in that their formulas are written CH_3Cl, CH_2Cl_2, $CHCl_3$. For each chlorine introduced a hydrogen must be eliminated. However, by the proper manipulation of some of these compounds, we are enabled to remove hydrogen, always in pairs of atoms, without replacing it with compensating groups. Hence such substances must be unsaturated. C_2H_6 is saturated, C_2H_4 and C_2H_2 are unsaturated, and can evidently take on either hydrogen or some other atoms or groups to make up the equivalent of C_2H_6. We call this condition the unsaturated condition, and establish a new device of bonds or linkages to represent it.

This device is the so-called double or triple bond, $H_2C = CH_2$, $HC \equiv CH$. Its significant features are these. It can exist only between pairs of carbon atoms, and represents unsaturation, and a definite reactivity and instability, in contrast to paraffins lacking these features.

Ethylene, $H_2C = CH_2$, is typical of a double bond hydrocarbon.

It may be prepared from ethane or its compounds by removing two units under such conditions that nothing replaces them.

$H_3C - CH_3$ by pyrolysis $\rightarrow H_2C = CH_2 + H_2$
$ClH_2C - CH_2Cl$, by removing two atoms of
chlorine $\rightarrow H_2C = CH_2$

The ready formation of hydrocarbons of the ethylene type serves as a ready means for forming paraffin derivatives. The following reaction in various phases is now a common industrial method.

$$+ Cl_2$$
$$H_3C - CH_3 \rightarrow H_2C = CH_2 \rightarrow ClH_2C - CH_2Cl \rightarrow$$
$$CH_2OH - CH_2OH, \text{ glycol}$$

Acetylene, C_2H_2, has a special interest. It is prepared easily, by an operation familiar to most, the action of water on calcium carbide. The high carbon content of the gas causes it to burn with a very luminous flame. These two facts have resulted in its extensive use for illuminating houses not connected with central lighting plants. The burning of acetylene with oxygen yields a very high temperature, and "acetylene welding" is now a common operation.

As the lack of two hydrogen atoms in the case of paraffin hydrocarbons leads to the unsaturated condition, so this condition may be established among paraffin derivatives. Two compounds will illustrate this.

Propyl alcohol $H_3C - CH_2 - CH_2OH$,
allyl alcohol, $H_2 = CH - CH_2OH$
Propionic acid, $H_3C - CH_2 - CO_2H$,
acrylic acid $H_2C = CH - CO_2H$

The oils, *i. e.,* liquid fats, are such compounds. Olive oil and similar oils owe their liquid condition to unsaturation. Linseed oil and other "drying" oils are even more unsaturated, and thus possess in great measure the tendency to attract other atoms, thus going through the process of "drying."

The use in foods of a solid or a liquid fat is to a considerable extent a matter of taste and usage. As the liquid fats, or oils, owe their liquid state to the unsaturated condition of the fatty acid, it is not unusual for such oils to decompose more readily, that is, become rancid, for the unsaturated condition means chemical reactivity. It is certainly true that, in cooking, solid fats are more popular than the liquid. Hence there has been developed the art of adding hydrogen to these liquid unsaturated compounds, converting them into solids and thus making a more attractive compound out of a less attractive one. This process is called hydrogenation, and is used in particular to make the liquid cottonseed oil, which is unsaturated, and comparatively unattractive, into solid compounds, containing more hydrogen, of distinctly more inviting appearance and properties. Several of the much advertised shortening agents now on the market are of this description.

Formulas representing three types of fats are as follows:

$C_3H_5(CO_2C_{17}H_{35})_3$ a normal saturated fat
$C_3H_5(CO_2C_{17}H_{33})_3$ an unsaturated liquid fat
$C_3H_5(CO_2C_{17}H_{31})_3$ a drying oil

The unsaturated condition has recently become a very serviceable means for synthesizing organic compounds. Two types of reactions are more outstanding than others.

a. Ethyl alcohol is now prepared in considerable amounts by the following reactions.

Ethane, $CH_3 — CH_3 \rightarrow$ Ethylene, $CH_2 = CH_2 \rightarrow$
$CH_3 — CH_2SO_4H \rightarrow CH_3 — CH_2OH$

b. Polymerization. One type of synthetic rubber is obtained by the following sequence of compounds.

Acetylene, $CH \equiv CH \rightarrow CH_2 = CH — CCl = CH_2$

The second compound by polymerization forms a type of artificial rubber represented perhaps by the formula $(C_4H_5Cl)_n$.

PART II

THE BENZENE OR AROMATIC SERIES OF HYDROCARBONS AND THEIR DERIVATIVES

Although all hydrocarbons are in many respects alike, the benzene hydrocarbons show some characteristics in which they differ from the paraffins. There is no such contrast as between metals and nonmetals, for example, but the differences are definite enough to make a differentiation possible and desirable. Four points of difference are to be observed. First, the benzenes contain less hydrogen than the paraffins—compare benzene, C_6H_6, with hexane, a paraffin, C_6H_{14}. One might suppose that the benzenes would, therefore, act as unsaturated substances, tending to unite eagerly with more hydrogen or its equivalent. This is, however, only exceptionally true, and the benzenes act on the whole as saturated compounds. The derivatives are formed, as in the case of the paraffins, by the replacement of one or more of the hydrogens by other groups.

Second, the configuration of the molecules is peculiar. The carbons of the paraffins are held together in open chains, thus, C—C—C—C—C—C. In benzene the carbons are held together by the so-called ring structure, really a

hexagon, 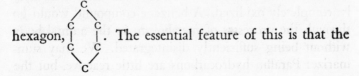 . The essential feature of this is that the units of the ring are all equally related to the whole. It would lead too far to explain the reasons for this assumption and the interesting features which it accounts for. As a matter of fact the assumption has been of the greatest value in the progress of organic chemistry.

So well is this ring established in chemical thought that its convenient form, the hexagon, is the fundamental device in the symbolism of benzene compounds.

The third feature of the benzene hydrocarbons is that they have a noticeably greater reactivity than the paraffin hydrocarbons. They react especially readily with nitric and sulphuric acids. This has had a very important practical outcome. It is only in recent years that there has been any considerable progress in the formation of paraffin derivatives from the parent hydrocarbon. Naturally occurring raw materials such as sugar and starch have been the raw materials for such compounds. By contrast the benzene hydrocarbons for many years have lent themselves very readily to the preparation of all kinds of derivatives, for which the hydrocarbon is almost exclusively the starting point, or raw material.

The fourth feature of benzene compounds is the stability of the ring, which is in contrast to the tendency of the ring as a whole to go into combinations. When this ring is a part of a more complex combination, it is often possible to destroy completely all the added parts, but the ring remains intact. For this reason a benzene derivative would not be suitable for foods, for foods must ultimately be completely oxidized. A benzene compound would go through the processes of metabolism in the animal body without being sufficiently disintegrated. We may summarize: Paraffin hydrocarbons are little reactive, but the carbon nucleus is rather easily disintegrated. Benzenes are reactive in that they readily form derivatives, but the carbon nucleus is a very stable one, persisting through a great variety of reactions.

Benzene, or benzol, must not be confused with benzine, a trade name for a mixed petroleum product akin to gasoline. Benzene is a definite compound in the form of a colorless liquid solidifying at 5° C., and boiling at 80° C. It is lighter than water, in which it is insoluble. It is an excellent solvent for such substances as the fats. Its odor is mildly pleasant, and promises to become familiar to users of motor cars, as benzene is now frequently introduced into gasoline. For this purpose it could never be used unmixed, as it solidifies a number of degrees above freezing. Although it burns with a sooty flame, on account of its high carbon content, it is said to be satisfactory in respect to any deposits of that substance. It has effective anti-knock qualities. The increasing use of benzene in the industries, especially for solvent purposes, has resulted in the unhappy complication of "benzol poisoning." The compound as one experiments with it in the laboratory seems to be a perfectly innocuous substance. When, however, it is dealt with constantly as in factory processes, contact of the skin with it and inhalation of the vapors make the situation a very different one. This is true of other seemingly harmless compounds, as, for example, aniline.

Just as methane, the first of the paraffin series, is followed by the other members, formed by the progressive substitution of the methyl residue for hydrogen, $CH_4; CH_3.CH_3; CH_3CH_2CH_3$, etc., so also from benzene a series is built up in more or less the same manner.

It is not so long a series, being limited for all practical purposes to about ten members, although many more are known. These ten "homologs" are:

Toluene, $C_6H_5CH_3$ (Toluol)
Three Xylenes, $C_6H_4.(CH_3)_2$ (Xylols)
Three trimethyl benzenes, $C_6H_3.(CH_3)_3$
Ethyl benzene, $C_6H_5.C_2H_5$
Cumene, $C_6H_5.C_3H_7$
Cymene, $C_6H_4.CH_3.C_3H_7$

It will be noted that these formulas always show a benzene nucleus to which the paraffin residues are attached. In a complete study of our subject, we would need to give great care to the fact that such hydrocarbons yield two sets of derivatives, those obtained from the original ring, and those obtained from the paraffin residue. The latter repeat the characteristics of the compounds already outlined under that head. The former, however, yield compounds of the new type, those typical of the benzene ring. Two illustrations will suffice. $C_6H_5CH_3$ yields $C_6H_5.CO_2H$, benzoic acid, wherein the variation is in the paraffin residue entirely, and the benzene nucleus is unchanged. While in trinitrotoluene, "T.N.T.," $C_6H_2(NO_2)_3CH_3$, the benzene nucleus is the one affected. Salicylic acid is typical of compounds in which both residues are affected, $C_6H_4OH.CO_2H$.

The application of these hydrocarbons as such in the industries is somewhat limited. They are useful as solvents, and the more volatile will in all probability be used to supplement the paraffin products for motor fuel. Their great use is to prepare "intermediates," compounds which are later developed into the finished coal-tar products.

DERIVATIVES OF THE BENZENES

A. (a) C_6H_5Cl, the halogen compound
   (b) $C_6H_5SO_3H$, the sulphonic acid
   (c) $C_6H_5NO_2$, the nitro compound
   (d) $C_6H_5NH_2$, the amino compound, aniline
   (e) C_6H_5OH, the hydroxyl derivative, phenol

B. (a) $C_6H_5NO_2$, the normal nitro compound
   (b) $C_6H_4(NO_2)_2$, the dinitro compound
   (c) $C_6H_4.NO_2.CH_3$, the derivative from the first homolog
   (d) $C_6H_4.NO_2.OH$, a mixed nitro and hydroxy derivative

Group A shows the simpler derivatives obtained from benzene: (a), (b) and (c) may be obtained directly; (d) and (e), only by indirect methods.

The second group of compounds shows the types of variations possible. These are (a) and (b), one or more of the substituting groups present in benzene. (c): The introduction of such groups in the benzene portion of homologs. (d): The introduction of several types of substituting groups in benzene or the benzene portion of any homolog. When to these possibilities the derivatives of the paraffin residue of the homologs are added, it may be seen that the number of compounds formed may be very large.

1. Halogen compounds.

The halogen derivatives are of minor importance, although in some of the more complex forms they are useful. They are obtained with great ease by the direct treatment of the hydrocarbon with chlorine or bromine. The readiness with which the halogens go into combination is consistent with the firmness with which they are held. Therefore these compounds are hardly available for conversion to others. Nevertheless one conversion is now industrially accomplished, and this is considered a triumph of modern chemical engineering.

$$C_6H_6 \xrightarrow{Cl_2} C_6H_5Cl \xrightarrow{NaOH} C_6H_5OH \text{ (phenol)}$$

A number of derivatives are shown in the following table. They represent all the simple types.

C_6H_5Cl	Monochlorobenzene.
$C_6H_4Cl_2$	Dichlorobenzene.
$C_6H_4Cl\ CH_3$	Monochlorotoluene.
$C_6H_4Cl.\ OH$	Monochlorophenol.
$C_6H_5.\ CH_2Cl$	Benzyl chloride, in which the halogen is in the

paraffin residue of the first homolog, toluene.

II. Sulphonic acids. The sulphonic acids are valuable intermediates, being readily transformed into other desired compounds. This sulphonic acid group in itself introduces certain properties of value. Its presence results in solubility and reactivity which previously may have been lacking.

III. Nitro compounds. The products obtained by treating the benzene hydrocarbons with nitric acid are called nitro compounds. $C_6H_5NO_2$, $C_6H_4(NO_2)_2$ and $C_6H_2CH_3 (NO_2)_3$ (T.N.T.), are examples. Like the sulphonic acids these compounds have a certain value of their own, as in dyes and explosives; but they also serve as intermediates for the formation of other compounds.

IV. Amino compounds. Type, $C_6H_5NH_2$. This is the famous aniline, so valuable as an intermediate for the manufacture of many of the dyes. It has some properties of ammonia, NH_3, due to the amino group,—NH_2, but the benzene nucleus is very prominent, as shown by the liquid state, by the combustibility and the readiness with which the benzene residue forms its typical derivatives.

PYREX GLASS IN USE IN A LARGE CHEMICAL LABORATORY. NEW
DEVELOPMENTS IN GLASS MANUFACTURE ARE OF GREAT IMPORTANCE
IN THE SCIENCES AND VARIOUS MANUFACTURING INDUSTRIES

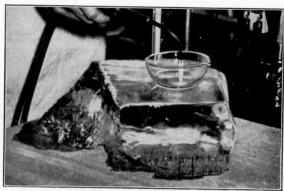

GLASS THAT DOES NOT BREAK BECAUSE OF EXTREME CHANGES IN HEAT AND COLD. THE GLASS DISH RESTS ON A CAKE OF ICE AND WITHSTANDS THE GREAT HEAT OF AN OXYGEN FLAME

THE CORNING LOW-EXPANSION GLASS SHRINKS DURING THE PROCESS OF MANUFACTURE—IN THIS INSTANCE FROM A DIAMETER OF 12 INCHES TO A DIAMETER OF $10\frac{1}{2}$ INCHES

Aniline is a liquid, only slightly soluble in water, and poisonous when absorbed in any considerable amount. In ordinary use no harmful effects are noticed, but factory operatives do feel it and especial attention is required in avoiding its harmful effects. Just as the amino group introduced into a benzene nucleus forms aniline, so the corresponding compound from toluene is toluidine, $C_6H_4NH_2CH_3$, with similar properties; and these are but typical of the many benzene amino compounds, over a hundred in number. They are formed according to the simple principles of substituting the amino group alone, or with others, in the benzene nucleus of these hydrocarbons.

V. The phenols. Type, C_6H_5OH. The phenols have a composition akin to that of the alcohols, and consequently many chemical characteristics in common. Yet the benzene nucleus introduces other characteristics, the most striking of which are poisonous character, and acidic nature, the latter characteristic a contrast to that of the paraffin alcohols, which are basic. This is shown in the names commonly applied, carbolic acid for ordinary phenol, and cresylic acid for cresol. Moreover the presence of the benzene nucleus is always apparent by its reactivity and stability. The chief member of the group of the phenols is the well-known carbolic acid. It is an easily melting crystalline solid, which assumes the liquid state when small amounts of water are mixed with it. It is usually slightly colored with small amounts of impurities, and only slightly soluble in water. The pure substance has a pleasant odor. It has valuable antiseptic properties, and is well known to be poisonous. Other phenols are formed when the hydroxyl group is introduced in other benzene hydrocarbons, and they have the same valuable properties. Thymol, $C_6H_3.OH.CH_3.C_3H_7$, in particular finds application in medicine.

In accordance with the usual modifications of benzene compounds, there exist phenols containing more than one hydroxyl group, $C_6H_4(OH)_2$, resorcinol, and $C_6H_3(OH)_3$, pyrogallol. These are soluble in water as the several hydroxyl groups have greater influence. These find application in photography, in medicine and in chemical manipulations.

The presence of the hydroxyl group in phenol facilitates the introduction of other groups. A compound thus
$$OH$$
formed is picric acid, $C_6H_2(NO_2)_3$, useful as a dye and as an explosive.

DERIVATIVES INVOLVING THE PARAFFIN RESIDUE OF THE HOMOLOGS OF BENZENES

In toluene, $C_6H_5CH_3$, we have two possibilities of derivatives, such as are obtained from the benzene portion, C_6H_5, and such as are obtained from the paraffin portion, CH_3. The latter simply repeat in a manner the compounds of the paraffin chapter. The most important are $C_6H_5.CH_2OH$, C_6H_5CHO, $C_6H_5CO_2H$, respectively benzyl alcohol, benzaldehyde, and benzoic acid. The aldehyde, oil of bitter almonds, has a pleasant odor and flavor, and the aldehyde group attached to the benzene ring is often associated with these conditions. Vanilla, for example, contains this group. Benzoic acid, as well as its sodium salts, is the most popular chemical food preservative. It is a mild acid, differing markedly in activity from the more familiar type of acids. Other compounds of these types are not uncommon. Salicylic acid, $C_6H_4.OH.CO_2H$, is a double compound, containing both the acid group in the paraffin residue and the phenol group in the benzene residue. Like benzoic acid it is used as a preservative, and it is one of the constituents of oil of wintergreen. Many other alcohols, aldehydes and acids, of single and mixed types, are known.

We have thus run over briefly the list of benzene derivatives. The number is very great, but some impression of their chief features may have been obtained. We have not touched to any considerable extent on the subject of mixed derivatives, compounds which like salicylic acid contain more than one substituting group. Their number is legion.

BENZENE COMPLEXES

There exist a number of hydrocarbons made up of several benzene rings linked together in one way or another. In these the rings show the chemical properties of benzene, forming derivatives in the same manner. Such are (a) triphenylmethane, CH $(C_6H_5)_3$, (b) biphenyl, $C_6H_5.C_6H_5$, (c) naphthalene, $C_{10}H_8$, (d) anthracene, $C_{14}H_{10}$, and (e) phenanthrene, $C_{14}H_{10}$. This list is much more than a list of names, for each of these has some points of specific interest.

The conventional ring formulas on next page will show the structure of these compounds more graphically.

The first special feature of these is that the first four are valuable bases of dyes. It will be seen presently that the first requisites for dyes is that the molecules show a high concentration of carbon. This then is the reason why they are associated with the benzene series and why the

Triphenylmethane   HC—

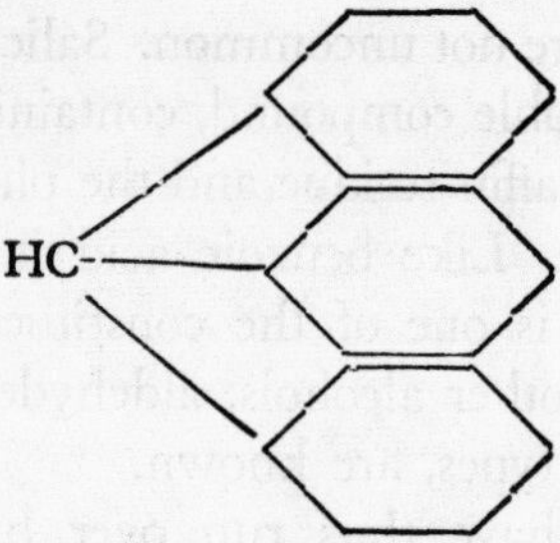

Biphenyl

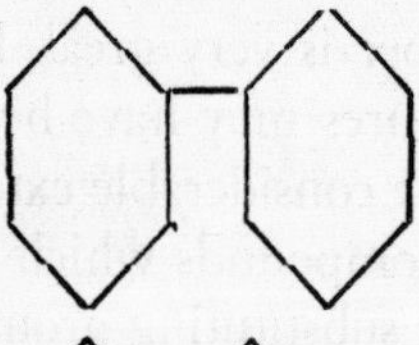

Naphthalene

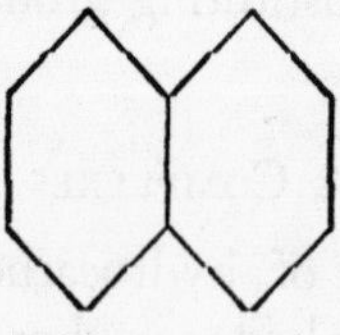

Anthracene

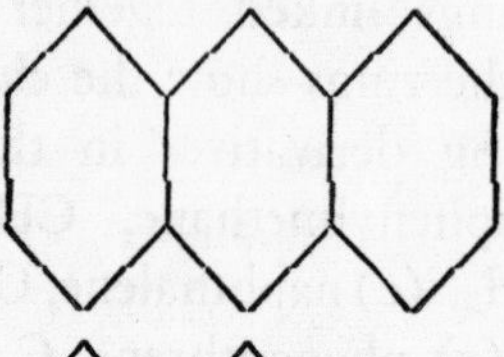

Phenanthrene

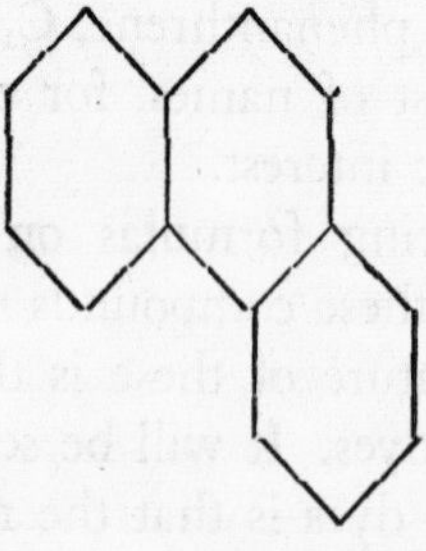

above compounds are of special value. Their chemistry
is on the whole similar to that of the single benzene ring.

Phenanthrene has been found to be of special interest since recent investigation has shown that this hydrocarbon is the nucleus of many biochemical substances, such as the sterols and certain hormones, as also of several opium alkaloids, as morphine and codeine.

THE TERPENES

There is a group of hydrocarbons based upon a five carbon unit, isoprene, C_5H_8. The fine points of the structure of these compounds would require a considerable discussion. It will be adequate for our purpose to touch on their main features.

Hydrocarbons as such have on the whole no place in the structure and processes of living organisms. They are too unreactive for any such function. Some terpenes, $C_{10}H_{16}$, occur as essential oils and in the gums of coniferous trees. Their activity may be attributed to their unsaturated condition, namely the presence of double bonds. Either as such, or when combined with oxygen, they form essential oils, as peppermint, lemon oil and camphor.

Rubber is a polyterpene, $(C_5H_8)_n$, the value of n being in the hundreds. Rubber will be discussed later (Chap. XXIII).

The famous *carotene,* related to vitamin A, belongs in this group. Its formula is approximately $(C_5H_8)_8$.

HETEROCYCLIC RINGS

This term signifies rings comparable to the benzene ring, made up however, not of six carbon atoms, but (as for example, pyridine) five carbon atoms and one nitrogen atom.

Quinoline includes both a benzene and a pyridine residue.

These form nuclei of the well-known drugs and poisons called alkaloids, which include nicotine, quinine, morphine, cocaine and many others.

Pyridine

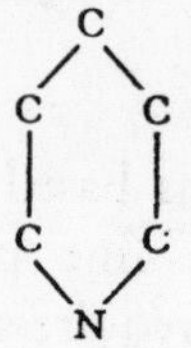

Quinoline

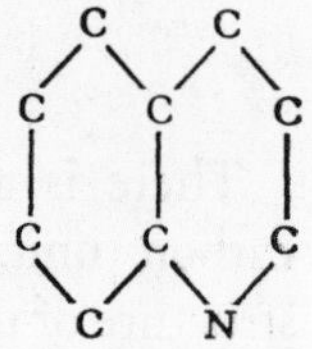

OTHER THAN CARBON SYSTEMS

The fundamental feature of organic compounds is the peculiar property shown by carbon in forming nuclei of extended chains or of closed rings. No fundamental reason appears why these characteristics should be confined to carbon. It is conceivable that other members of the carbon family might build up similar nuclei. Attempts to do this have been successful to some extent, and compounds analogous to ethane, propane and butane have been built up from the elements germanium and tin. Typical of such compounds are monogermane, GeH_4, digermane, G_2H_6, trigermane, G_3H_8, and a much more complex tin compound, $Sn_5(CH_3)_{12}$ in which the tin skeletal chain corresponds to the five carbon chain of pentane. Silicon chains also have been prepared with as many as seven atoms of silicon.

CHAPTER XXII

THE INORGANIC CHEMICAL INDUSTRIES

THE great realm of inorganic nature is one in which chemical activities have spent themselves. Affinities have had endless time and opportunity to become satisfied and the chemical energy of matter has been dissipated. It is like a clock that has run down. Inorganic chemical industries are impossible until some means are found for winding up the clock again. That is, we must find some source of energy outside this spent matter which may be available for unlocking the combinations made in the course of the ages, thus making available the matter and energy which we desire. These outside sources of energy are not difficult to locate. They make our industries possible, and we should realize that when certain irreplaceable resources are used up, we have spent fundamental assets.

The sources of energy which we now use are limited in number. They are: 1. The energy of the sun stored up in fuel supplies, either of contemporary origin, like the wood of our forests, or of remote origin, like the coal and petroleum supplies. 2. The energy of the sun stored up in the water power of our rivers and streams. It is but natural that we should turn to these sources of energy which are being ever renewed. The growth of electrochemical industries is the outcome of increasing ability to utilize our water power through hydroelectric installations. 3. The utilization of the energy of the tides and the direct heat of the sun still lies mainly in the future.

A very few mineral substances are found whose affinities have not been satisfied. Sulphur and metallic sulphides offer the best illustrations of this. Although this energy is ordinarily utilized, it is of little moment in comparison with the vast amount of energy needed in the electro-chemical industries.

It is scientifically proper to note that the unsatisfied affinity of the oxygen of the atmosphere is necessary for the utilization of the energy stored up in the coal. We are so likely to take oxygen for granted that this fact is not sufficiently appreciated. Oxygen is as truly our source of energy as is the coal which is used for fuel.

When by the preparation of chemically active substances from inert compounds we have established chemical affinities anew, that is, wound up our clock again, we are ready for a second phase of chemical activities. Given active reagents as sulphuric acid, sodium hydroxide, or chlorine, further chemical reactions are in the line of least resistance, and in operations both small and large, they usually present no difficulties. The great problem of chemical industries is the unlocking of the stable combinations as we find them in a spent or burned-out system. A less difficult problem is the application of these un-locked forces to the needs of men. The first is gathering resources together, the second spending them. The organic chemical industries are on the whole in a third class. In these no great sources of energy are stored up, nor yet applied. They are practically merely fine readjustments of the forms of matter, without the great energy changes of inorganic chemistry.

In spite of the profound and subtle difficulties confronting chemical manufacture, there have been developments of the industry in the remote past which challenge our admiration. In some fields, glass, ceramics, varnishes, our theoretical knowledge is only beginning to enable us to make improvements. In the end highly developed learning is bound to overtake and pass mere experience in every field; the greater the skill of the empirical industry, the greater will be the accomplishments when it is placed on a scientific basis.

Chemical manufacturing is spreading out in so many directions that only the most conspicuous fields may be profitably discussed here. In many of these fields the work of the engineer is all-important. In the open-hearth process of steel making, for example, the beautiful chemical manipulation would be impossible without the high temperature obtained by the structure of the furnace. Engineering details must perforce be omitted from our discussion, but any conception of chemical industries would be grossly inadequate if it failed to include the wonderful engineering achievements upon which their success so often depends.

METALLURGY

In the main, the processes of extraction of the metals from their ores must accomplish the solution of two problems. One problem is the proper manipulation of the mass of foreign material, "gangue," which may be mixed with the true ore. In the case of silver and gold the metal is present in exceedingly small proportions, and larger amounts of useless material must be handled. The second problem is the chemical change necessary to convert the compound of the metal as it is found into the free metal, the form in which it is usually desired.

The first problem is solved in various ways. Concentration may be accomplished by hand picking; by driving before a current of water, when the heavier metallic portions are left behind; flotation involves the rising of metallic sulphides with the foam generated by means of certain oils; the magnet is used for the separation of some rich iron ores from material of no value. Fluxing is an almost universal method of disposing of foreign matter when the operation is one at high temperatures. This consists in the proper combination of the foreign matter with other substances so that the whole forms a molten mass, through which the heavy metallic portion will sink and thus accumulate at the bottom. Fluxing is in a sense salt formation of a certain type. If the foreign matter present contains an excess of nonmetallic, that is, acid, constituents, as silica, basic fluxes will be added, while if bases such as magnesium and calcium oxides predominate, acid silica would be the flux added. In certain other operations having concentration for their purpose, the metal desired may be converted into compounds soluble in water, so that it may be leached out from the mass of inert rock. This applies to few cases, gold, silver, and copper. Amalgamating gold and silver ores with mercury, so that the mercury settles out with the precious metal in solution is a method akin to this.

The second problem is the proper chemical manipulation of the ores. Ores fall into various groups according to their chemical composition, and each group requires its own proper treatment. The sulphides form one such group, including ores of silver, mercury, lead, copper, arsenic, antimony, zinc, cobalt, and nickel. The essential features of the extraction are two. First, the sulphur must be removed, which is done by heating with an abundance of oxygen in the form of air. The sulphur burns away, $ZnS + 3O \rightarrow ZnO + SO_2$, forming sulphur dioxide, while the metal, also in combination with oxygen, is left in the residue. The escaping sulphur dioxide is not alone a waste, but a nuisance, as it is destructive to vegetation. Where the conditions are favorable, it is made into sulphuric acid. The residual oxide of the metal is now heated with carbon, usually in the form of coke, and thus its oxygen is removed and the metal obtained free.

Another class of ores is represented by the oxides, including also hydroxides and carbonates. At the high temperature of the operations the hydroxides lose water, and the carbonates lose carbon dioxide, so that each is converted into the oxide. $Cu(OH)_2$, copper hydroxide, $\rightarrow$ $CuO + H_2O$, $CuCO_3$, copper carbonate, $\rightarrow CuO + CO_2$. The oxide is reduced by means of carbon with varying degrees of ease, and carbon monoxide or dioxide is formed according to the conditions. Ores of lead, copper, tin, iron, manganese, chromium, and zinc fall under this head.

Electrolytic methods are becoming important in the obtaining of a number of metals. Aluminum is thus obtained as well as sodium and magnesium. In the first case the actual electrolysis is comparatively simple, the problem being to prepare a suitable raw material. The fundamentals of electrolysis are simple, but the proper control of certain details determines the practical success of the operations.

It must always be remembered that the above descriptions of metallurgical operations are given only in the barest outline. Practically the manipulation is often more complex. The conversion, for example, of a few grams of silver sulphide into pure silver is performed in the laboratory with the greatest ease. When, however, the operation becomes an industrial one, the handling of large quantities of lean ore, mixed with earthy matter, involving remote regions, and long distances, raising the question of water and fuel supply, the cost of labor and necessities, the ease of the chemical transformation becomes a comparatively small portion of the whole. Engineering and economical questions often quite overshadow it.

In addition to the first great step, the extraction of the metals from their ores, methods of refining are often required, and further manipulations needed. Copper and lead are cases in hand of metals which must be further treated in order to give them the required purity. In both cases the more valuable silver may be present as impurity, and its recovery is a partial compensation for the operation. In such refining the details are too varied for a general statement; yet one important principle often applies, namely, the oxidation of a more active impurity. If copper containing iron, sulphur, and other active elements is melted and treated with air, these more active elements oxidize, and rising to the surface of the heavy metal may readily be removed. Silver is "parted" from gold by treatment with hot sulphuric acid, in which the silver is soluble.

Another general principle of refining is the electrolytic method, described in Chapter XVIII. This is of great effectiveness, inasmuch as in one step of the process, the metal in hand is freed from all the less active metals, and in the other step, from those which are more active.

The iron and steel industries in great part are applications of mechanical appliances for shaping the metal in the desired forms. Such are the foundries, the forges and the rolling mills. But preceding each application of a given form of metal is the chemical transformation needed to give it the desired properties. Such transformations have been discussed in a brief way under iron and involve the addition or subtraction of other elements. In connection with the complicated structure, both chemical and physical, of the many forms of iron and steel now in use, as well as of other metals, the science of metallography has grown up. It is the study of the relation to one another of the various elements in the formation of compounds, and of the various compounds present in the formation of more complex mixtures, the whole making up what we call iron and steel. The resources of chemistry are supplemented by the microscope. A smooth surface of the metal is treated with an active reagent, as iodine. This dissolves some portions of the complex mass leaving others in such pronounced shapes that it is possible to derive information from the microscopic examination. Among the substances identified in these mixtures are the following: ferrite, pure iron; graphite, carbon; cementite, Fe_3C, an iron carbide; perlite, an alloy of cementite and ferrite; martensite, a solution in varying proportions of carbon in iron.

The mixing of metals with other elements takes two general forms. The first of these is the ordinary alloy, familiar in brass, bronzes, German silver, coinage and many other forms. Copper, zinc, tin, lead, are predominant in the common alloys, while antimony, bismuth, aluminum and the noble metals are constituents of others.

The second group of alloys includes those in which one metal is altogether predominant, but other metals or non-metals are present in small amounts, yet give the whole special properties. Two per cent of beryllium added to copper gives an alloy which upon proper heat treatment is strong, hard and fatigue-resistant. Phosphorus and silicon bronzes are illustrations of a large class of such combinations. Stainless steel and other modifications of steel fall into this class.

Surface treatment of metals is another form of metallurgy. Tin plating and galvanizing of iron to protect it from rusting are familiar processes. Electroplating has reached a high state of development, a conspicuous form being chromium plating. A particular form of surface treatment consists of giving to aluminum a thin coating of the colorless and transparent oxide, so that the metal then retains its high finish.

THE NON-METAL INDUSTRIES

Chlorine is manufactured in increasing amounts, and finds application in bleaching textiles and in disinfecting water supplies. The old method of freeing the chlorine from hydrochloric acid by oxygen in some form is now replaced by the electrolytic method. Liquid chlorine is frequently prepared and marketed as such, but much of it is still converted into bleaching powder, $CaOCl_2$, which is efficient either for bleaching or for disinfecting.

The recovery of bromine from sea water is spectacular. Some years ago there was sent out an experimental vessel, which, working in the Atlantic, proved the feasibility of such a method. Since then recovery has been conducted on a commercial scale at Cape Fear in North Carolina.

The bromine in the sea water, low in proportion, 60–70 parts per million, but vast in the aggregate, is liberated and collected and is later used in the preparation of "ethyl gasoline." This recovery focuses attention on the sources of materials from the sea and from salt lakes, operations which are already reasonably active, and in the working of which modern physical chemical knowledge has led to marked success.

Other nonmetals are either found native, as sulphur, or prepared in quantities demanded by the industries. The various forms of carbon, lampblack, coke, charcoal, and graphite are prepared in great quantities. Phosphorus is the basis of the match industry; boron and silicon are used for special purposes.

GASES

Chemistry, as well as modern engineering, has progressed greatly in the matter of manipulating gases. One of the hindrances to the formation of derivatives from the petroleum hydrocarbons has been the difficulty of obtaining the individual hydrocarbons in a sufficient state of purity, in addition to the fact that these individuals are gases. Methane, ethane, propane and pentane are now available, and are manipulated by pyrolysis or by chlorination. Liquid air is a source of both oxygen and nitrogen, as well as of argon and neon. Helium from gas wells of the West is obtained on a vast scale. Hydrogen is produced in various ways, and used for hydrogenation operations. The electrolysis of water yields hydrogen and oxygen, the latter used medicinally and for the production of high temperatures. The production of carbon dioxide for beverages and dry ice has already been mentioned.

Experimentally the cooling by means of liquid air, now readily available, has made investigation of gases easier, as they may thus be converted to the liquid form.

Those communities which are within the range of natural gas supplies are fortunate in having available a relatively cheap source of heat. Other communities must depend upon artificial gas which is obtained by the distillation of bituminous coal, or by the water gas process. The latter consists in the passing of water vapor through a mass of glowing coke. The reaction results in a mixture of hydrogen and carbon monoxide ($C + H_2O \rightarrow CO + H_2$), suitable as a source of heat, but not for light without enrichment. The compressed gas industry for isolated homes is of some magnitude. In the industries a fuel gas is at times required, and the need is met in one way by "producer gas," formed by passing steam and air over heated coal.

THE SALT INDUSTRIES

Salt deposits, salt lakes and the sea offer a vast field for recovery of salts. In this country common salt is obtained from salt deposits, in Louisiana by actual mining, in other places by bringing up the salt in the form of brine, fresh water being introduced in wells and allowed to become saturated. In warm countries salt is obtained by the spontaneous evaporation of sea water. Other salt deposits which bulk large in the industries are the sodium nitrate deposits of Chile; the potash deposits of Germany and Alsace, and the deposits of Death Valley. The potash deposits of Texas and New Mexico are supplying salts in promising amounts. Searles Lake in California and the Dead Sea are producing profitably. The latter yields compounds of sodium, potassium, calcium, magnesium, chlorine and bromine.

THE ACID INDUSTRIES

The great acid industry is based, in the first place, upon the manufacture of sulphuric acid by making a combination of the constituent elements. From this finished product the other acids desired are made by a simple double decomposition reaction. The making of sulphuric acid has already been described. The steps are: sulphur in any available form, to sulphur dioxide, to sulphur trioxide, to sulphuric acid. Further steps in the making of acids are simple, provided the raw material is available. Salt and sodium nitrate are easily converted into their corresponding acids by mixing them with sulphuric acid and heating. The new product is more volatile than the sulphuric acid and may readily be separated from the mixture. The gaseous hydrochloric acid is absorbed in vertical towers by coming in contact with a descending stream of water; the nitric acid being a liquid, is simply condensed. Other acids do not compare with these three in importance, but they may be prepared, given the necessary salt, with equal facility. Carbon dioxide, so much used for beverages, being an acid oxide, is prepared from calcium or magnesium carbonate by this method. The choice of these is decided by the value of the by-product.

THE ALKALI INDUSTRIES

Just as there is a group of acid industries closely correlated, so there is a group of alkali industries. Before the modern development of industrial chemistry the basis of this was the making of lime from limestone. By mere heat calcium carbonate, an abundant mineral, can be converted into calcium oxide, this into the hydroxide, and thus an active base obtained. This is convertible into the other active bases, sodium or potassium hydroxide or ammonia, in a way comparable with the conversion of sulphuric acid into other acids. This was the operation followed in the olden days when wood ashes were made into lye by treatment with lime.

Historically the great problem of the alkali industry has been the manufacture of sodium carbonate. Descriptions of the old Leblanc process and the modern Solvay process fill many pages of an industrial chemistry. As the Leblanc process has been almost completely superseded by the Solvay process, the latter will be the only one described. Naturally the source for the sodium is common salt. Its main reaction is $NaCl + NH_4.H.CO_3 \rightarrow NaHCO_3 + NH_4Cl$. This is merely a double decomposition reaction of the usual type, based upon the comparatively low solubility of the sodium hydrogen carbonate, and involves no important energy changes. Energy changes are involved in the preparation of the ammonium hydrogen carbonate, $NH_4 H CO_3 (NH_3 + H_2O + CO_2)$, which requires the preliminary release of the ammonia from ammonium chloride,

$$2NH_4Cl + Ca(OH)_2 \rightarrow 2NH_3 + H_2O + CaCl_2.$$

Applications of energy from without, requiring the use of fuel, are in the formation of the calcium hydroxide from limestone, and the conversion of the resultant $NaHCO_3$, baking soda, into the sodium carbonate. The by-products, ammonia and carbon dioxide, are used in further operations, but chlorine and calcium are wasted. The efficiency of this process depends upon the skillful application of engineering principles in the designing of the apparatus. With laboratory apparatus it is not easy to carry out the process. Yet through proper design of machinery, it is made a basic chemical industry. It is to be noticed that baking soda, $NaHCO_3$, is the first product made by the Solvay process. It is used in large amounts for baking powder, but its chief application is for conversion into the normal carbonate.

Sodium hydroxide, caustic soda, also called lye, is made from the carbonate by double decomposition with lime, that is, calcium hydroxide. Electrolytic methods have assumed a large place in the manufacture of sodium hydroxide. This is the electrolysis of sodium chloride, which supplies chlorine at the anode, and the sodium released at the cathode acts upon the water present to form sodium hydroxide and hydrogen.

THE FERTILIZER INDUSTRIES

Agriculture should and does make good use of such wastes as our civilization may supply. Tankage, garbage, even sewage disposal products are commercially manipulated in order to return to the soil that which originally came from that source. The present chapter deals with the three inorganic fertilizers which agriculture requires in addition to the more natural plant foods of agriculture and other industries. These are nitrogen, potassium (conveniently called potash) and phosphorus.

The term potash indicates, when used exactly, the oxide, K_2O, but is applied to any compound in which the potassium is in available form. The great bulk of potash produced, approximately 90 per cent, is used for fertilizer purposes. Formerly practically the entire supply came from the Stassfurt deposits. These deposits were formed by the evaporation of sea water, under unique conditions, so that all its constituents were left in place. Sea water salts are 78 per cent of sodium salts and only 4 per cent of potassium salts. The latter are very soluble, so that in the evaporation of sea water the small proportion of potassium salts is usually either never deposited or removed by solution after deposition. Nevertheless deposits in Germany and in the Southwest, both as salt deposits and salt lakes, have been successfully developed.

The phosphate industry is a simple one. It happens that in some of the South Atlantic states calcium phosphate occurs in abundance. This phosphate is in a form so insoluble that plants cannot utilize it. It is therefore ground fine and mixed with sulphuric acid, when the following reaction takes place:

$$Ca_3(PO_4)_2 + 2H_2SO_4 \rightarrow CaH_4(PO_4)_2 + 2CaSO_4$$

Both products are slightly soluble and are valuable as fertilizers.

A recent successful modification in the conversion of phosphate rock into usable form is as follows: A part of the rock is treated as is iron ore in the blast furnace. Phosphorus is thus formed free and promptly burned to its oxide. This with water forms phosphoric acid, which is then used to render some of the rock soluble and ready for the market.

$$Ca_3(PO_4)_2 \rightarrow P \rightarrow P_2O_5 \xrightarrow{+H_2O} H_3PO_4 \xrightarrow{+CaPO_4} CaH_4(PO_4)_2$$

Other forms of phosphate worked up for fertilizers are bone products (for bone is merely calcium phosphate) and phosphate slags of steel making, obtained in the linings of steel converters when the iron is rich in phosphorus.

Nitrogen fixation was discussed in Chapter VII. For agricultural purposes, most nitrogen compounds will serve the purpose of supplying the plants with that element, because in the end nitrogen in any combined form is oxidized to the nitrates necessary for plants. Industrially nitrogen is supplied to agriculture in several forms. Ammonium salts are obtained from the products of soft coal distillation. Sodium nitrate is obtained from the niter beds of Chile, and is also produced synthetically on a vast scale. Any nitrogenous refuse such as slaughterhouse waste or garbage residue may be used as such or mixed with other substances of fertilizer value.

CEMENT, GLASS, POTTERY

Portland cement is an artificial combination of limestone and clay which is highly heated and then ground to a fine powder. The proportions were determined in the first place by natural mixtures found to give the desired results. Cement may be called a mixture of calcium silicate and calcium aluminate. Its setting when mixed with water is difficult to explain, but is said to be due to hydrolysis of these salts, followed by recombinations between the bases and acids present and of these new salts with water, and subsequent crystallization with the formation of a solid mass of interlocking crystals.

Glass.—The making of glass, as well as that of pottery, is an ancient industry, developed to a high degree of perfection before the age of theoretical knowledge. They are both silicate industries, involving the combination of silicon dioxide with one or more bases, the combination being fusible according to its complexity. These are then of the nature of salts.

Glass in its common form is a mixture of silicates of calcium and sodium. Its complex nature causes a delayed crystallization (glass is a supercooled liquid) giving the glass two of its chief virtues, transparency and the property of softening before melting. Other virtues of glass are insolubility and general inactivity toward reagents. Glass is made by fusing together sodium carbonate or sulphate, calcium carbonate, and sand. The nonmetallic oxides of carbon and sulphur in combination with the bases are expelled in the process of heating. While this soda-lime glass serves many purposes, it is nevertheless too susceptible to sudden changes of temperature and the solvent action of water and alkalies. Hence other oxides are introduced, and the result is an improvement. Bohemian glass contains potassium in place of sodium, Jena normal glass contains zinc and aluminum oxides. Several other metallic oxides are applied as well as the nonmetallic oxides of boron and phosphorus. Lead glass is noteworthy in that it is brilliant but very soft.

Glass must be annealed, that is, cooled with care, so that the interior may not be left in a state of tension. The Prince Rupert drop illustrates this state of tension in an exaggerated degree. These drops are made by sudden cooling of molten glass. If the small end of the drop is broken off, it causes the whole to fly into pieces with almost explosive violence.

Glass manufacture has made great progress from the standard industry of a generation ago. In addition to the products of that time we now have safety glass (mainly a mechanical arrangement), a glass so strong that objects made from it are almost unbreakable, and particularly fiber glass. Fiber glass is glass spun out in fine threads, which are then woven into the desired shapes. Hundreds of products are thus formed. Glareless glass and structural glass are now developed products.

The coloring of glass is accomplished in one of two ways. Certain substances, insoluble in the glass, are mixed with the mass. They remain diffused in a very even manner and give an effect of color or milkiness. Ruby glass is colored by very fine particles of gold or cuprous oxide. Milk glass contains such substances as tin and zinc oxides, which are suspended through the glass and render it opaque. Other effects are produced by the introduction of metallic oxides which form true colored compounds with the silica. These compounds are evenly diffused through the entire mass. Among the most striking is the compound formed with cobalt oxide, which is of an intense and beautiful blue color.

The chemical features of glass making may be stated approximately as follows: Metallic oxides like those of calcium, magnesium, and aluminum fuse with great difficulty. The same is true of the nonmetallic oxide used, silicon dioxide. When, however, the two are mixed and heated, they combine with the formation of a more fusible complex, which is virtually a salt. On the whole, the more complex this is, the more fusible it is, and the more suitable it is for glazes and fluxes. Glazes both for metal objects and for pottery are then forms of readily melting glass. Fluxes are compounds used in metallurgy to render objectionable foreign material fusible and therefore removable. For metallic oxide impurities nonmetallic silicon dioxide and boron oxide are used. To remove the acid silicon dioxide, a basic flux is used, as calcium oxide. The impurities are thus converted to fusible glasses.

Pottery.—Clay is a hydrated silicate of aluminum, possessing the property of plasticity when moist, and capable of burning to a hard mass, which, in that it does not actually fuse, retains the shape given while soft. Ordinary brick and the crude forms of earthenware represent this plainly. The burning, or adherence of the clay particles is probably due to a very superficial melting of fine projections and foreign substances. The article, though it shrinks, retains its shape, and unless heated very hot is porous. When the article is designed for impermeability to water, it is glazed. This glaze consists of feldspar and other silicates which are applied to the article in the form of a thin layer. On account of their greater complexity, they are more fusible than the original clay, and when the article is fired again, this layer melts over the whole surface, making a watertight glaze. The various grades of pottery vary according to the purity of the materials and the manner of mixing. When the glaze is diffused throughout the original clay, the whole mass is more fusible, requiring more delicate handling, but the product is translucent and attractive. This is often called china, while the name porcelain is applied to less translucent ware, glazed on the exterior, but opaque within. This glaze can be colored after the manner of glass. The design in the proper material is placed on the ware before or after applying the glaze, the former giving the more permanent result.

ELECTROCHEMICAL PROCESSES

The present era is justly criticized because of its inattention to the conservation of our natural resources. Coal, the usual source of energy, is being consumed at an increasing rate as our industries grow. Coal deposits are among the natural resources which, once used, are irreplaceable. Hence we may feel gratified that economic pressure is resulting in the utilization of water power in increasing measure, with consequent saving of coal. Such power is conveniently converted into electrical power, which in its turn is available for chemical manufacturing purposes in two ways quite independent of each other. One of these makes use of the electricity merely as a convenient source of heat, while the other is strictly electrochemical, depending altogether on the special relations between chemistry and electricity.

In the former set of operations the electric furnace is applied. In this the heat is developed either after the manner of arc lights, or by the resistance of the mass of material through which the current flows, illustrated by our domestic electric heating devices. Steel, graphite, carborundum, silicon, calcium carbide and carbon disulphide are products of such furnaces. In them the use of electricity is solely as a source of heat, which is applied to greater advantage, both technically and economically, than when produced by the combustion of coal.

The second set of operations involves actual electrochemical changes. Such operations are: A, electroplating; B, electrorefining and the recovery of metals from wastes; C, the preparation of certain metals as sodium and aluminum; D, the preparation of secondary products like sodium hydroxide.

The first principle of all these operations is a simple electrolytic separation of the positive and negative constituents of a suitable electrolyte. In some cases this is the end of the process, as when aluminum is obtained, or silver is plated on a brass object. In other cases complications ensue, as when sodium is liberated in presence of water. Then the complication must be avoided by proper contrivances; or, on the other hand, advantage may be taken of this secondary reaction. When sodium chloride is electrolyzed, there are three possibilities. Sodium and chlorine may be desired, in which case the sodium must be prevented from reacting with chlorine or water. If sodium hydroxide is wanted, the arrangement is such that sodium may react with water, but not with the chlorine. When sodium hypochlorite is the object, the resulting sodium hydroxide and chlorine must be brought together, but other possibilities prevented. Many details are of great moment. The intensity of the current, the nature of the electrolyte, the nature and size of the electrodes, and contrivances for separation or uniting the products of the electrolysis are among the features which require careful regulation.

CHAPTER XXIII

THE ORGANIC CHEMICAL INDUSTRIES

THE practical side of organic chemistry touches our lives at many points. In the first place living processes and products are concerned with organic chemistry. In the second place there are well-established industries which have furnished useful products through many years. On top of all this there has been a recent renaissance of organic chemistry so striking that new processes and products are reported with great frequency. To some extent the first of these interests, involving foods and biochemistry will be touched on in the chapter, Chemistry of Foods (XXVII). The organic industries proper, the subject of this chapter, will be taken up somewhat in the order in which the subject of organic chemistry was developed in the chapter devoted to it (XXI).

PETROLEUM

The industries of the hydrocarbons of the paraffin series are practically all concerned with petroleum. The main features of the refining industry have already been outlined. However, research has been so active in this field that recently principles have been applied with outstanding results.

The first chemical modification in petroleum refining was the operation of *"cracking."* The great demand of the present age is a volatile liquid, which requires a molecule with six to ten carbon atoms. The amount of this in crude oil is limited. By overheating under pressure larger molecules are broken down, with a consequent increase of the gasoline yield. This operation is not new. However, the opposite operation, building up complex molecules from simple by the help of catalysts, is new; and it has some applications in the way of redeeming the waste products of cracking (the disintegration of the large molecules may have gone too far), in using natural gas as the raw material of gasoline—if market conditions make this desirable—and lastly in the building up of lubricating oils, which require a molecule of some complexity. This building up of complex molecules by causing simple units to combine is called polymerization, and is very important in the modern developments of synthetic rubber, plastics and fibers.

The question of the action of *antiknock compounds* is an engineering question. The chemist, however, must solve the problem of the production of these substances. Tetraethyl lead, Pb $(C_2H_5)_4$, has revolutionized the gasoline industry. It is poisonous because of its lead content; but since the public has learned to take proper precautions, accidents are now unheard of. It has been found in course of time that the antiknock effect could be obtained in other ways, in particular by certain forms of paraffin hydrocarbons (isooctane), by unsaturated chain hydrocarbons related to ethylene, and by hydrocarbons of the benzene series. Petroleum refining has been modified to meet these conditions.

The preparation of *derivatives* directly from the hydrocarbons has been the prime feature of the benzene industries. It is but natural that this fact should be a challenge to the chemist to accomplish this result in the paraffin series. In recent years this challenge has been met with some success and with promise of greater results. The first problem that needed solution has been the isolation of reasonably pure individual members of the series, a feat accomplished successfully only with the recent success in the handling and separation of gases.

The most obvious method of approach has been by means of the halogen derivatives. The method so far as it is applicable is illustrated by the preparation of amyl acetate. The starting material is pentane.

$$C_5H_{12} \rightarrow C_5H_{11}Cl;$$
$$\text{pentyl chloride}$$

$$C_5H_{11}Cl + NaCO_2CH_3 \rightarrow NaCl + C_5H_{11}.CO_2CH_3$$
$$\text{sodium acetate} \qquad \text{(pentyl) amyl acetate}$$

This second step is an organic synthesis, of a type repeated many times in this branch of chemistry.

Pyrolysis is a dignified term designating the breaking down of complex substances by means of high temperatures. This has been applied to paraffin hydrocarbons with the result that a pair of hydrogen atoms is split off and the unsaturated reactive condition established.

$$CH_3 - CH_3 \rightarrow CH_2 = CH_2 + H_2$$

This active compound is now treated with hypochlorous acid, HOCl, with the formation of a mixed oxygen and chlorine compound. $CH_2OH.CH_2Cl$, which is readily converted to glycol, $CH_2OH.CH_2OH$, a compound much like glycerol, and serving the same purpose to some extent. Glycerol and ordinary alcohol are prepared commercially by methods akin to this.

Direct oxidation of higher hydrocarbons to acids and subsequent conversion of these into soaps, is practiced fairly often and promises considerable results in the future.

Halogen derivatives are prepared directly for use as such. CH_3Cl, CH_2Cl_2, CCl_2F_2 are of use as refrigerants. $CHCl_3$ is chloroform and CCl_4, carbon tetrachloride, is used as a noncombustible solvent and as a fire extinguisher. The immediate future may find an increasing value in halogen derivatives as solvents. In particular fluorine compounds are only recently receiving attention. Their future usefulness is still a question. The preparation of halogen derivatives as intermediates for the formation of other compounds has already been touched on.

Organic Compounds

The chapter of oxygen derivatives includes the subjects of fermentation industries and of solvents. The first of these will be discussed later. *Solvents* will be treated at this point. In order that one may appreciate their function in modern organic industries one should recall the usefulness of water in the inorganic world. It is difficult to summarize the applications of organic solvents. The use in lacquers is perhaps the most striking illustration. A modern lacquer is composed of a solid material, as a gum or a cellulose derivative, dissolved in a suitable liquid. To this is added the proper pigment. When the lacquer is applied, the liquid evaporates and the solids remain in the desired form.

At present the organic industries make use of at least one hundred different solvents, and new ones are being offered from time to time. The list includes the first five alcohols, a number of ethers and esters, and many compounds which have a structure involving several types. Acetamide $CH_3.CONH_2$ may be taken as an illustration. It has solvent action due to three different influences, hydrocarbon residue and oxygen and nitrogen groups. In particular there may be mentioned the synthetic preparation of methyl (wood) alcohol from carbon monoxide and hydrogen, $CO + 2H_2 \longrightarrow CH_3OH$; of ethyl alcohol from ethane; of propyl alcohol from propane. Other alcohols are formed by fermentation processes. Other solvents of varying physical properties are prepared in various ways by methods not readily summarizable.

Among oxygen compounds the new types of *soaps* present both theoretical and practical interest. Standard soap has a structure represented by the name and formula, sodium stearate, $C_{17}H_{35}CO_2Na$. This structure may be interpreted as a large hydrocarbon residue converted into a salt by means of the — CO_2Na group. Serviceable as soap is, it has one great disadvantage, in that it is acted upon by the calcium and magnesium of hard waters, forming an objectionable scum, and the value of the soap to that extent is lost. The new soap, starting with a higher acid, for example $C_{13}H_{27}CO_2H$, is by the action of hydrogen reduced to a corresponding alcohol, $C_{13}H_{27}CH_2OH$. This, being a base, will react with sulphuric acid to form $C_{13}H_{27}CH_2SO_4H$. The sodium salt of this new acid $C_{13}H_{27}SO_4Na$ is the new soap. It is, like the old soap, the sodium salt of an acid involving a long carbon chain. Its special virtue is that moderately hard waters do not interfere with its action, as the calcium and magnesium salts which it might form are soluble.

The Oils, Fats, and Waxes

Although the liquid oils have a larger percentage of unsaturated fatty acids than do the solid fats, the distinction between them is on the whole a practical one, in that the name oil is applied to fats which are liquid at ordinary temperatures. The word oil is carelessly used to denote a number of unrelated substances, being applied to such different substances as petroleum, oil of wintergreen, and even sulphuric acid, and to obviate any confusion the substances discussed in this chapter could be designated as the fatty oils, or better, the liquid fats. Solid and liquid fats are used interchangeably to some extent, and if need should arise could be interchanged even more. Tradition and usage are firmly fixed, and long-established habits are altered only slowly. Another distinction which is from a chemical standpoint arbitrary, is that of animal and vegetable origin. Prejudice here too plays a part not justified by any difference in chemical composition. But attractiveness and minor convenience play a rôle which must be reckoned with in any practical consideration.

The presence of fats in vegetable as well as in animal organisms is a familiar fact. Nuts are conspicuous for their oil, and we are very familiar with olive, cottonseed, and linseed oil. In animal rations fats and carbohydrates supplement each other, serving more or less the same purpose, but practically no carbohydrate is stored by the animal. In the storing by vegetables, carbohydrates are more abundant than fats, and only when the former drop off are the latter abundant, as is illustrated in nuts. The animal fats in greatest use are lard, tallow, and butter fat. The vegetable fats best known are those from seeds, castor, cottonseed, hempseed, linseed, poppy, and sunflower; from nuts, walnut, almond, peanut, cocoanut; also olive oil, palm oil, and cocoa butter.

Fats are in the main extracted readily enough from the

OIL GUSHING OVER THE TOP OF A DERRICK IN THE OKLAHOMA OIL
FIELD

AN OIL REFINERY AT RICHMOND, CALIFORNIA. THIS IS THE LARGEST
OF THE REFINERIES OF THE STANDARD OIL COMPANY OF CALIFORNIA

fiber and other material in which they are imbedded. They are easily melted, when not already liquid, and are thus extracted, especially with pressure. Or they may be extracted by means of solvents like gasoline and carbon disulphide, which dissolve out the fats without affecting other ingredients. The first use of fats is for foods; not alone for such uses as those of butter, olive oil, and lard, but a large amount is taken more or less unknowingly in the food, as in milk, oatmeal, and prepared dishes. Soap making may be considered next in interest. Its preparation has been discussed under the head of sodium in a previous chapter. Much fat is hydrolyzed, instead of being saponified, and this operation liberates the free fatty acids for any use desired. The free fatty acids can then be used for making soap, by uniting with sodium hydroxide (lye).

They can be used for making candles, as they are solid enough to be firm, yet melt easily as the candle is burned, and are rapidly vaporized at the wick. The paraffin used so much for candles is mechanically imperfect, as it softens too readily in warm weather. Tallow and the natural waxes are also used for candle making. The fatty acids are advantageously mixed with paraffin for the better grade of candles, as they make them firmer and therefore less likely to collapse or to drip.

Fats and fatty oils are used as lubricants, in medicinal preparations, as ointments, and in various textile operations, as treatment of hides in making leather. The unsaturated oils have a unique application in paints and varnishes.

The hardening, or hydrogenation, of oils is a most interesting process which has come into prominence in recent years. The liquid fats are usually not considered so serviceable as the solid. This may be due to the mere liquid condition or to the fact that some of them are less stable, and readily become rancid. The chemical feature of these liquid fats is that they contain less hydrogen than solid fats. As an example, the fat, $C_3H_5(C_{18}H_{35}O_2)_3$, is a solid. The corresponding liquid fat is $C_3H_5(C_{18}H_{33}O_2)_3$. Upon treatment with hydrogen in presence of a catalyst (nickel is much used) enough hydrogen can be added to the liquid fats to convert them into solids. Cottonseed oil is thus made into a very attractive solid product.

Glycerol belongs to the chapter on fats. The formula shows that the proportion of glycerol obtained from a fat must of necessity be small. Stearin yields only 10 per cent of its weight theoretically. Its chief use is for nitroglycerine, one of the great agents of modern engineering. Other applications are in toilet soaps, pharmacy and medicine, antifreeze, and for keeping fiber moist and soft, as it does not evaporate and attracts small amounts of water from the air.

PAINTS AND VARNISHES

As introduction to this brief discussion, attention may be called to two phases of the subject. The first is illustrated by the use of shellac and lacquers. Shellac consists of a resinous substance dissolved in alcohol. When this is applied to a surface, the alcohol soon evaporates and leaves the resinous matter spread over the surface in a thin, even, hard layer, which serves the desired purpose. The action of many modern lacquers is similar. The other illustration is the application of linseed oil and other drying oils. The oil does not evaporate, but absorbs oxygen, and owing to oxidation and polymerization, the liquid linseed oil is changed into a solid, sufficiently hard and tough to protect the surface underneath. If to these two ideas we add that of pigments, the whole ground is briefly covered. Pigments are solids, white or colored, which are mixed with linseed oil, making it opaque, and giving it a desired color.

Varnishes may be described as solutions of certain resinous substances in alcohol, turpentine, or linseed oil, so selected and modified that when the mixture is spread over a surface there results presently, owing to evaporation or oxidation, a glossy durable solid. The chemical changes are not altogether clearly understood, though the features already suggested are rather apparent. The resins used, amber, copal, lac, and others, of well-known physical appearance, are of the nature of complex organic acids. However, they are used solely for their physical properties; their chemical nature does not come into consideration. For many of the products in which linseed oil is used, the oil is first boiled. It is heated, often in presence of oxidizing catalysts, metallic oxides, the practical effect of which is to hasten the oxidation when the oil is later applied. For ordinary paints, linseed oil is not boiled so much as formerly. Paints consist essentially of linseed oil or other drying oil, as tung oil, mixed with a solid to give the paint body, and a pigment in addition, perhaps, to give the desired color. The chemistry of the drying of the oil has already been discussed, and it may be well to discuss the body and pigment, although they are mostly inorganic products. White lead, basic lead carbonate, $Pb_3(CO_3)_2(OH)_2$, is the standard body, although other compounds, such as zinc oxide, barium sulphate, other combinations of zinc and lead, and titanium oxide are coming into use. For some purposes these are superior to white lead. Their requirements are durability, fineness, and opacity, which means covering power. When a color other than white is desired, a pigment must be added, and for this purpose colored substances of the greatest variety have been used. Compounds of iron are common, as Venetian red, siennas, ochers, and umbers, all forms of iron oxide. Other metals which furnish colored compounds suitable for pigments are chromium, copper, lead, cobalt, and mercury. Organic pigments can be made in great variety by combining mordants with dyes, and applying the solid substances thus formed. These are less permanent than the inorganic pigments, but serve many special purposes.

THE CARBOHYDRATE INDUSTRIES

Glucose, maltose, sucrose, dextrin, starch, and cellulose are the carbohydrates which figure largely in the industrial world. Cellulose falls under the textiles. All the rest, excepting sucrose, are alteration products of starch, so that in the discussion of sucrose and starch we will cover most of the field.

Cane sugar, saccharose or sucrose, is obtained mostly from the sugar cane and the sugar beet, and, in spite of the popular impression, there is no difference in the fully refined products. Extraction is achieved by pressing out the sap or by diffusion into water. In each case the sugar solution resulting is then evaporated to obtain the solid sugar. In the case of beets, the beets are chipped and then systematically extracted by means of separate lots of water. We here have an illustration of a device much employed in chemical engineering. The fresh chips, holding much sugar, come in contact with the extracting solution when it is almost at the end of its absorbing capacity, while the beets which are almost exhausted are treated with the fresh water, and so on through, so that there is a maximum of extraction with a minimum application of water.

After the aqueous solution is separated from the fiber, the sugar recovery is essentially the separation of what gummy, resinous, and albuminous matter can be removed by a coagulant, the evaporation to the point of crystallization of the sugar, and finally the refining of the crude product. There are many steps and details, too technical and involved for mention here. A considerable amount of foreign matter accumulated toward the end interferes with further crystallization. Therefore there is a mother liquor, high in sugar content, which is the molasses. In the case of cane sugar this molasses has attractive properties and is to some extent utilized directly, but part of it is treated further for its sugar content or allowed to ferment to form alcohol.

The maple tree is in certain regions a source of sugar. Maple sugar owes its attractiveness to the delicate flavor of the foreign matter present, and no doubt to its romantic source. It is ordinarily an article of luxury, used as a sirup, and commands a price, in accordance with its sugar content, of from four to five times that of ordinary sugar. Sorghum "molasses" is too impure for profitable extraction, but is used in localities as a sweetener for home consumption.

Starch is manufactured in large amounts, being extracted from corn, wheat, potatoes, and rice. Arrow-root starch, a very pure form, has some uses, while certain palm trees yield sago. Tapioca comes from a tropical plant. The last two are artificial modifications of the original product, hence their special form and appearance. The process of starch extraction is in great part mechanical, but fermentation processes are used to assist in the liberation of the starch grains from the other material present. Starch is used as food and in laundry work; in the textile industry it is used for dressing goods, as a thickener, and for sizing paper; it is used for paste and for making dextrin and glucose. The maltose formed in some industries, as in brewing, is usually made from starch still incorporated in the grain, and is not separated out as a pure product.

Solid *dextrin* is made by the action of heat, or of heat and acids, on starch. It is used for its adhesive value (British gum). When diastase is used the product is sirupy, and is applied as such in candy making and in brewing.

In the making of *glucose* from starch the process of hydrolysis, that is, the splitting of the highly complex starch into simpler complexes, and finally into its constituent units, is practically complete. In dextrin the molecule is a less complex polysaccharide than that in starch, in maltose we have a disaccharide, while in glucose we have reached the monosaccharide stage. The starch is heated with water and one to three per cent acid for an hour or more. The acid is then removed by means of calcium carbonate (marble dust) and the by-product, calcium sulphate, allowed to settle out. Glucose is now produced as an attractive product, vying in appearance with cane sugar. The former prejudice against its use has virtually disappeared, and glucose is now accepted legally as a regular food. As stated in another place, *levulose* is now recovered from the Jerusalem artichoke for the purpose of sweetening and the manufacture of alcohol. The dahlia bulb is also utilized as a source of levulose.

THE FERMENTATION INDUSTRIES

The process of fermentation is usually associated with the formation of ethyl alcohol from sugar or starch. Yet other alcohols are obtained at the same time and are valuable by-products. Such a one is amyl alcohol, named on account of its relation to starch. Vinegar making is a fermentation process and other acids as butyric and lactic are also formed by similar methods.

The simplest form of alcohol fermentation is that of glucose, or mixtures of glucose and levulose, the sugars of ordinary fruit juices. Almost as soon as this juice is extracted, that is, exposed to the air, spores fall into it and fermentation begins.

Alcoholic fermentation requires no chemical reagent from without, the change being simply the rearrangement of the hydrogen and oxygen already present. Ethyl alcohol and carbon dioxide are such predominating products that other substances formed are usually little considered. Besides alcohol and the residual sugar, the acids from the fruit are important, not alone for their own acid taste, but also on account of their delicately flavored esters or organic salts which they develop with the alcohols. These, as well as other foreign substances are present in small amounts, but these small amounts are sufficient to influence the taste of the product. One familiar with the wine industry knows the great importance of delicate gradations in flavor when no other difference can be established. The details of wine making are many, and the industry is taken very seriously in wine-growing regions, like that of the Rhine, where schools for its study are established. Cider making is familiar, yet it is an illustration of a common experience with very little knowledge of the nature of the real facts. In this process the course of the changes is as follows: The sugar begins to ferment very promptly, and in two weeks the sugar may be mainly converted into alcohol. The cider now seems sour, not on account of the increase in acid, but on account of the decrease in sugar, so that the sour taste of malic acid originally present in the apple is apparent. If not protected from the air (oxygen and mother of vinegar) acetic acid fermentation may now begin. Ten per cent of sugar should yield theoretically a five per cent alcohol solution, and a vinegar containing 6.7 per cent acid. The usual result is a lower one, and ordinary vinegar contains about four per cent.

The essential feature of the brewing industry is that the sugar to be fermented is obtained from the starch of grains. Malt is barley partially germinated, there being formed the enzyme diastase, which is capable of converting starch into maltose. It is this maltose which ferments under the influence of yeast. From the standpoint of the brewing industry these statements are most meager. There are many fine points involving economy, flavor, and keeping which would involve a highly technical discussion.

The third class of alcohol industries involves the concentration by distillation of the alcohol formed in one of the above fermentation processes. When the raw material is the fermented fruit juice, brandy is the product. Sugar residues yield rum, and the various grains, fermented, yield whiskey. The alcohol content of these beverages is roughly 40-50 per cent, and the difference lies mainly in the small amounts of other ingredients, such as flavors, color, and other alcohols besides ethyl. These last are supposed to be injurious. These details are given weight in popular interest out of all proportion to their importance in the eyes of a chemist. On the other hand, the chemist should not put too light an estimate upon popular impressions concerning minute differences in much used articles. They may contain the germs of important truths.

The manufacture of alcohol as such is a phase of the distillation process. Grain is allowed to ferment, alcohol is developed and then distilled off. In this country sugar waste is now the chief source of alcohol, although a portion, perhaps ten per cent, is made by the synthetic process. Stills have been designed which accomplish a satisfactory separation of the alcohol and water in one operation, usually no easy affair. The apparatus is so arranged that the vapors do not at once go to the condensers, but are retarded with the effect that the more easily condensible water is in part returned to the still, while the more volatile alcohol retains the vapor form and so passes on to the main condensers. From such a still, alcohol of high percentage may be obtained. For absolute alcohol, that is, 99 per cent or better, the water must be removed by chemical means. In order to avoid hindrance to the industries, alcoholic beverages being taxed as luxuries, denaturing is resorted to, in order to make the alcohol available for the one purpose and to prevent its use for the other. Wood alcohol, mixed with pyridine, is much used as a denaturant, and though not ideal, has served the purpose reasonably well. For special purposes other substances may be used as denaturants.

The above-mentioned fermentation processes are of long standing. By the use of special cultures other processes have come into vogue. Sugar and especially starch serve as the raw material, and the cultures must be prepared with great care. Acetone and butyl alcohol are typical products. The latter, in conjunction with certain cellulose nitrates, has been an important element in the modernization of automobile lacquers.

THE TEXTILES—CELLULOSE AND ITS MODIFICATIONS, WOOL, SILK, SYNTHETIC FIBERS, RUBBER, LEATHER, PLASTICS

In the use of these materials the physical properties are the outstanding features which regulate their value. But the chemical composition is interesting in itself, and the knowledge thereof leads to modifications which are of great value.

The chemistry of *cellulose* has already been explained under the heading of carbohydrates. Cellulose represents the composition of cotton and linen. The other cellulose fibers, hemp, jute, ramie, contain the cellulose either in modified form or in combination with a modified woody form. Their properties are determined by such characteristics as the length of the fiber, its pliability, its heat conductivity, strength, and brittleness.

On the whole cellulose is an inactive insoluble substance. Yet its chemical properties are made available in a number of instances about to be described.

The essential feature in the modifications of cellulose which have assumed such importance is that on account of its basic nature it may be combined with certain acid groups. The compounds thus formed are soluble after a fashion in various solvents, forming gelatinous masses. This jelly may then be pressed out in threads or sheets with the formation of the desired articles. Three types will be explained.

Cellulose dissolves in, that is, forms a compound with, a mixture of carbon disulphide and sodium hydroxide, the whole forming the typical jelly. This is then forced in fine threads into dilute sulphuric acid (or another substance) which sets the thread and removes the added chemical. This is the viscose process and yields the rayon thread. The other operations are mechanical. Cellophane making differs in that the jelly is pressed out in sheets.

When the cellulose is combined with the acetate group, the product known as acetate serves many purposes, particularly the making of slow-burning films, to be used instead of the dangerously combustible nitrate films.

When cellulose is converted to the nitrate there are various possibilities. First, guncotton with its well-known uses. Second, the conversion of this into such products as collodion, celluloid and photographic films. When, however, the nitration is less complete, these lower nitrates serve as excellent bases for the modern automobile lacquers which have revolutionized that industry.

Wool is a protein in its chemical structure. This means that it is very complex, that it contains nitrogen and is made up of animo acids held together by nitrogen. Wool is therefore amphoteric, that is, it has both acid and basic nature, a matter of great moment in the application of dyes. It does not burn readily, and when it does, it gives off the "burnt feather" odor. Toward bleaching agents wool is rather sensitive, and may not be treated with chlorine. Hydrogen peroxide and sulphur dioxide are satisfactory bleaching agents.

Silk is also a protein. The setting of the gelatinous thread spun by the silk worm into the serviceable thread is similar to other coagulations of proteins (white of egg). The attractive appearance of the thread is now imitated in the various artificial textiles. Silk, like wool, is amphoteric.

Textiles are often loaded with foreign material for the purpose of accomplishing certain results. They are impregnated with inorganic compounds to render them less inflammable, with gummy materials to render them stiff, with fats and soaps to make them soft, and with various compounds to give them body and weight.

Synthetic fibers. The spinning of a gelatinous thread by the silk worm and its subsequent coagulation is the model upon which the development of the modern synthetic fiber is based. The list of such fibers is becoming longer each year. Their composition in detail is not always known, but in a general way it may be said that they are polymerization or condensation products of various units, among them the amides, units suggestive of the structure of the proteins. There is a close relation between the chemistry of the synthetic fibers and that of the plastics.

Rubber (or caoutchouc) is a polyterpene $(C_5H_8)_n$. The value of n is several hundred. Rubber comes from the sap (called the latex) of the rubber tree, in which the rubber is in colloidal suspension, and from which it is separated by the addition of an acid. Inasmuch as rubber softens when heated, the vulcanization with sulphur to render it more permanent is vital. In this process the presence of catalysts, organic compounds called accelerators, shortens the time required. The technique of rubber production is very elaborate, and much research is spent on the subject with valuable results. For many of its applications various foreign substances are added.

The possible shortage of the rubber supply envisaged years ago stimulated the rubber plantation industry, which now supplies the world with a very superior article. Studies have also been made to the end of supplying an artificial rubber. Three fairly successful products may be mentioned.

Isoprene, C_5H_8, the unit of the terpenes, an unsaturated hydrocarbon, can be polymerized to form a serviceable rubber, not as good as native rubber, to be sure, and somewhat costly. The success of the rubber plantations has postponed any great development of this product.

Neoprene (commercially known as 'duprene') is made as follows. Acetylene (from calcium carbide, which in turn is made from lime and coke) is combined with hydrogen chloride, and the product polymerized to a high grade rubber.

$$C_2H_2 \xrightarrow{\text{by polymerization}} C_4H_4 \xrightarrow{+ \text{ HCl}} C_4H_5Cl$$

$$\xrightarrow{\text{polymerization}} \text{neoprene, a polymer of unknown complexity.}$$

This product is expensive, but has superior qualities.

Buna rubber is a polymerization product of butadiene, C_4H_6.

In each of these three polymerizations the unsaturated condition of the simple hydrocarbon unit is the essential feature.

Leather differs so much externally from the fibers just

discussed that it is not usually classed with the textiles; yet the chemical composition of leather is much the same as that of wool. The essential portion of the hide is the dermis or true skin. When this ordinarily dries, a substance like glue or gelatin, the coriin, in among the fibers, stiffens, and this cements the whole together into the hard mass familiar in dried skins. The tanning operation seems to be the combination of the tanning materials with this coriin, thus altering it, so that it is no longer capable of this cementing action. It is interesting that the tanning materials are the same as those used for mordants in dyeing. Tannin, a compound of doubtful composition, derived from gallic acid, the best known of the tanning materials, is obtained from various sources, such as oak and hemlock bark. Metallic compounds are also used, especially those of chromium and aluminum. In the latter case the compound formed is unstable, being decomposed by water, hence such leather is spoiled by wetting. In the case of oil tanning the process is aided by a removal of as much of the coriin as possible.

Plastics have been called the "jewels of organic chemistry." Like synthetic fibers they are the polymerization or condensation products of simple units. They can be molded when soft and harden afterward, and they lend themselves to shaping otherwise. Two have been known for years: celluloid, composed of guncotton and camphor; and bakelite, the condensation product of formaldehyde and phenol. Plastics are now made from many constituents and in various proportions. A list of two hundred has been published. To be commercially successful, the raw materials must be drawn from readily procurable sources. Such are formaldehyde, glycerol, phenol, cresol, cellulose, urea, casein and the unsaturated hydrocarbons, the last now so readily obtained from the paraffins. The plastics promise to take a leading place in respect to the so-called molded articles, and may even become materials of construction.

PERFUMES, FLAVORS, AND THE ESSENTIAL OILS

Although the substances collected from the ends of the earth for the satisfaction of men's desires along these lines are gathered with no reference to their chemical nature, they have some chemical resemblance, and when their chemical structure is understood it is seen that they fall into some one of a very few classes. They are almost exclusively vegetable products; sometimes so nearly a pure simple compound that the artificial duplication is practically identical, sometimes so blended with small amounts of various other constituents that their properties can less easily be imitated. The name essential oils applied to many of them must not be misunderstood. They are not oils, and simply possess some of the external characteristics of oils. For purposes of food (flavors), personal enjoyment (perfumes), and medicinal value these comparatively rare substances play an important part. The industry is to some extent a haphazard one, the products being gathered up here and there as stray producers or collectors provide them. But taken all in all, especially for a few favorites, such as camphor, vanilla, and peppermint, the amount produced in the end is large, and they are important articles of commerce.

The classification of these substances is as follows:

1. Compounds containing oxygen. These are both paraffin and benzene derivatives containing one or more

of the groups; esters, ethers, alcohols, aldehydes, phenols, or ketones. Banana oil is amyl acetate. Vanilla, $C_6H_3(OH).(CHO) (OCH_3)$, includes three of these groups.

2. The second class is included in the group of the terpenes, $C_{10}H_{16}$. This group includes not only the hydrocarbons, but certain oxygen derivatives. The hydrocarbons themselves possess unique properties, and form a group of over a hundred individuals. Clove and lemon oils belong here, as also caraway, rose, orange, peppermint, camphor, and many others.

THE COAL TAR INDUSTRY

The forms of soft coal which are distilled for the making of coke are popularly looked upon as forms of carbon, with considerable impurity. When we consider it from the present standpoint, we must appreciate that soft coal is probably a compound of carbon, very rich in carbon, to be sure, but still a compound. Formulas like $C_{24}H_{18}O_3$ have been suggested, although there are also small amounts of nitrogen compounds present. When this coal is heated, the highly complex molecules decompose before they can volatilize, and the atoms present rearrange themselves in more simple and stable forms. These are the products of coal distillation. The purpose of the distillation of coal is in the coal regions to produce coke, in the cities to produce gas, but the main operation is in each case the same. The soft coal is placed in retorts which are heated from without, and the gas begins to pass off at once. The gas consists mostly of hydrogen and methane, over 80 per cent, and when it is to be used for illuminating purposes without a mantle, needs to be enriched by the addition of other hydrocarbons high in carbon. But there is a growing tendency to use the gas for heating purposes only, therefore to neglect the enriching, and if light is needed, to make use of the Welsbach mantle. Besides the gas, which needs some purification, there is obtained by condensation an aqueous liquid containing ammonia. This is not only the source of the ammonia used as such for ice machines and other purposes, but much of it is applied simply as a convenient nitrogen compound in fertilizers. Ammonia may be oxidized to form nitric acid and nitrates, useful for explosives and fertilizers. This has altered the nitrogen industry to an appreciable extent.

The most interesting product from our standpoint is the tar. About 20 per cent of the weight of the coal appears in this black confused mixture of all the nonaqueous liquids formed in the process. This is distilled to obtain the various products, but about half of it remains behind as a pitch, of such a nature that it must be used simply as a tar for roofing, paving, and similar crude purposes. About 40 per cent of the coal tar can be separated into various hydrocarbons: benzene, toluene, xylene, cumene, naphthalene, and anthracene, which are used in part for the raw material of the benzene products, and in part as solvents and fuel. Of another type are the products of the phenol group, so-called carbolic and cresylic acids, valuable as antiseptics and disinfectants. Pyridine and a number of minor products are obtained in addition.

Though these products are to some extent applied directly in a more or less purified form, their chief interest lies in the fact that they form the raw material for the manufacture of the intermediate and finished products of the drugs and dyes. Specific as it is, the subject is one of great interest, for the deprivations of the first World War showed that the dye industry is a key industry, that upon it depend so many other industries that its stoppage was felt in many lines. It is the opinion of most American chemists that this branch of chemistry in both its theoretical and industrial aspects should be fostered with the greatest care.

The dyes will be discussed directly. The industry is an elaborate one and requires the application of many complex processes. From the coal tar, mentioned above, nine crude products are obtained, mostly hydrocarbons. These are made into almost 300 secondary products, called intermediates, and from these about twelve hundred finished products are prepared, three-quarters of them dyes. However, only about half the dyes are actually manufactured and used, as these seem to be sufficient to fill the needs.

Wood Distillation

The wood distillation industry should be mentioned. When the wood is heated to a high temperature, it is decomposed with the formation of various products. One-fourth of the wood is recovered as charcoal, one-fourth as combustible gases. The distillate is an aqueous mixture yielding wood (methyl) alcohol and acetic acid. Small amounts of creosote also are obtained.

Dyes and Dyeing

A scrutiny of the compounds of organic chemistry will reveal the fact that they are chiefly colorless. The few

colors which are noted in the preparation of organic substances are due either to the inorganic elements, as iodoform, or to impurities, probably of a complex nature.
Color is associated with a very special structure of a
somewhat elaborate molecule. The conditions which
must be fulfilled are, first, that there must be an accumulation of carbon in the molecule and a certain special
linkage between the carbon atoms. These conditions are
found practically only in the benzene ring. It will be apparent that the dyes must then be derived from the benzene
series, C_6H_6, rather than from the paraffin series, C_6H_{14},
for in the latter the carbon is diluted, so to speak, with
twice as much hydrogen as in the benzene compounds.
A second condition for color is that there shall be present
a special combination of atoms, in a group called the
chromophor (color-bearing) group, and to this group the
color is due. In some cases this group is pretty well
defined, in others less so. The possession of color alone is,
however, not enough to constitute a dye. The substance
must also possess such chemical characteristics that it will
form a compound with the fiber which is to be dyed. The
commonest relation of chemistry is that of the acids and
bases, and we find that repeated here. The dyestuffs must
contain an acid group, SO_3H, OH, or CO_2H, or a basic
group, NH_2. Without one of these they will not attach
themselves directly to fiber.

Wool and silk being amphoteric react readily with all
dyes, as acids to basic dyes, and as bases to acid dyes.
Cotton, however, not having such pronounced chemical
properties, does not ordinarily respond and requires a
mordant or go-between. However, there are some conditions under which it is advisable to use a mordant with

wool and silk, and there are some dyes of such chemical activity that even cotton will unite directly with them.

The structure of the molecules of the dyes is very definite and an alteration in the chromophor group may destroy the color. Indigo is easily converted into a compound, indigo white, which, because it lacks the chromophor group, is colorless. Changes in the rest of the molecule in the way of increasing its complexity often enhance the color value of the dye. The simplest dyes are yellow, but if the structure is made more complex, the color intensifies, yellow to orange, then red, purple, and finally blue or green.

$C_6H_5 — N = N — C_6H_4 \ NH_2$ is the formula of a yellow dye.

$HSO_3.C_6H_4 — N = N — C_6H_4 \ N \ (CH_3)_2$ is the formula of an orange dye. They have the same skeletal structure, but the complicating units of the second compound bring about an intensification of the color.

The process of dyeing is more than the simple impregnation of the fiber with the color. It is perhaps a chemical union of the dye with the fiber, resembling in many respects the simple union of base and acid. The fiber is placed in a dilute solution of the dye, containing dye to the extent of 1 to 3 per cent of the weight of the fiber, and the whole is heated with careful mixing for about thirty minutes. The fiber will now have taken all of the dye with which it can unite, and the process is practically done. When cotton is to be dyed a mordant must often be used to bind the dye to the fiber. For basic dyes, the mordant is acid, as tannin and the fatty acids of oils and soaps. For an acid dye the basic mordants used are the hydroxides of aluminum, iron, chromium, tin, antimony, zinc, and lead. Some of these influence the color, and advantage is taken of that fact.

THE ORGANIC EXPLOSIVES

Explosives owe their efficiency to the rapid development of gases, which, owing to their great bulk, must find some vent. Inasmuch as these explosions are accompanied by a heat development, there is added force given to the gases by the expansion due to the heat. Finally the suddenness of the action is the most important factor in the shattering effect of the explosive. In the old black powder the carbon and sulphur present burn at the expense of the oxygen of the potassium nitrate, and three gases, carbon dioxide, carbon monoxide, and nitrogen, are formed. These gases form comparatively slowly, so that the shattering effect is slight. In a high explosive, on the other hand, like nitroglycerine, $C_3H_5(NO_3)_3$, all the atoms entering into the action are exceedingly close to one another, being parts of the same molecule. It is estimated that its disintegration is about a thousand times as rapid as is that of black powder, hence its violent shattering effect.

Explosives are of two main types. High explosives are used purely for shattering, as for blasting and for filling shells in warfare. Decomposition is so rapid, and the force of the shock applied so suddenly, that its force cannot be transmitted to the movement of any body as a whole. Hence it fractures whatever resists its action. The other type is used for throwing projectiles, and must be slower in its action, for otherwise there would be no interval for transmitting motion to the projectile, and the gun would burst. Modern smokeless powder is made from guncotton, but so diluted and grained that its action is slowed down. The projectile will then begin to move with the first gases formed, and later receive its full motion with the full explosive force of the charge.

The four explosives most discussed are: nitroglycerine, nitrocellulose, trinitrotoluene, and trinitrophenol, or picric acid.

Nitroglycerine, glyceryl nitrate, is not a nitro compound, but a nitrate, a salt of glycerol and nitric acid. Like all these compounds, it is made by treating the raw material with a mixture of nitric and sulphuric acids, the sulphuric acid being used to maintain the strength of the nitric acid. Nitroglycerine itself is too explosive, and therefore it is usually applied in the form of dynamite, which is made by absorbing the liquid nitroglycerine in a convenient absorbent, as sawdust or wood pulp, or the fine earthy material called infusorial earth. Different proportions are used, and the products have different names, as dynamite and forcite, but the essential constituent is nitroglycerine. The decomposition of nitroglycerine may be represented by the equation,

$$2C_3H_5(NO_3)_3 = 6CO_2 + 6N + 5H_2O + O$$

The products are gases at the explosion temperature.

Guncotton, cellulose nitrate, like nitroglycerine, is a salt, the base being cellulose, which on account of its alcohol groups acts like glycerol. Guncotton has the appearance of the cotton from which it was made, but is heavier and coarser. It burns quietly though quickly, and when properly prepared is considered safe. When detonated it explodes violently, even when wet. Pure guncotton is used as a shattering explosive, but when modified and diluted it is the basis of the slow-burning smokeless powders.

Trinitrotoluene (T.N.T.) has recently come into great prominence. It shows no vital difference from previously used explosives, but in certain details, as ready fusibility and safety in handling, it has found some favor. It is a true nitro compound, containing the group, NO_2, and is formed thus:

$$C_7H_8 + 3HONO_2 \rightarrow C_7H_5(NO_2)_3 + 3H_2O$$

Picric acid, trinitrophenol, $C_6H_2OH(NO_2)_3$, has come into prominence in modern wars. It is a nitro compound, and although less satisfactory than other explosives, it has found considerable application.

It is frequently said that these substances, when lighted, will burn quietly. But for the purpose for which they are to be used a violent action is desired, and they are therefore "detonated"; that is, a small charge of fulminating mercury, $Hg(ONC)_2$, is exploded in close contact. Under these conditions the disintegration takes place with great suddenness and violence. Fulminating mercury decomposes explosively upon being struck or upon application of heat, and, either by the violence of the shock or the nature of the vibration, transmits its decomposing action to the main charge, which then decomposes with equal violence.

PROCESSES OF THE ORGANIC INDUSTRIES

A summation of outstanding principles which have marked the great advance in organic chemistry will be in order. These principles were initiated in the laboratory and have thence been extended to the industries. The industries have done much, both in research and applications, to extend the scope of organic chemistry.

Hydrolysis (resolution by means of water) is the splitting of complexes like starch or the proteins into their constructive units by the addition of the elements of water. This is an old story. The reverse, building up such complexes, has been successful in the case of simple compounds, even in the case of such large molecules as the fats. More elaborate syntheses have not progressed far.

Pyrolysis (resolution by means of heat) is a general term which includes the breaking down of complex molecules by the action of heat. Phases of this should be differentiated.

(a) Destructive distillation, especially of soft coal and wood.

(b) Cracking of petroleum.

(c) The splitting off of two hydrogen atoms from paraffin hydrocarbons to form unsaturated hydrocarbons, which owing to their reactivity may be acted on further as follows:

$$CH_3 - CH_3 \rightarrow CH_2 = CH_2 + H_2$$

Polymerization. The building up of complexes by the union of a number of similar active groups, usually under the influence of a catalyst. Illustrations of this are:

(a) The forms of artificial rubber $nC_5H_8 \rightarrow (C_5H_8)_n$.

(b) Paraffin complexes leading to high quality lubricating oils.

(c) Building up liquid fuels from natural gas.

(d) Synthetic fibers and plastics.

The knowledge of the possibilities of polymerization is only in its beginning.

Condensation. This is again a building up of complexes from simples. It differs from polymerization in that the units are diverse, and that there are outside chemical affinities which are instrumental in establishing the union, as, for example, oxygen in one unit and hydrogen in the other.

(a) The great illustration of this is the formation of the many different plastics which are known and successfully applied.

(b) The triphenyl methane dyes are formed in most cases by condensation of simpler molecules.

Hydrogenation. The addition of hydrogen to such compounds as are capable of accepting it.

(a) The chief illustration is the hydrogenation of unsaturated liquid fats to form solid fats.

(b) The Bergius process by which soft coal, a compound of carbon low in hydrogen, is converted into a liquid hydrocarbon with a normal amount of hydrogen. This is one of the more promising methods of supplying gasoline substitutes.

(c) It has been found possible to restore to usefulness petroleum refining by-products formed by pyrolytic decomposition.

(d) It is used to reduce sugars to polyalcohols, which then can be used for purposes akin to those of glycerol.

(e) It is used to convert fatty acids into alcohols, which then are convertible into the modern soaps.

(f) It may even be used for breaking down higher hydrocarbons into lower molecules by rupturing the carbon chain. $C_{12}H_{26} + H_2 \longrightarrow 2C_6H_{14}$.

Synthesis. This is best illustrated by recalling the formation of amyl acetate.

$$(C_5H_{11})Cl + Na(CO_2CH_3) \rightarrow NaCl + (C_5H_{11}).CO_2CH_3$$

amyl chloride   sodium acetate   amyl acetate

This is the standard method for the upbuilding of larger molecules. Its application is fundamental, common in the laboratory and is increasing in the industries. This and other methods of synthesis and formation of compounds have led to the commercial preparation of so many compounds that in any short discussion it is impossible to do them justice. The list includes solvents (including even ethyl alcohol and glycerol), medicinals, insecticides, textiles, dyes, and fine chemicals.

Catalysts. Even if their action is little understood, the effects accomplished with them are very real. There are hundreds available, mainly positive catalysts, but negative catalysts, inhibitors, are now frequently applied.

SUMMARY

A generation ago a summary of a chapter on organic chemical interests would have gone something like this. Organic interests fall into two groups: (1) Those of the paraffin series take natural products and modify them or simplify them in various ways. (2) The benzene industries begin with the fundamental hydrocarbons, and substitution and synthetic operations build them up into many useful complexes. This type is conspicuously lacking in the case of the paraffin hydrocarbons.

Today a résumé of such a chapter reveals a very different situation. New developments among the benzenes are not lacking, especially among the medicinals. However, the great number of modern industrial developments of today concern derivatives of the paraffin series. They include extensions of the old type mentioned above, but more conspicuously new compounds obtained by operations of a synthetic nature, comparable with those of the long established benzene industries. The raw material is often an original hydrocarbon converted into a derivative by methods already mentioned (page 277). To these methods a new type of attack has been added, namely, nitration, the introduction of the nitro group — NO_2 by direct action of nitric acid, thus duplicating the formation of nitro-benzene, the fundamental form of attack in the benzene series.

The list of such new compounds now available is a long one, and it is difficult for the layman to appreciate the services they can render. For example, they count as solvents for lacquers, for extractions, for preparing textiles and smokeless powder. They serve as the raw materials for synthetic compounds of many types. Two new departures are "penetrants," which greatly increase the wetting and penetrating power of water, and the nitro compounds, as CH_3NO_2, $C_2H_5NO_2$, $C_3H_7NO_2$, claimed to be of promise in "new worlds of chemical exploration."

It will be recalled that the proteins, one form of the essential nutrients, are complexes made up of combinations of approximately twenty comparatively simple amino acids. These amino acids have commanded a great interest in the study of nutrition. They have gradually become available in pure form, and quite recently practically the entire list has been placed upon the market. Their first value will be in studies of nutrition. They are also under investigation for a possible medicinal value and they may conceivably lead to many new developments.

CHAPTER XXIV

ANALYTICAL CHEMISTRY

A PRACTICAL study of chemistry very promptly develops a need for methods of testing and analyzing the substances with which we deal. Some of the simpler tests are used with great frequency, as the litmus test for acid and alkali, the silver nitrate test for hydrochloric acid and chlorides, and the barium chloride test for the sulphate group. In any given case we recognize a substance by manipulating it so that some very characteristic property will become apparent, most frequently one that is recognized by the appearance, less frequently by the odor, and still less often by the application of one of the other senses. The theory and technique of these specific tests, with the study of separation and distinguishing the several members of a mixture, is the study of "Qualitative Analysis." When the operations are so modified that, in addition to the nature of the substances present, their quantities and the percentage composition of the whole are established, the study is "Quantitative Analysis."

QUALITATIVE ANALYSIS

It will not be profitable to attempt to give the whole scheme of qualitative analysis, but enough may be shown to illustrate the logical orderliness of the procedure.

Inorganic substances which we usually meet with are of comparatively few types. They may be in the form of elements, or they may be compounds. The compounds may be compounds with hydrogen or oxygen, or they may be in the form of acids, bases, or salts. Recognition is most readily accomplished by identifying first the metal present, and then the nonmetal or the nonmetallic group. A number of elements, as chlorine, bromine, iodine, carbon, and sulphur have such striking properties that they are easily identified as elements. But the metals are so much alike in their external properties that it is more convenient to convert them into salts, and to make our tests upon these. Qualitative analysis deals chiefly with the elements in the form of soluble compounds, and its tests are then not so much for the elements themselves as for the positive metal ions, on the one hand, and for the negative nonmetal ions on the other.

The common test for silver, for example, is not a test for silver as metal, but for silver in the form of an ion. If we wish to find what metals are present in a silver coin, we first dissolve the coin in nitric acid, when the metals present will be converted into soluble nitrates. To the solution of these products in water we add a little hydrochloric acid. The negative chlorine ions of the latter unite with the positive silver ions present, forming a characteristic insoluble silver chloride. From its appearance and other tests applied, we are certain that this is silver chloride, and therefore know that there was silver in the original coin. Other metals, as copper, will not respond to this test. If we now remove all the silver ions by the means just discussed, and add ammonia to the rest, a striking blue color is developed. This is due to the presence of copper ions, and we know that the coin contained copper as well as silver. It is customary to speak of silver and copper and other metals as being present in a solution.

This is inaccurate and allowable only by convention. In the solutions we have the salts and consequently the ions of silver and copper and other metals, and our tests are usually for these ions.

It may be assumed that each ion has its own characteristic tests. Those for silver and copper have been mentioned. Just as the chlorine ion is a test for the silver ion, so the silver ion is a test for the chlorine ion. Most tests are thus used in two ways. Barium ions and sulphate ions form a much used pair of mutually reacting ions. That is, barium ions form with sulphate ions a characteristic precipitate which serves for the identification of both. The identification of a pure substance is a very easy matter, and may be accomplished in a few minutes. When, however, several substances are mixed, the problem becomes complex and the various tests must be reduced to a system. This system is to be described briefly.

The metals usually met with, either as metals or in their compounds, number about twenty. They will be arranged in the groups into which they fall according to the analytical scheme. This conforms roughly to the electrochemical list, reversed, and is based upon the nature of the compounds which these metals form with the various reagents. In the classification and discussion many details will be omitted.

Group   I   Silver, and mercurous mercury.
Group   II   Copper, lead, mercuric mercury, cadmium, bismuth, tin, antimony and arsenic.
Group   III Iron, aluminum, and chromium.
Group   IV   Zinc, cobalt, nickel, and manganese.
Group   V   Calcium, strontium, barium, and magnesium.
Group   VI   Sodium, potassium, lithium, and ammonium.

If the substances which are engaging our attention are

not in solution in water, they are converted into soluble compounds by proper treatment. In a few cases this is not possible and the tests are carried out along other lines. Ordinarily, however, the scheme here given applies completely.

Let us assume a mixture containing all these metals in solution in water, in the form of salts. If to this complex mixture we add hydrochloric acid, HCl, the chlorine ions will form insoluble chlorides with a limited number of the metals. These chlorides will settle out and may be filtered off. The solid collected on the filter paper will consist of the chlorides of silver and mercurous mercury, while in the clear liquid running through will be included all the other metals of the list. We therefore say that silver and mercurous mercury are the metals of group I, and that hydrochloric acid is the group reagent.

To the clear solution containing all the other metals, as well as some of the hydrochloric acid added as above, a sufficient amount of gaseous hydrogen sulphide, H_2S, is added. This will form insoluble precipitates with the metals designated as group II, and the precipitates may be collected on a filter paper. All the remaining metals will be found in the clear solution running through. Hydrogen sulphide therefore is the group reagent for the metals of group II.

Before proceeding further, any hydrogen sulphide remaining in the solution must be removed by boiling, and then the reagent for group III may be added. This is ammonia, or ammonium hydroxide, NH_4OH, which forms precipitates of insoluble hydroxides of the three metals. As before these may be collected on a filter, and the clear filtrate will contain the remaining metals.

The group reagent for the next group is ammonium sulphide $(NH_4)_2S$. When the precipitate thus formed is removed, the solution is ready for the group reagent of group V, namely, ammonium carbonate. The procedure is here the same as in every previous case.

There is no convenient substance which forms insoluble compounds with the metals of group VI. From any ammonium compound the ammonia with its characteristic odor is easily obtained, but for the others the identification is not so easy.

The scheme of analysis continues in that now it is necessary to establish tests to identify one metal of a group in distinction from the others of the same group. This is not difficult, provided there is only the one metal present, for each metal has one or more reactions so characteristic that it may be identified with certainty. When two or more metals of the same group are mixed, the problem is greatly complicated and various methods must be applied for separating them before each may be identified. The details of these operations are very important, but for our purpose they may be omitted entirely.

The metals of the sodium group do not form characteristic precipitates, and their identification in mixtures is surprisingly difficult. The flame color and the spectroscope are helpful, for these metals give striking colors to the Bunsen flame.

The nonmetallic radicals, or ions, are grouped after the same manner as are the metals. There are fewer such ions, and they are more promptly recognized, so that they present fewer difficulties than do the metals. The classification of the most important negative ions is as follows:

SULPHURIC ACID TANKS AT A SMOKELESS POWDER PLANT

(See page 301.)

GUNCOTTON ON THE WAY TO THE MIXER WHERE MANUFACTURE OF SMOKELESS POWDER IS COMPLETED

(See page 301.)

Group I Chlorine, bromine, and iodine.
Group reagent, silver nitrate in presence of nitric acid.
Group II Sulphate SO_4, sulphite SO_3, carbonate CO_3, borate B_4O_7, phosphate PO_4.
Group reagent, barium chloride in neutral solution.
Group III Nitrate NO_3, nitrite NO_2, chlorate ClO_3.
There is no group reagent.

As with the metals, after the group in which a negative ion belongs has been established, special tests are required to determine the particular members of the group. Most of them show such striking reactions that the matter is comparatively simple. For example, in group I, the free halogens may be liberated and easily recognized.

Having established the positive and negative ions which may be present, we may assume that our problem has been solved. These ions may be put together according to certain probabilities, but there is often uncertainty as to what combinations were originally present in a mixture, and the question is best left unanswered.

This résumé of the plan of qualitative analysis is exceedingly brief and superficial. A little practical experience would soon show how the scheme works out. There are many special problems and complications and some abbreviations. Blow-pipe analysis, used much less now than formerly, is often a convenient supplement to the above methods.

The microscope promises many improvements on the methods outlined, and some extension of its scope. As we ordinarily obtain a precipitate, we can judge of it only by its gross features, color, and general appearance, as crystalline or gelatinous. Under the microscope small crystals ordinarily indistinguishable from others show their characteristic crystalline form. The shape, size, and some optical properties of the crystals are easily determined. The reliability of the conclusions, the observation of added characteristics and the small amounts needed, all unite in making the microscope useful in this particular field of chemistry.

QUANTITATIVE ANALYSIS

Quantitative analysis is the study of the theory and technique for the determination of the amounts of the different constituents of any substance. The processes must be conducted with great care and are very time-consuming. For special purposes there are many excellent shortened methods, but, on the whole, the work requires time and deliberation. There are two sets of methods used, those in which the substances involved are weighed, called gravimetric analysis, and those in which the volumes of the solutions of substances used are measured, called volumetric analysis. The latter methods are usually much more rapid, and in some cases are very accurate. But their application is often impossible. To give some impression of the scope of each, concrete illustrations will be adduced.

Let the problem be to determine the proportion of silver present in the metal used in a silver coin. A bit of the metal is weighed. The amounts used in gravimetric analysis are very small, as care and accuracy are thereby greatly aided. Two- or three-tenths of a gram would be ample for the cases in hand. The sample is then dissolved in nitric acid, that is, the silver and any other metals present are converted into the corresponding nitrates. Every precaution is used throughout to prevent loss. When the metal is all dissolved the solution is diluted with water, and hydrochloric acid is added. The silver forms an insoluble precipitate with the chlorine, which, after being stirred and warmed, collects in an easily handled mass. There is now prepared a filter of finely divided asbestos, like a layer of paper, over the perforated bottom of a crucible. This is weighed after careful preparation and drying. When the solution containing the silver chloride is poured out upon this filter, all soluble matter runs through with the water, and the silver chloride is left in the crucible. This is carefully washed, dried, and weighed. From the weight of silver chloride the amount of the silver can be readily calculated by the proportion,

$$\frac{\text{Known weight of silver chloride}}{\text{Wanted weight of silver}} = \frac{\text{AgCl}}{\text{Ag}} = \frac{\text{Mol. Wt. of AgCl}}{\text{Atom. Wt. of Ag}} = \frac{143.4}{107.9}$$

The comparison of the amount of silver present to the whole metal may now be made.

This operation is repeated in its main features for most gravimetric determinations. The sample under investigation must be weighed and brought into solution. To this solution a reagent is added which forms a new compound with the part under discussion, separable and weighable with accuracy. The methods by which these conditions are fulfilled form the technique of analytical chemistry.

Volumetric analysis applies frequently to the determination of acids and alkalis, although its extension to other substances is considerable. One or two characteristic processes or methods will be explained. The methods are based upon the use of solutions of substances of known concentration, and the work is simplified if these are made up of a certain normality, for example, tenth normal. If all solutions used were tenth normal, then the volumes applied would always bear a simple relation to each other. As the preparation of solutions of an exact concentration is a very considerable trouble, it is more profitable to make them of approximately the desired concentration, then to determine the error and apply the correction arithmetically.

Let us take for an example the determination of the amount of acid—we will call it acetic acid—in vinegar. We will measure out with great accuracy, by the use of a pipette, 10 c.c. of the sample. This is placed in a beaker with a convenient amount of water. There is now added an indicator, like litmus—though there are other better ones—which will tell when all the acid has been neutralized by the addition of the base. From a graduated burette, set at 0, there is now allowed to run into the vinegar, with constant mixing, a solution of sodium hydroxide of known strength, until the indicator tells us that the acid is just neutralized. If we now take the reading on the burette, it will tell us how much of the sodium hydroxide was required, and from this a simple calculation will tell us the amount of acid in the vinegar.

This method applies especially to the balancing of acid and basic solutions, but is of extensive application in other ways. A number of typical illustrations of other methods could be given, but they are of very technical nature, and follow out the same ideas as that already explained. These methods usually depend upon the ready determination of the end point, that is, the moment when just enough of the second solution has been added to react exactly with the first solution. Indicators, like litmus, phenolphthalein and others, show by the change of color that the acid and base just neutralize each other. Iodine is a very common reagent in these operations, as it combines a ready activity with a striking color effect when starch is present. That is, if iodine solution of a known concentration is added to certain solutions, a little boiled starch being present, these substances will combine with the iodine until they are completely used up. One drop of iodine solution in excess will then develop a strong blue color with the starch. Potassium permanganate solution is another useful reagent. It has the double virtue of

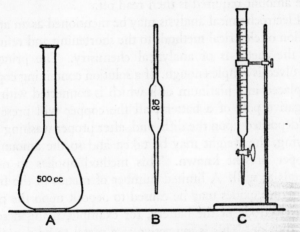

THE MOST COMMONLY USED VOLUMETRIC APPARATUS
A., the measuring or graduated flask; B, the pipette; C, the burette.

supplying oxygen, and of losing its striking color as long as it is losing this oxygen. The moment the substance being treated fails to assimilate more oxygen, that moment the color of the permanganate remains and the result is apparent. There are other color changes which are useful for these determinations. By proper manipulation, a method may be varied and so lend itself to a number of useful applications.

The volumes, which are the essential features of this type of analysis, are determined mostly by three pieces of measuring apparatus, the pipette, the burette, and the measuring flask. The graduations must be made with great care. The pipette, in sizes from 1 to 100 c.c., and the measuring flask, in sizes from 25 to 2,000 c.c., can be used only for the stated amounts. The burette, on the other hand, is used to deliver any required amount, and the amount required is then read off.

Electrochemical analysis may be mentioned as an application of electrical methods to the shortening and refining of the methods of analytical chemistry. The principle involved is simple enough. If a solution containing copper is placed in a platinum dish which is connected with the negative pole of a battery, all the copper will presently be deposited upon the dish, and, after proper washing and drying, the weight may be taken and so the amount of copper present known. This method applies to other metals as well. A limited number of metals in the form of higher oxides may be caused to deposit upon the positive electrode of the battery, for example, manganese as the dioxide. This is too active as a metal to be deposited upon the negative pole as in the case of copper.

In Conclusion

The above outline of analytical chemistry represents the classic procedures in the two branches. There are tendencies to shorten and to refine them by various devices. Of these brief mention may be made. Specific tests for some of the metals have been found, thus obviating the following out of the regular scheme of analysis. Volumetric methods of quantitative analysis are so rapid and convenient that there is a constant tendency to substitute them for the slower gravimetric methods. Colorimetric methods consist in comparing the intensity of color produced by given reagents with those obtained by prepared standards. Various somewhat obscure physical methods are used in special investigations. For the chemist the results obtained are more interesting than these methods, which properly belong to the domain of physics.

Microanalysis is a method for obtaining results with very small amounts. Among its applications are analyses of the minute amounts of lead and arsenic which might be residual in the fruit of sprayed orchards.

Investigations of the vitamins have required the use of the nonchemical methods of biological analysis with living animals. The desired results have not yet been attained by strictly chemical methods.

CHAPTER XXV

PHYSICAL CHEMISTRY

PHYSICAL chemistry concerns itself with the determination of the physical constants of substances and the use of physical methods for the investigation of chemical relations. The subject illustrates Lord Kelvin's dictum to the effect that real knowledge can begin only after measurements have been attained. In this connection we often hear the expression, "the borderland between chemistry and physics." The results obtained from these studies have often led to generalizations from which the theories underlying the subject of chemistry have been developed, and even to the explanation of the causes underlying chemical phenomena. The dependence of numerous chemical conclusions upon such data will be pointed out in the sequel. Even when physicochemical measurements have not led to important generalizations, they have served many useful purposes in less important respects. The knowledge of specific gravity of solutions has not been reduced to important laws or theoretical conceptions, but in the way of analysis and practical convenience it is of the greatest service. On the other hand, certain measurements connected with solutions have led to the theory of ionization, which has helped to solve so many problems of chemistry.

In an ordinary study of descriptive, or general chemistry, we assume certain generalizations and theories as established. Such are the gas laws, and the molecular and atomic theories. By means of these we can comprehend the phenomena of chemistry as parts of a whole and we can summarize our experience of the past and prepare for future developments. It is the work of physical chemistry to acquire the necessary data by careful measurements, and from them to derive the laws and theories by which we weave the whole together. Even a brief consideration of general chemistry is incomplete without some physical chemistry, and of the twenty-one chapters here devoted to the subject of general chemistry, five are taken up mainly with physical chemistry. Physical chemistry, however, is too extensive a subject to be thus incidentally included. The following brief discussion can barely do more than indicate the outstanding lines of interest and show how intimately and usefully they are associated with our comprehension of chemistry.

The subject is outlined below under nine major topics. Wherever the subtopics have been treated fully enough in the foregoing text, you are referred to that place. Otherwise, there is appended in each case a brief comment in the treatment that follows.

TOPIC I, THE THREE STATES OF MATTER
- A. The solid, liquid and gaseous states
- B. Latent heat
- C. Melting point and boiling point
- D. Vapor pressure
- E. The "super" state
- F. The gas laws

TOPIC II, SOLUTIONS
- A. Solubility
- B. Ionization
- C. Osmotic pressure
- D. Electrochemistry

TOPIC I, THE THREE STATES OF MATTER

A. *The solid, liquid and gaseous states.* The physical state, superficially considered, is but an external feature in connection with elements and compounds. The non-metals all form acids, regardless of whether they are solids like sulphur or gases like nitrogen. When, however, definite comparisons can be established, the subject of physical state at once becomes interesting and instructive. Chlorine, bromine, and iodine, as will perhaps be recalled, are three elements of great similarity. They are of striking physical properties, all very active chemically, and they form salts of remarkable similarity. The differences which they exhibit are differences in degree, and the physical state is a very apparent index of this difference. Chlorine is a gas, bromine a liquid, and iodine a solid. The atomic weights, 35.5, 80, and 127, respectively, show an arithmetic relation bearing out the first suggestion of the solid, liquid, and gaseous states. The chemical properties also follow in order, as do the physical properties. Here there is a close relationship between the variation in the physical state and the variations in other properties, both physical and chemical.

In the series of organic compounds, as the hydrocarbons, alcohols, and acids, changes in the physical state follow very closely upon the increasing complexity of the molecule. CH_4 is a gas, C_6H_{14} is a liquid, and $C_{20}H_{42}$ is a solid. The simplest alcohols, methyl and ethyl, CH_3OH and C_2H_5OH, are liquids, but those containing a large number of carbon and hydrogen atoms, as $C_{18}H_{35}OH$, are solids. The same is in a general way true of the acids and all other organic compounds. These facts are of profound significance in the field of biochemistry. Tissue must be solid on the whole, and yet must be built up of the elements carbon, hydrogen, oxygen, and nitrogen. The difference in the physical state and other physical properties connected with the structure of the molecule results in insoluble solid compounds when the molecule is complex, and soluble solid, liquid, or even gaseous compounds when the molecules made up of the same kinds of atoms are simple, each state serving the special needs of the animal organism.

B. *Latent heat. See* Chapter IV.

C. *Melting point and boiling point.* The melting point of solids and the boiling point of liquids are but phases of the subject of physical state. A solid melts easily, or passes to a gas easily, other things being equal, when it has a simple molecule. The boiling point of each alcohol of a series is higher than that of the one before with some semblance of regularity. The boiling point of any substance, moreover, is associated with its chemical structure. The influence of a hydroxyl group (— OH) for example, is to raise the boiling point about 100° C. Propyl alcohol, C_3H_7OH, a monohydroxy derivative, boils at 97° C. The dihydroxy derivative, propylene glycol, $C_3H_6(OH)_2$ boils at 188° C., while glycerol, the trihydroxy derivative, $C_3H_5(OH)_3$, boils at 290° C.

The influence of any substance upon the boiling point or freezing point of another in which it is dissolved is so regular that it has been of very great use in determining the composition of chemical substances. In a rough way these facts are commonly appreciated. In candy making, the determination of the boiling point of the sirup indicates the composition of the sugar solution. It is well known that the presence of alcohol or some other substance lowers the freezing point of water to such an extent that it may be kept from freezing in automobile radiators. This influence of different solutes on the solvent is regular, determined, however, not by the number of grams of the substance dissolved, but by the number of the molecules. One gram of ordinary alcohol, molecular weight 46, contains over seven times as many molecules as one gram of cane sugar, molecular weight 342. To obtain equal effects for the two substances they must be introduced in the proportions of 46 parts of the alcohol, or 342 parts of the sugar in equal amounts of water; these proportions contain equal numbers of molecules. The use of ordinary alcohol for this purpose is so common that it may be interesting to apply the formula which expresses this general relation. The formula, modified for the sake of compactness, is:

$$\text{Depression of freezing point in degrees, F.} = \frac{3400 \times \text{alcohol per cent}}{46 \times \text{water per cent}}$$

The number 3400 is a so-called constant, correct only for water. For other liquids it has another value. The molecular weight of the alcohol is 46. For 5, 10, 20, and 30 per cent alcohol we may very readily compute the lowering of the freezing point, which will be found to be 4°, 8°, 14°, and 32° F., respectively. The same method of calculation would apply to any other usable substance.

A simple reversal of the formula will permit us to determine molecular weights from the experimental determination of the freezing point depression. This determination is a very common one. A small amount of the substance under discussion is weighed and added to a known weight of the solvent. For this purpose water only is exceptionally adapted. The mixture is cooled carefully, being stirred all the while, and a thermometer of very special construction, reading to 1/100th of a degree, is used to measure the lowering of the freezing point. The apparatus and operation for boiling point elevation are very similar. The constant used varies for different solvents and is also different in each case for the boiling point and freezing point determination.

When the methods just outlined were applied to acids, bases, and salts dissolved in water, the results obtained did not conform to the theoretical values. The effect was always greater than the calculation called for. In the end, these deviations have led to the development and adoption of the theory of ionization, discussed in a previous chapter. According to our conception of ionization, a salt like sodium chloride, dissolved in water, yields two ions, Na^+ and Cl^-. The influence upon the boiling point and freezing point is determined, not by the one unit, or molecule, of sodium chloride supposedly present, but by the two units, the ions formed when the salt dissolves in water. A salt like barium chloride, $BaCl_2$, has an even greater effect, inasmuch as it is dissociated into three ions, Ba^{++} and $2Cl^-$. The conclusions thus established are confirmed by the study of the conductivity of solutions, a branch of electrochemistry.

D. *Vapor pressure.* The melting points of solids, and the boiling point of liquids, as has already been implied, are associated to a considerable extent with their chemical composition. The influence of substances in solution has also been discussed. Further considerations are still before us. When a liquid is heated, and begins to boil, the gas in expanding into vapor must overcome the pressure of the atmosphere. And as this pressure varies the boiling point varies. On a mountain 10,000 feet high the boiling point of water is only about 90° C., 194° F., while under pressure in a steam boiler the boiling point may be as high as 180° C., or 356° F. If the temperature of a liquid is raised indefinitely, there is reached a temperature at which the liquid is converted to a gas regardless of the pressure. This is called the critical temperature of the liquid. Before this fact was appreciated, it was found impossible to convert certain gases to liquids, because pressure alone was applied, and above its critical temperature a substance cannot exist as a liquid. The name "permanent gases" formerly applied to oxygen, nitrogen, and other gases no longer has any meaning. These gases are now liquefied very readily by the combined action of high pressure and low temperature.

The boiling point of a liquid is the temperature at which its vapor pressure overcomes the atmospheric pressure. Vapor pressure is the tendency to pass into the gaseous form. A knowledge of the vapor pressure of water is needed in making gas measurements when these gases are in contact with water, for part of the space supposedly filled by the gas is taken up by water vapor. The vapor pressure of a liquid is altered by the presence of a substance in solution, the extent of the alteration being determined by the proportion of molecules present. From such studies the molecular weight may be found and so the chemical composition of a substance determined. The separation of the constituents of a mixture by means of their different vapor pressures is a very frequent practice in organic chemistry.

E. *The "super" state.* In the conversion of matter from one state into another, the change is often delayed after more than sufficient heat or cold has been applied. Vapors partially filling the space in which they are confined are common. When cooled they are not always condensed. They need nuclei to condense about, and since dust and smoke form such nuclei, fogs are prevalent over cities in moist regions. The rapid formation of clouds and gathering of rainstorms may be connected with this condition of supersaturation, which, due to its sudden cessation, causes great accumulations of liquid water. The reverse condition, overheating of a liquid without its boiling, is a source of constant annoyance to the chemist. The condition applies most often to concentrated solutions. When these overheated solutions do finally give off vapor, they do it with such violence that they may throw the liquid from its container. In a smaller way this sudden evolution of the gas causes the "bumping," which is at times extremely annoying. Liquids may be supercooled, and often such a supercooled liquid may be caused to solidify with great suddenness. Exact measurements show supercooling to be very common. An interesting application of this idea is the explanation of the peculiar properties of glass. Glass is such a complicated substance that its constituents do not crystallize out as it cools. This state of supercooling is never ended by a real solidification, namely, crystallization. The supercooled liquid has no definite solidifying or melting point. It softens gradually on warming, and hardens gradually on cooling. The transparency of the liquid condition is maintained throughout. Thus two of the valuable characteristics of glass are due to the supercooled condition. The only change of state which shows no delayed action is the conversion of a solid into a liquid. Supersaturation is a phase of this delayed action.

F. *The gas laws. See* Chapter XII.

Topic II, Solutions

A. *Solubility.* The knowledge of the solubility of inorganic compounds in water is still a matter based mainly on experiment. There are a few generalizations such as the solubility of the compounds of the sodium group of metals, and a regularity in the comparative insolubility of the hydroxides and sulphates of the metals of the calcium group. The solubility and insolubility of the compounds of all the metals is the basis of the scheme of qualitative analysis. In quantitative analysis the exact determination of solubility and "solubility product" are fundamental. As we know more of the structure of atoms and molecules, there will probably be developed some understanding of the underlying reasons.

In organic chemistry the case is simpler. The presence of the hydroxyl group, — OH, and of the amino group, — NH_2, makes for solubility in water. The influence of these groups disappears when they are outweighed by the organic residue. Solubility of organic compounds has become a major factor in industrial organic chemistry.

B. *Ionization. See* Chapter XIII. A modern modification of the theory of ionization involves also the structure of crystals. The ionic condition applies to the crystalline form of ionogens as well as to their aqueous solutions. Crystals of sodium chloride, for example, are made up, not of molecules, but of ions of sodium and chlorine, mutually surrounding one another. When in solution, the complete ionization fails, because some agglomeration of ions takes place, due to the electric charges. This agglomeration is one, however, of ions, not of molecules. This modification does not nullify the use of the older theory of ionization as applied to ordinary reactions.

In connection with the ionization of acids and bases, a sharp distinction must be made between the actual amount of those substances present, and the degree of their ionization. Their effectiveness is determined by the latter value, and therefore it is convenient to consider it in many relations. To this end the hydrogen ion concentration is measured and indicated by the sign pH. The mathematical meaning of the symbol pH is obscured by logarithmic relations. Practically it is less complicated. pH 14 indicates the normal concentration of a base, OH^- ions. pH 0 indicates a normal acid concentration, H^+ ions. pH 7 therefore represents a neutral condition.

C. *Osmotic pressure.* A substance in solution tends to diffuse through the entire mass. This tendency is called the osmotic pressure, and has a definite resemblance to the tendency of gases to diffuse, obeying the same mathematical laws. Osmotic pressure is an important feature physiologically, in the absorption of the products of digestion.

D. *Electrochemistry.* The simplest elements of this subject have been outlined (*see* Chap. XVIII). The whole is very extensive, and in ways both theoretical and practical would carry us very far. This branch of physical chemistry has become so important that it has grown to be a subject of itself, and by the side of other branches commands its own textbooks and journals.

Topic III, Other Physical Properties

A. *Specific gravity.* The specific gravity of pure substances is of value as a means of identification. This applies particularly to minerals. It is connected to some extent with chemical nature. Metals of the sodium and calcium group are light, while the rest, excepting aluminum, are distinctly heavier. Metals with high atomic weights have high specific gravities, a fact true also of their compounds. There are exceptions to this statement, but as a rough generalization it is correct. Aside from any relation to the nature of elements and compounds, the specific gravity of solutions is used with great frequency for determining the proportions of the constituents. In books containing the physical constants of chemical substances, tables covering this matter fill many pages.

B. *Crystalline form.* Crystals are studied by mathematical and optical measurement, but that which gives them their crystalline form must be the chemical composition of the substance. For this reason chemically similar substances often crystallize in similar crystal forms. The crystals of chlorides, bromides, and iodides of sodium and potassium are all very much alike, for these salts are chemically similar. The alums form an interesting group of substances. Their formula may be written thus: $M^{I}M^{III}(SO_4)_2, 12H_2O$. They are double sulphates, containing always a metal of the sodium group and one of the aluminum group, crystallizing with twelve molecules of water. For all of them the crystalline form is so similar that a crystal of one placed in a solution of the other continues to grow, although one may contain the metals potassium and chromium, and the other ammonium and aluminum. This relationship is called isomorphism and was of some value for establishing the relationship of elements before certain better methods were established. In the case of these alums, for example, the metals which go to form them must belong to the M^{I}, the sodium group, or to the M^{III}, the aluminum group. The internal structure of crystals has been submitted to investigation by the so-called X-ray analysis. Such studies, besides opening up new lines of thought, often serve to establish more firmly assumptions previously held.

TOPIC IV, REACTIONS

A. *Speed of reactions.* The speed and completeness of chemical reactions are determined to a considerable extent by certain physical conditions, temperature, concentration, solution, and the presence of a catalyst. It is a very common experience that an elevation of temperature greatly accelerates the speed of reaction. In fact, some reactions seem to stand still, and for all practical purposes do stand still, at ordinary temperatures. When heat is applied, these reactions proceed rapidly. It is a convenient laboratory rule that an elevation of 10° C., 18° F., doubles the speed of reactions. It is natural to attribute this increased velocity to an increase in molecular and atomic motion, but it is evident that the rate of increase of the molecular motion is far exceeded by the increase of chemical activity.

B. *Equilibrium. See* Chapter XI.

C. *Concentration.* If an active metal is contained in a test tube with some water, and a little sulphuric acid is added, we may look for a reaction between the two. If no action takes place, the natural impulse would be to add more of the active acid. We here illustrate in a simple way the law of mass action, that the speed of the reaction is proportional to the reacting masses. In this illustration the concentration of the acid alone counts, as the extent of the metal surface exposed does not vary. If the concentration of both participants in the reaction can be varied, the speed of the reaction, other conditions remaining constant, will be represented by the product of the metal and acid concentrations, a $\times$ b (the law of mass action).

D. *Catalysts.* There is scarcely a more useful chapter of chemistry than that treating the catalysts, even though in so many respects the nature of their action still remains unknown. Although our first thought may concern the inorganic catalysts of the type of the oxides of nitrogen and of platinum, illustrated in the two great processes for the manufacture of sulphuric acid, the influence of catalytic action covers a much greater field. The accelerators of the rubber industry, which hasten the process of vulcanization, the metallic catalysts so important in hydrogenations, as of cottonseed oil, and the catalysts used in polymerizations illustrate their increasing use. In one field alone, that of petroleum, hundreds of catalysts have been applied. On the other hand, negative catalysts and inhibitors show the opposite effect, so that hydrochloric acid can be extensively used for disintegrating the limestones holding back the natural petroleum deposits, yet it does not attack the metal pipes used in the operation. Antioxidants, whose action is indicated by the name, fall into this class.

Catalysts of the biochemical type are in their way quite as important as those mentioned. These are the substances of such physiological importance that they occupy a prominent place in the research of today, such as the enzymes, vitamins and hormones. The catalytic action of the first of these seems clearly established; the action of the others can hardly be considered less catalytic.

The subject of catalysis is still to a great extent in the empirical stage. Many catalysts are known and used to great advantage, but knowledge of the underlying principles involved is not so far advanced. It seems likely that the progress in this field will now be rapid.

Topic V, Optical Properties

A. *The spectroscope*. The spectroscope is a physical instrument which lends itself to the solution of chemical problems in a unique manner. Reference has already been made to the fact that potassium and sodium compounds color the Bunsen flame violet and yellow, respectively. Lithium colors the flame red, and strontium and barium produce such striking effects that they are used for making red and green fire. The prism of the spectroscope refracts the different kinds of light emanating from any source at different angles, and thus disperses it, that is, spreads out the different constituents upon a screen, so that they may be examined in detail. Ordinary white light is a complex made up of the colors of the rainbow, usually said to be violet, indigo, blue, green, yellow, orange, and red; and when white light is examined in the spectroscope, all these colors are seen ranged in their proper order. The light from sodium, however, is pure yellow, and as seen in the instrument consists of only a narrow yellow band, no other colors being present. Potassium and lithium similarly show bands in the red region, and cesium and rubidium also have marked lines. The metals of the calcium group emit light which is somewhat complex, hence their spectra show several lines. Other elements also have spectra which are characteristic. They serve as clear methods of identification.

When sunlight is introduced into the spectroscope, it forms the regular multicolored spectrum due to the glowing mass of the sun. The gaseous elements on the surface of the sun also show their characteristic lines, but on account of the greater intensity of the light from the main body of the sun, these lines appear as shadows against the bright background of the rainbow colors. From these shadows, called the Fraunhofer lines, the various elements in the gaseous layers of the sun may be positively identified. The result from these studies and those of other heavenly bodies shows them to be composed of the same elements as the earth. In 1869 helium was thus discovered in the sun, and thirty years later it was discovered on the earth, also by the spectroscope.

B. *The polariscope.* When light passes through a prism (the Nicol prism), it is altered so that its rays may be said to be rotating in one plane only. Certain substances, the sugars, some of the food acids, the amino acids of the proteins, turn this "plane of polarization" to the right or to the left. This not alone enables chemists to use the polariscope as a means of measuring amounts; it has also served as a means of establishing the nature of molecular structure.

C. *Index of refraction.* Another optical observation is often made use of, namely, the index of refraction. Like specific gravity, melting point, boiling point, and crystalline form, this physical property may be of use as a means of identification, especially in connection with the fats.

TOPIC VI, HEAT

A. *Heat of reactions.* Measurements involving heat are, next to those of mass, the most common physicochemical measurements. Temperature changes indicate development of heat, often from chemical sources, a fact in which we are interested every moment. We must understand thermometry and appreciate the meaning of the absolute

CHEMISTRY

zero, and of absolute temperature, points already brought out.

When a chemical reaction of the more ordinary kind takes place, heat is evolved and may be measured by the calorimeter. At first thought it would seem that we have in the amount of heat evolved a valuable physical measure of chemical affinities. It is of great value, but most chemical reactions involve so many features that the exact meaning of many results is lost. When carbon burns, the heat developed involves not the result of the union of carbon and oxygen alone, but also the conversion of solid carbon to gaseous carbon dioxide; and perhaps chemical changes in the disintegration of the complex carbon molecule. Yet in many ways the determination of the heat of a chemical reaction is valuable, as, for example, in the study of the fuel value of foods. This leads simply enough to the relation of chemical energy to heat and other forms of energy.

B. *Specific heat.* Specific heat is the relative heat capacity of various substances compared with water. It takes only about one-eighth as long to heat up a pound of iron through a certain number of degrees as it does a pound of water, using the same heat supply. Hence the specific heat of iron is only one-eighth. Specific heat has been a valuable means of checking atomic weights, for the product of the atomic weights by the specific heats of the elements has been found to be uniformly about 6.3. Chemical analysis tells us that silver has a combining weight of 108. This may mean an atomic weight of 108 or a multiple of that number. The specific heat of silver is .056, and when this is divided into the constant 6.3, the result, 112, shows that 108 is the atomic weight of silver.

TOPIC VII, THE ATOM

A. *Radioactivity and atomic structure.* See Chapter XX.

B. *Periodic classification.* See Chapter XIX.

C. *Atomic weight.* The atomic weight is more nearly a chemical function than most of the other topics discussed in physical chemistry. Yet the determination of masses (weighing) is physical, the knowledge of the molecule so closely related to the atom is physical, and there are various other considerations of similar nature coming into play. The determination of the atomic weights is a delicate and intricate affair and requires a combination of physical and chemical processes differing greatly for the various elements. The periodic classification of the elements is usually considered a chapter of physical chemistry.

D. *Molecular weight.* Discussed under Topic I, C.

TOPIC VIII, FURTHER PHYSICAL CONSIDERATIONS

A. *Research tools.* Some appreciation of the increased use of methods of analysis of physical types may be obtained from a consideration of the following list of refined physical tools: "Dipole Moments," giving information concerning the arrangement of atoms in the molecule; "High Temperature Research"; "High Pressure Technique"; "Colorimeters"; "Photoelectric Cell"; "Spectrograph"; "Polarograph." These are among devices now used in research and analysis. The discussion of most of these lies properly in the field of physics, but the chemist finds them increasingly useful in solving problems hitherto beyond his reach. Brilliant illustrations of this are the field of X-ray analysis and the whole scope of the investigations of the radioactive elements.

B. *Photochemistry.* The most striking manifestations of this are photography and plant growth.

C. *The quantum theory.* A modification of our ideas of the emission of energy is the "quantum" theory. This assumes the emission of energy in a discontinuous stream of energy, "quanta," corresponding somewhat to the discontinuous composition of matter in the form of atoms. This subject is one of great difficulty, and until its conceptions are simplified it may be omitted from further elementary consideration.

As mathematical and physical conceptions come to play more important parts in the interpretation of chemical phenomena, there are developed new theories which present difficulties too great for an elementary elucidation. Difficult as they may seem, they bring us nearer to the goal of the research student, the understanding of the underlying causes of the reactions of chemistry. In such respects there has been considerable progress in recent years. The difficulties and the importance of physical chemistry go almost hand in hand.

Topic IX, Colloid Chemistry

Between the condition of true solution, in which the molecules are diffused through a liquid, and a condition like that of coarse particles of sand in water, there are many phases of an intermediate condition, called the colloidal condition. This has been described as small aggregates of one substance more or less permanently surrounded by films or layers of another. Illustrations will make this clearer. A dust cloud represents fine particles of a solid in a gas, the air. Foam represents such a relation between a liquid and a gas, although we may produce a foam with a solid. The colloidal conditions most considered, however, involve suspensions of fine particles of solids, as of the metals, in water, emulsions of oils in water, and finally the hydrosols and hydrogels represented by a gelatine solution before it has set and after. None of these are true solutions. They consist of small particles of the substance surrounded by films of water. The different forms which these associations of particles and surrounding water take on run into each other, and sharp classifications may not be made.

The colloidal condition applies to small particles of substances mechanically divided, or to molecules or molecular aggregates so large that they do not form true solutions. The realm of the colloidal particles may be set as between the particles which are more or less apparent, and capable of settling out, and those of true molecular dimensions. These fine particles are kept from aggregation for a number of causes. The Brownian movement is a movement among particles small enough to be affected by the blows of the ever-moving molecules, and hence they are in a small way kept stirred up. Further, colloidal particles are charged electrically with charges of a similar nature, hence they cannot collect, as particles with similar charges repel one another. When this mutual repulsion is the cause of suspension, the colloidal condition is brought to an end by the introduction of an electrolyte, when the particles lose their charges and can collect and settle. Another cause for the colloidal condition is the formation of films, which are persistent and prevent the particles from coming together. Such films around the fat globules of milk are familiar.

The colloidal condition has certain characteristics by

which it may be recognized. The particles are observable by the ultramicroscope. The particles themselves are not actually seen, but only the reflections of a strong beam of light sent through the solution. The Tyndall effect is comparable. It is the visible path of a beam of light sent through a colloidal solution. Such solutions are opalescent, that is, not quite clear, and are likely to be viscous and easily shaken into a froth. Coagulation, most familiar in the hardening of egg white and the curdling of milk, is an interesting characteristic of some colloids. Besides this form of gelatinization, we know also the setting of jellies upon cooling. Colloidal metals and other substances can be made to precipitate, especially by the addition of an electrolyte. Some forms of coagulation are simply comprehended thus: in the solid or liquid state, the solid is surrounded by the liquid and the liquid phase predominates: in the coagulated mass, the conditions are reversed and the solid form predominates.

The applications of colloid chemistry are many, and when the subject is more fully understood we will find therein explanations of many phenomena now simply passed over in wonder. The following list of applications indicates the large possibilities which may open up the better understanding of this absorbing subject. The chemistry of soap and of cleansing, leading on to the question of emulsions connected with the fats and greases, lubricants, and salves; the question of milk and milk products; paints with their suspended pigments; varnishes; inks; adhesives, starch, gums, and glue*; gelatine and its use in foods; rubber, collodion, celluloid, products like imitation rubber, plastics; photographic emulsions and negatives;

---

* The Greek word for glue, collos, has given its name to the subject.

artificial textiles, tanning; clay and the ceramic industries, including coloring and enamels; the application of dyes; the purification of water and the disposal of sewage; certain methods, as flotation, in metallurgy. Many of the problems of biochemistry are likely to find their solution in the field of colloid chemistry.

It may be difficult at first sight to see the connection of all these substances with one another. The connection lies in the intimate and somewhat permanent association, which is not solution nor yet mere mechanical mixture, between different constituents. The final products are comprehended under such ideas as viscous solutions, as water-glass, varnishes, and glue; jellies, gelatinous solids, as rubber, celluloid or coagulated masses; pastes, as clay; emulsions, as milk, paint and photographic plates. Adsorption and contact catalysis are phenomena whose association with the others is not apparent, but their problems are nevertheless the same.

CHAPTER XXVI

GEOCHEMISTRY

THE experiences upon which the ordinary study of chemistry is based are drawn from operations connected with material collected and applied to the common human needs, as fuel, soap, or lime. Or the material may have been even more specially segregated for the study of chemical phenomena, pure and simple. But before leaving the subject we should take a look at chemical phenomena as exhibited in the natural process of the inorganic world. That is, the chemistry of the original material of the earth's crust, the nature of the minerals making up the rocks, and of the changes taking place which result in the accumulations of the specific substances of interest.

The great bulk of the earth's crust is made up of comparatively few elements, in stable and inactive combinations. This must naturally be so, as the whole drift of chemical activity is toward a stable equilibrium, and in the long periods of time which come under consideration this equilibrium will have been in great part attained. It is not surprising that substances of chemical activity should be found only exceptionally in nature. Their activity would have been satisfied sooner or later in one way or another. Men find, for the most part, these affinities satisfied, and the various substances around them in a sluggish chemical condition. The energy of the sun's rays, of water power, and that which is stored up in coal and other fuels, furnish us means to overcome this condition of equilibrium and inactivity.

Unless the quiescent state has been overcome and new systems of chemical unequilibrium and activity established, chemical operations and industries are impossible. The chemistry of the animal and vegetable world is a field in itself. In this field there is a constant cycle of affinities satisfied and reëstablished, of compounds made and unmade, of energy stored up and again liberated. The discussion of this field is left to the chapter on the chemistry of foods and agricultural chemistry.

The molten magma of the earth in solidifying formed the solid earth. Our attention must be confined to the outer layers of this mass, as there is no definite knowledge of the interior. The thickness of the layer which is known is ten miles or more, a comparatively meager distance. This knowledge comes from no penetration to that distance, but because through the upheavals of nature layers of the crust for such a depth have been folded and bent, and the broken edges exposed so that we may study it upon the surface. It is this mass of rock, making up the outer layers of the original material of the earth which makes the beginning of our study. Above this is the layer of secondary sedimentary rock formed from the material of the first, sediment and fragments, with the original material interpenetrating it in many outcrops. And on top of this is the uppermost layer of loose matter, sometimes of very meager depth, clay and gravel, and, what interests us most, the soil.

To some extent the general nature of all three layers, from the chemical standpoint, must be somewhat the same, as each is derived from the one below it. Here and there, however, there are segregations, accumulations, concentrations, of substances radically different from the chief mass of the earth. There are formed veins and pockets of deposits of material which supply us with the salts, minerals, and ores, which are the basis of the mineral wealth of the land. The purpose of this chapter is to follow briefly the changes and their causes, which result in the modification of the original primary rock material into these deposits of special interest. There is a chemistry of the reactions by which the primary rock was formed. But this is a study beyond our scope, and we will simply begin with the primary rocks as we find them.

The chief elements of the earth's surface are these eight. Their proportions, including the sea and the air, are, according to Clarke:

	Per cent
Oxygen	50.0
Silicon	25.8
Aluminum	7.3
Iron	4.2
Calcium	3.2
Magnesium	2.1
Sodium	2.4
Potassium	2.3

We must stop for a moment to make clear the significance of the terms minerals and rocks. By mineral is meant a true chemical substance (it may be an element, but is more usually a compound), as found in nature, as part of the earth's crust. A mineral may occur in such masses that it goes to form a rock, as quartz or marble, but more frequently the rock is made up of a number of minerals, as granite, which contains the well known minerals, quartz, feldspar and mica or hornblende. Chemical considerations concern only the individual minerals.

The minerals made up from the above elements are, as we would expect, salts, silicates, formed by the combination of the metallic oxides with the one over-abundant nonmetallic oxide, namely silica. Besides silica, SiO_2, which makes up about 12 per cent of the earth's crust, the main mass of all minerals consists of silicates. The most common of these are the feldspars, $NaAlSi_3O_8$, $KAlSi_3O_8$, $CaAl_2Si_2O_8$, hornblende $(Ca,Mg,Fe)\,SiO_3$, pyroxene, of similar composition, mica (muscovite), $H_2KAl_3Si_3O_{12}$, all silicates differing in the relation of the oxide of silicon to the metallic oxides. In any given silicate, as feldspar, the variation of the metal changes the mineral, with no important difference in the general composition.

Silicates thus represented can account for the original form of all the more active metals, as their oxides may be included in the complex salt. With some modifications, silicates may include the nonmetals sulphur, chlorine, and boron. Apatite, a phosphate, includes phosphorus, fluorine, and chlorine. Many of the less common metals, such as copper, lead, cobalt, nickel, and zinc, are found in small amounts in these silicates, even when they are not directly apparent. Although certain information is not available, we may agree that all the elements, save carbon perhaps, have their origin in these silicates, being exceedingly thinly scattered through the rock. They have been extracted somehow, and concentrated in the deposits with which we are familiar. Without such concentration the search for them would be well-nigh hopeless.

The process by which the various elements have been removed from the primary rock, converted into certain compounds, and then deposited in the locations where we find them, is to a very great extent unknown to us. We will content ourselves with following those processes which we can understand, assuming a somewhat parallel history for the others.

Granite is a typical rock, and its constituent feldspar is a typical silicate mineral. Stable as this and other minerals seem to be, they are nevertheless subject to slow disintegration, first physical, then chemical. Changes of temperature cause rocks to crack, and the effect of the freezing of water, the wearing action of water, air, and glaciers, the disruption due to plant growth and solution in water, are all physical agencies which result in a large exposure of surface to further chemical action. To appreciate chemical action most readily, it will be convenient to assume the structure of silicates to be the union of the respective oxides. The constituent oxides have varying degrees of chemical activity and therefore are capable of separation. The prolonged action of water and carbon dioxide, that is, carbonic acid, withdraws the most active constituent and the mineral is thus disintegrated. Another active agent is the oxygen of the air which acts on ferrous compounds. It is very common to see gray rock containing ferrous iron changed to a product which is red, due to ferric iron now present. Sulphur too, in pyrites, combines with oxygen, and the sulphuric acid ultimately resulting has further disintegrating action. The juices of plants also have some chemical action, but the most important is the action of the water and carbon dioxide of the air. As a result the more active metals go into solution as carbonates, and thus start on a career of changes. Some pass on to the sea, which is the final storehouse for a number of them, but most of the potassium and calcium are intercepted and deposited on the way. That portion of the primary rock which does not pass into solution remains behind in the form of silica and clay.

The chemical decomposition of most primary rocks results in the formation of salts, soluble and insoluble, of the more active metals, sodium, potassium, calcium, and magnesium, which are found later in solution in the sea or salt lakes, or deposited by some chance in salt beds of one kind or another. Secondly, there are formed the inactive insoluble residues, like silica and clay, which may subsequently be transported to other locations or agglomerated into a secondary rock. Calcium and magnesium carbonates, at first soluble, are often later deposited in insoluble forms, and make vast masses of secondary rock.

From the above interpretation of physical and chemical changes of rock, we should have formed a picture of the secondary rock formed by changes taking place in the primary rock, and of the loose material resting on top of both, known as the soil. From all these there has been leached out, by incredibly slow processes, the two sets of mineral concentrations found in salt beds and in ore deposits.

THE SALT CONCENTRATIONS

The amount of mineral matter dissolved in surface and spring waters is usually very small, but the process has been going on for ages, and the amount thus carried away is enormous. American rivers in the rainy regions carry 80 to 140 parts per million, about 1/100 per cent of mineral matter, one-tenth of it being common salt. In arid regions the mineral content of waters is 8 to 10 times as high. Besides common salt the mineral matter consists mostly of carbonates and sulphates of calcium and magnesium, much of which is derived from secondary rocks. From the analysis of primary rocks we might expect fairly equal amounts of the four chief metals, but we notice a great dearth of potassium compounds, for they are held by the soil. Further we would naturally expect the sea to have somewhat the same composition as the waters which feed it, even if more concentrated. Here again there is a discrepancy. For neither the proportions existing in the primary rock or in the dissolving waters are found in the ocean. Here sodium predominates over all the others. The salts of the sea are about 3.5 per cent of the whole mass of the ocean, and of this four-fifths is common salt, sodium chloride. The origin of these large amounts of chlorine has never been satisfactorily explained.

As has already been implied, the salt deposits which we know were formed in all probability by the evaporation of landlocked bodies of sea water. Some of these are so vast that we must assume a frequent replenishing of the brine, and consequent accumulation of the salts. Sodium chloride, common salt, is of course the most conspicuous mineral of these deposits. But in the famous Stassfurt deposits the potassium and magnesium salts are also still to be found.

It might be assumed that all sorts of compounds must have found their way into the sea, and should be found there with sufficient searching. This can be true however, to only a limited extent, as so many of the metals, for example, are likely to form insoluble compounds through interaction with other substances with which they come in contact, and to be deposited rather promptly. Yet a number of elements are found indirectly, as iodine in the ash of seaweed. The perennial interest in gold in sea water is based upon considerations such as these.

The salt deposits of desert regions (alkali) have a history similar to that of the salts of the sea. But they come from restricted sources and their composition is not the same. Sodium carbonate and sodium borate (borax) deposits are conspicuous variations from sea-water deposits. Another familiar deviation is that of the sodium nitrate beds of northern Chile.

ORE DEPOSITS

From what has already been stated it must be evident that ore deposits of the less abundant metals are concentrations of material which has previously been highly diffused, so highly diffused in fact that it may not in many cases be traced to its original location. The meaning of the word "ore" is based upon practical values. It usually means an accumulation of a metal or its compound (applied mainly to the heavy metals) of such a character that the extraction of the metals therefrom is profitable. Ordinary yellow sand contains more iron than there is of metal in a rich gold ore, yet in the one little attention is given to the iron content, while the other is of great value. Iron ore should contain about 50 per cent of iron to pay for its extraction, while a gold ore may be profitable with a gold content of 1/200 per cent. It is a question of economics, not of chemistry. In a remote region where transportation is difficult and supplies costly, there must be a larger return than where the outlay is less. The market value of silver determines whether the silver mines of Nevada are to be worked or not.

The ores of the ordinary metals may contain the metal either as the free or native metal, or in some form of compound. Evidently only the less active metals will be found free in any amount, for the rest would in time have asserted their activity and formed some kind of combination. Referring to the electrochemical list, it may be observed that only the metals below hydrogen are found free. Sulphides are abundant as are also the oxides, hydroxides and carbonates. In fact, these five forms include 90 per cent of all ores. Metals occur also as chlorides, as silicates, and in combination with arsenic. Gold, copper, and platinum occur as free metals. Silver, mercury, copper, lead, arsenic, antimony, zinc, cobalt, and nickel occur as sulphides. Copper, iron, aluminum, manganese, and zinc have important oxides. Pyrites, FeS_2, though exceedingly abundant, hardly ranks as an ore of iron, on account of the difficulty of extracting the iron in sufficiently pure form. It does, however, rank as an ore of sulphur and has been used extensively for the making of sulphuric acid.

How were the metals removed from their original combinations, transported, and deposited in the places and forms in which they are found? The first answer is this: It is likely that now and then the conditions of cooling of the molten mass of the earth resulted in some partial concentration of one or the other of the heavy metals free or combined. From such incipient concentrations the action of water caused them to go into solution. In such cases water may have acted under very unusual conditions. The temperature and pressure may have been very high and the water may have contained carbon dioxide, alkalies, or even acid from the products of oxidation of sulphur compounds. The periods of time involved were very long, and no matter how slow the action it may yet have been complete. In the rocks, primary or secondary, there developed fissures, as the result of geological changes, cooling, drying, shrinking, and folding of rocks, with subsequent extension by erosion and solution. Now the compounds of the metals carried in solution traversed these openings and the conditions of solution changed. There was alteration in the pressure, temperature, evaporation of the solvent, loss of carbon dioxide, or there was contact with other substances and solutions which exerted a chemical action. As a result of these changing conditions the compounds previously held in solution were deposited. The deposits are not solely of the valuable ores. The greater portion may be useless material, the gangue material through which the ore is scattered in one form or another. The most abundant gangue minerals are quartz, SiO_2, calcite, $CaCO_3$, barite, $BaSO_4$, fluorspar, CaF_2, and a number of silicates. Although this explanation assumes long periods of time, there are cases in abundance under observation showing the solution, concentration, and redeposition of ores in short periods of time. Deposits so formed may be subject to a second concentration, by either physical or chemical processes. Or they may be modified chemically, the upper layers of lead sulphide, for example, are sometimes converted into lead sulphate and carbonate by the action of the oxygen and carbon dioxide of the atmosphere. Ore deposits are not necessarily in the form just described. Other conditions may result in beds of ore, or in impregnations of permeable rock, which can be mined and treated for the extraction of their constituents.

MINERALOGY AND CRYSTALLOGRAPHY

Minerals have been defined in a former paragraph as individual chemical substances, sometimes elements, more often compounds, as they are found in nature. They are the units of which the rocks are built and they are the starting points for any serious consideration of chemical changes.

From even a brief study of the minerals, it may be seen that they fall into two groups, the first that of the silicates and their modifications, which go to make up the mass of the primary rock; the second that of minerals of a very different chemical composition, made up in great measure of modifications and extractions from the first. The total number of species identified is about one thousand, one hundred being somewhat common forms. Of these last about half belong to the first class, the silicates, and the rest to the other class. Each group has its own features of interest. In the first group the geologist finds a greater interest than does the chemist, for in them he finds the interesting evidence for his study of the history of the earth. In the second group are the more reactive substances which, through chemical manipulation, become of service to men. The German expression, "aufschliessen," to unlock, as applied to the silicates, is very suggestive. It is no easy matter to pass from most of the silicates to the compounds of the other type. Witness the vast amounts of potash locked up in the feldspar of granite rocks, while the only forms which are available to us are those which, through the slowly acting operations of nature, have been segregated from the original rock and concentrated in secondary deposits.

The identification of minerals is accomplished by the study of their physical and chemical properties. The latter applies to only a limited extent to the many silicates, as they are too inactive, but with the help of the blowpipe much can be accomplished with the minerals of the second group. The presence of sulphur and arsenic is determined by the odor of their oxides. Halogen acids are easily liberated and identified. Carbon dioxide is easily detected, and other chemical tests, not differing from the usual tests of qualitative analysis are useful in establishing their nature.

The physical properties which are of use are: luster; color, both of the mass and of the powder; hardness; malleability; nature of the fracture, which is cleavage when it follows the lines of crystallization; fusibility; specific gravity; optical properties; and especially crystalline form.

The luster is described as metallic, vitreous, resinous, dull, and otherwise. Superficial as it may seem, it gives a very prompt clue to the nature of a mineral. The metals and some of their sulphides and oxides have such a pronounced metallic appearance that they may be distinguished with great certainty from the more stony or glassy materials of other composition. The color is often characteristic, due to the nature of the mineral itself, or to rather consistent impurities. Of special interest is the color of the powder obtained most easily by making a "streak," that is, rubbing the mineral against a rough porcelain surface. The material rubbed off as a powder gives the desired information.

Hardness is determined by comparison with a fixed scale of accepted minerals.

Malleability serves to distinguish with certainty between a metal and a compound. A few compounds are so metallic in appearance that they are deceiving. Their conduct under the hammer shows whether the specimen is a metal or not.

Minerals often break with a fracture which is characteristic and instructive. Most important in this connection is the fact that in many crystals or crystalline masses there are predetermined lines along which the fracture will take place. This is the cleavage, and when it does apply is readily recognized. Cleavage has the appearance of the regular breaking of a lump of cannel coal when placed upon the fire, but the latter is not due to crystalline structure.

Fusibility, like hardness, is determined by comparison with a fixed scale. The specimen, in the form of a thin fragment, is heated in the blowpipe flame and from the readiness of the melting the number representing the fusibility is assigned.

Specific gravity is determined in the regular way by comparing its weight in water and out of water. With respect to specific gravity there is again a rather sharp distinction between different classes of minerals, as there is between the two great classes of metals, the heavy and the light. The simple compounds of the heavy metals, when they occur as minerals, usually have a specific gravity of five or above, while the other minerals, particularly the silicates, have a specific gravity of from 2.5-3. Within narrower limits the determination of this property gives more exact data.

Crystalline form. The crystal form is one of the most important features connected with the appearance and structure of matter. Most men have a vague idea of a crystal as being a glassy, geometric solid. But the mineralogist has reduced the study of crystalline forms to a mathematical science. A piece of glass cut out in a proper shape is, of course, not a crystal. The external crystal form must represent an internal arrangement of the molecules, and although the relation of crystalline form to chemical structure is a subject not yet worked out to any degree of completion, the mineralogist has applied the matter satisfactorily in a descriptive way.

A true crystal is bounded by plane faces, with no reëntrant angles. Although the faces are the most conspicuous, that which really determines the crystal form is the angle which the faces make with each other. On this interpretation, using a homely illustration, all ordinary boxes with squared edges and right angles would represent the same crystal form, whether they were perfect cubes or elongated in one direction or another or were large or small. Fortunately, in any given case one kind of crystal usually assumes more or less the same form, and so the matter is in practice less complicated. The angles are measured with great accuracy by means of a goniometer, and from them the crystal form calculated by methods by no means simple. For ordinary practice, the crystal forms are usually readily apparent to the trained crystallographer, and he can use this knowledge for the solution of his problems.

CHAPTER XXVII

THE CHEMISTRY OF FOODS

THE chemistry of living matter and its products and processes is included mainly within the scope of organic chemistry. We may call this biochemistry, or, if we are interested in certain phases of it only, chemistry of foods. It is almost a self-evident necessity that the chemical nature of tissue and of the foods needed to build it up must be the same. In order to make some beginning of the consideration of these substances, we will make a classification of the constituents applicable, with slight reconsideration, to both organisms and their foods. The classes thus distinguished are six—carbohydrates, fats, proteins, simpler organic compounds, water, and mineral matter. The human body is made up of about 60 per cent water, 18 per cent protein, 16 per cent fat, 6 per cent mineral matter, while the carbohydrate present is only about 0.1 per cent. Plants vary considerably in their composition, and it is difficult to make an exact statement which is at the same time brief. But some idea may be obtained from the following rough averages. The nutritious parts of plants average about 24 per cent water, 10 per cent protein, 5 per cent or more of fat, and 60 per cent carbohydrate. In the nonnutritious parts of a plant the water may run as high as 90 per cent, and most of the rest is likely to be carbohydrate in the form of cellulose. A usable estimate of the amount of mineral matter in plants is about 1 to 2 per cent. The remaining class of substances mentioned, the simpler organic compounds, like alcohols, acids, flavors, and essential oils, are present in such irregular ways that no general statement may be made for them. They will be mentioned as the occasion arises.

It is apparent that protein and fat are predominant in the human, that is, the animal body, while carbohydrates, particularly cellulose and starch, predominate in plants. For our present purpose, a convenient distinction between animals and plants lies in the manner in which each obtains its food, including both functions of foods, namely the supply of material and the supply of energy. The animal must have its food ready in a highly organized form, such as is found in other animals or plants; the digestive process consists in assimilating these, so far as the material is concerned, and in burning them up, to utilize the energy stored up within them. Plants, on the other hand, use simple inorganic matter for their food, and build it up into complex forms, storing up in them the energy gathered from the sunlight. The animal is dependent upon the plant, and the latter makes use of the waste products of animal life, carbon dioxide, CO_2, water, H_2O, and certain nitrogen compounds. When the plant is through with its process, we have the complicated carbohydrates, fats, and proteins, ready again for the animal's consumption. We thus again meet with the cycles of carbon and nitrogen in nature, in which these elements go the rounds of the three kingdoms of nature, mineral to plant, plant to animal, then animal back to mineral.

By contrast the energy changes involved in the life of plants and animals, however, do not form a cycle. The

CARBON AND HYDROGEN CYCLE

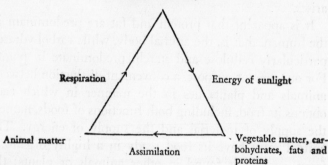

Carbon dioxide and water
CO_2 and H_2O
The initial and final
compounds of the cycle

Respiration

Energy of sunlight

Animal matter

Assimilation

Vegetable matter, carbohydrates, fats and proteins

original source of our energy is the sunlight. The plant gathers this and stores it away in its compounds. The animal burns up these compounds and thus utilizes this energy. But now this energy is lost by being dissipated as heat to the surroundings. Materials are used over and over again. But the movement of energy is in only one direction; when it is used up it must be replenished from the original source, the sunlight.

CARBOHYDRATES, FATS, AND PROTEINS

The chemistry of the carbohydrates has been fully presented and needs little further mention here. Glycogen, a polysaccharide similar to starch, sometimes called animal starch, assumes a conspicuous place in the process of food absorption. The fats, too, have been touched on sufficiently. However, mention should be made of a number of solids, strongly resembling the fats, yet of different composition. Along with the fats they are classed under the name of lipins, meaning fatlike substances. Such substances are the higher fatty acids, palmitic and stearic, $C_{15}H_{31}CO_2H$ and $C_{17}H_{35}CO_2H$; the sterols, which are higher alcohols, $C_{27}H_{43}OH$; the waxes, similar to fats, but containing an alcohol other than glycerol for a base, $C_{30}H_{61}(OCO.C_{15}H_{31})$, and certain fats complicated with phosphoric acid, called phospholipins. These all function to some extent as do the fats, and we may assume that they offer more possibilities for the complications useful for living processes.

The chemical composition of the proteins is briefly this: They are made up of various combinations of different amino acids, held together by the group NH. The total molecule is apparently very large, the individual groups being repeated until the total number is perhaps in the neighborhood of one hundred, and the total molecular weight about 15,000. It is possible that this is an understatement. There are external signs of this large molecule, in that the proteins are colloidal, that is, they do not crystallize or diffuse readily, and their solutions foam on shaking. When acted on chemically they break down, and before simple substances are obtained a long series of intermediate compounds can be identified, of which some are apparently of greater importance than others. It is quite possible that the special importance of some of the amino acids is associated with a relation to the hormones.

We may summarize. Proteins (the name means "substances of the first importance") are complex nitrogen derivatives, more conspicuous in the animal organism than in that of the plant, of an average composition; carbon

52 per cent, hydrogen 7 per cent, nitrogen 16 per cent, oxygen 23 per cent, sulphur 2 per cent. Some also contain iron and phosphorus. They are solids, odorless and tasteless and almost white. Their solubility with respect to water, alcohol, and salt solutions is variable. Most of them are amorphous (not crystalline) and colloidal. They occur only exceptionally without foreign admixture, and in the animal at least only in the living cell, not in reserve stores. Their most characteristic property is that of coagulation, familiar in the hardening of the white of an egg and the curdling of milk. There is more than one variety of amino acid present in any given molecule. They are amphoteric, that is, act either as bases or acids, which is to be expected, as they contain both the acid and basic groups of the amino acids.

Beside the nature of the units, the amino acids, of which the proteins are composed, the significant feature of their structure is the linkage by which they are held together. This is comparable with the linkage in the oxygen system in the case of the polysaccharides. It may be crudely represented by $A - \underset{H}{N} - A' - \underset{H}{N} - A'' -$ and

so on, A, A' and A'' representing different amino acids. By chemical and physiological processes these complexes may be resolved by the addition of the constituents of water, into the simple units. The units preserve their integrity and in living processes are capable of recombination into new proteins suitable to the animal needs.

The theoretically possible number of proteins is a fabulous one, and the actual number known is very large. Out of all the mass of known proteins, the following classification will bring some simplification:

Class 1. The simple proteins, namely, proteins which, no matter how complex the molecule, contain no other constituent besides the amino acids. The variation among them must be due to different combinations of the amino acids. As far as food value goes they are not equal, for some seem to lack certain amino acids apparently necessary for proper building of tissue.

Class 2. These are called the conjugated proteins, because in addition to a composition similar to that of group 1, they have other groups of altogether different nature superadded. They include very vital substances, such as the hemoglobin (red corpuscles) of the blood, and the material of the nucleus of the cell. The variety and complexity of these seem to be the features making them of special value in the more vital parts of the organism.

Class 3. These proteins are called the derived or modified proteins. Proteins are readily altered, probably in the direction of simplification, by the action of heat, water, acids, alkalis, and enzymes. The range of intermediate products, before the constituent amino acids are reached, is considerable.

Among the modified proteins may be mentioned especially the polypeptides, artificially prepared by synthesis of amino acids, or obtained from the natural proteins by disintegration. In them the living processes and the laboratory processes meet and they have in consequence a special meaning.

SIMPLER ORGANIC COMPOUNDS

The fourth group of substances included in organisms and their foods, after carbohydrates, fats, and proteins, may be designated as the simpler organic compounds. When these do not contain nitrogen they present no new features. They are simply the alcohols, aldehydes, acids, and other familiar compounds of organic chemistry. But if they do contain nitrogen they have a more particular relation to the animal body. It is likely that they are formed from the proteins, by processes either normal or abnormal. The most important is urea $CO(NH_2)_2$. It is the compound by which the bulk of the nitrogen is excreted from the system. The elimination of the other common elements, hydrogen, oxygen, and carbon, is very simple. The first two are readily disposed of as water. Carbon leaves the body as carbon dioxide, which is active enough and soluble enough to be capable of absorption, yet not so much so but that it may be thrown off in the lungs.

The nitrogen problem is less simple. As an element it is inactive and insoluble, and its simple hydrogen and oxygen compounds are corrosive. In urea the great activity of ammonia is toned down by the carbonic acid, and the result is a compound of a neutral nature. Urea has a structure represented by the formula $CO.(NH_2)_2$. It is carbonic acid $CO.(OH)_2$ with the two hydroxyl groups replaced by $— NH_2$. It is excreted in the urine, and its amount is considerable, about 30 grams, or one ounce, per day. It undoubtedly has other functions.

A small portion of the nitrogen never reaches the form of urea, but becomes part of compounds of the type of uric acid, $C_5H_4N_4O_3$. To some extent these may be considered normal. Beyond that they give rise to complications from an excess of uric acid in the blood and in the urine.

Mineral Matter

This expression is used to designate the portions of any animal or vegetable substance which do not pass off as gases when the substance is burned. This ash approximately represents the amount and, less exactly, the forms in which the original elements are found in the foods and tissues. There are found the nonmetals, sulphur, phosphorus, chlorine, fluorine, and silicon, and the metals, sodium, potassium, calcium, magnesium, and iron, and occasionally one or two other elements. The function of mineral matter is varied. It supplies hard material for building up skeletons (calcium phosphate) and protective coverings as shells (calcium carbonate). Salts in the blood and digestive juices influence their solvent power and their diffusibility while the action of acids and bases in the digestive juices may be readily comprehended. Some metals seem to have special functions, perhaps as catalysts, as iron in the blood. Phosphorus is helpful in building up a variety of molecules, which through a greater complexity serve as the seats of vital processes. It is significant that sea water, with its abundance of mineral matter, is so favorable to the thriving of living things. Small as the amount of mineral in plants and animals is, its rôle is always of definite importance. The mineral matter is excreted regularly and must be renewed constantly, thus indicating its intimate relation to the changes taking place in the living tissue.

Water and the Animal Body

In the study of inorganic chemistry the peculiar relation of water to many important reactions is repeatedly noticed.

The relation of water to acids and bases, and the ionization of salts in water are good illustrations. This fundamental importance of water in ways both physical and chemical is repeated in the chemistry of the body. Water exhibits certain physical properties to an unusual degree. It has high capillarity, high heat capacity, both as liquid and on changing to vapor, and is a good nonconductor of electricity. Water acts physically by its warming and cooling action, and by its serving as a carrier to disseminate matter through the various parts of the body. It fills the tissue spaces and makes them firm and rigid. Chemically it serves as the medium for the reactions between active substances and can in no way be of less service than it is in the laboratory. The hydrolytic action of water, that is, its power to split carbohydrates, fats, and proteins into their simple constituents, is one of its chief functions. But still another relation of water comes to the front in this matter, namely the relation of water to the colloidal condition. Colloidal solutions represent the phases of matter related to water intermediate between true solutions and complete lack of any relation. It includes fine suspensions or sediments, jellies and emulsions, as when oil is thoroughly beaten up with water and yolk of eggs. In this colloidal state, as in jellies or emulsions, we have an ideal condition for living tissue, namely, a combination of the solid condition for rigidity, and the liquid condition for chemical reactivity. If a gelatine solution containing salts is allowed to set, it will illustrate this, for it will be rigid, yet will permit chemical reactions to take place. A crude picture of protoplasms may be suggested by the following: Water containing salts in solution is emulsified, that is, churned up, with the desired solids, the proteins, fats, and carbohydrates. Such a mixture, if we can imagine it to be according to some orderly principles, might serve from its physical and chemical characteristics as a proper seat of the chemical reactions of living things.

DIGESTION, ABSORPTION, AND UTILIZATION OF FOOD

The proteins, fats, and carbohydrates which constitute the main portion of our foods are to a great extent insoluble. Even soluble dextrin and cane sugar have molecules so large that they are not directly capable of absorption. The purpose of the digestive process is then to so simplify these complex, insoluble or nondiffusible compounds that they may become absorbable. Water, salts, the simple sugars, and a few other substances need no preliminary simplification. But these form a comparatively small fraction of the whole. The digestive tract, consisting of stomach, small intestine, and large intestine, is adapted to the storing of the food, converting it chemically into the soluble and diffusible alteration products and finally absorbing it into the body proper.

The three nutrients owe their physical and chemical properties to a great extent to the fact that they are complexes of simpler units. The proteins are made up of many amino-acids, starch of monosaccharide units, and fats of glycerol and the higher organic acids. In each case simplification may take place by the assumption of water, and the simpler units thus liberated are ready for absorption.

The changes in all cases are of a similar kind and may be accomplished in the laboratory by the influence of various reagents. In the digestive processes the reagent is the digestive juice belonging to the respective portions of the digestive tract. The active influence in each case is the enzyme suited to the particular need. These enzymes are catalysts, for they do not seem to be a part of the final products, and a small amount influences a very large amount of material. The action of enzymes in digestion is hydrolytic, that is, splitting by action of water, as shown above, and they are usually classified and named according to the compound upon which they react. Those hydrolyzing starch are called amylases (*amylum,* starch); proteases act on proteins, and lipases (*lipos,* fat) on fats. Invertases change double sugars (disaccharides) into monosaccharides. Specific names are given for particular enzymes, as maltase for that one acting on maltose.

The digestive juices are the saliva, the gastric juice of the stomach, the pancreatic juice introduced into the digestive tract just before the food reaches the small intestine, and the enteric juice of the small intestine. The total amount of these juices is about five quarts; they are mostly water, the solid content being at the most only a few per cent. The active agent is always an enzyme, suited to the work which it must do. The saliva is practically neutral, the gastric juice acid with hydrochloric acid, and the pancreatic juice alkaline with sodium carbonate. Each enzyme is effective only in its proper medium.

The final effect of all these juices containing the various enzymes is that the complex nutrients are resolved into their simple units, the "building stones," in part soluble, but all capable of passing through the walls of the digestive tract to be received by the circulatory system of the blood and lymph. These units preserve their identity and are presently resynthesized for the uses of the body or burned for heat and energy.

Absorption of the digested foods begins in the stomach, but is more rapid in the small intestine, which, with its large surface exposure, is well constructed for this purpose. Absorption is completed in the large intestine, and the unabsorbed residue, which is not large, is excreted. After passing the intestinal wall, the absorbed monosaccharides pass into the blood, are carried to the liver, there resynthesized into glycogen and temporarily stored as such. This glycogen is reconverted into glucose and passed on to the tissues as needed. The fats, partly finely divided, but mainly in the form of fatty acids, pass into the lymph (the fluid supplementary to and emptying into the blood), are reformed into fats and stored or used as needed. The protein fragments pass into the blood and presently are built up again to serve the particular needs of the body.

The Utilization of the Different Nutrients

Proteins are needed to build up new tissue and to replace old tissue, for there is a considerable wastage inherent in the mere process of living. In the end, after it has served its main purpose, protein is burned up and supplies heat and energy. As protein is the most difficult nutrient to procure, and also involves the most complex methods of excretion, the use of protein as food beyond its special requirement is disadvantageous.

The fats, after they are reformed, are carried by the blood to the different tissues, where they are either oxidized at once or stored for future use. Some may be incidentally converted into glucose, but its ultimate utilization is the same.

The carbohydrates are utilized to some extent directly by the oxidation of the monosaccharides. Some may be stored temporarily as glycogen, either in the liver or the muscles, but apparently never for a long time. For more permanent storing, the carbohydrates are converted into fat, for the ultimate aim of both is the same, the supplying of the body with heat and energy.

FUEL VALUE AND FOOD REQUIREMENTS

In the study of chemical reactions, the development of heat is such a striking feature that we soon come to look

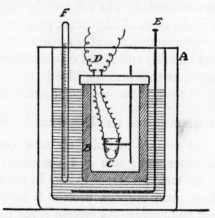

DIAGRAM OF THE BOMB CALORIMETER

A is a case designed to prevent the passage of any heat to or from its contents. It contains water in which is immersed the strong bomb B. The sample is placed in C, and the chamber is filled with compressed oxygen. When all is ready, the sample is fired by the current introduced at D. The heat of the combustion is communicated to the water surrounding B (which is stirred by E), and the change of temperature is recorded by the thermometer F.

upon it as a sign of the intensity of chemical affinities. Measurements of the amount of heat liberated offer valuable information. In the case of fuels this is of course particularly true, and in the case of purchases on a large scale the heat value of coals is carefully determined. This is done by means of the calorimeter, a tight chamber in which the sample under consideration is burned in an atmosphere of oxygen. This chamber is immersed in an outer cylinder filled with water, and all the heat of the action is absorbed by the water. Knowing the amount of the water and the elevation of its temperature, one can easily calculate the amount of heat. It is measured in calories, namely the amount of heat needed to raise the temperature of a unit weight of water one degree.

All this applies to foods, for they are used in part for the amount of energy which they may develop upon being burned. When measured in such a calorimeter, it is found that one gram of fat yields 9,300 calories, that is, heat enough to raise the temperature of 9,300 grams of water 1° C. One gram of protein yields 5,700 calories and 1 gram carbohydrate 4,100 calories. This variation is due to the fact that they are already oxidized in varying degrees. When the nutrients are burned in the body, it would be a fair presumption that the amount of heat liberated would be the same as in the calorimeter.

For the purpose of testing this point the respiration calorimeter has been devised, in which a man could be enclosed and measurements of matter and heat carefully made. The results confirm the presumption and we now know that the fuel value is the same when developed in a calorimeter or in the body.

To this statement the proteins offer an apparent exception, as they are not completely burned up but leave the body as urea. For this reason 1,600 calories are lost, and the body fuel value of proteins is only 4,100 calories.

These numbers being inconveniently large, the major calorie, 1,000 times as large, is ordinarily used as the unit, so that our fuel values may be stated as respectively, 9.3 Cal., 4.1 Cal., and 4.1 Cal., or even more conveniently as 9, 4, 4 Cal.

FOOD REQUIREMENTS

The ordinary food requirements are six: proteins, carbohydrates, fats, water, mineral matter and the condiments, like the flavors, organic acids, and similar substances. To the list of these six the vitamins should be added as a seventh, although we know little more about them than that they are essential. All these classes of food necessities are of course supplied to us by our daily menu. A brief analysis of our foods will reveal the fact that they are very similar, differing only in the proportions in which they include the same nutrients, and in the condiments which accompany them. Further, a survey of all our foods will show that the list of these is a comparatively short one, comprehended under the following few classes; (1) meats, including (2) fish; (3) fats, including oils; (4) milk and milk products; (5) eggs; (6) cereals; (7) bread; (8) starch and sugar; (9) fruits; (10) vegetables; (11) potatoes; (12) nuts; (13) condimental substances.

1. Meats. A convenient impression of the composition of meat, free from bone, is that it is made up of water 60 per cent, protein 20 per cent, and fat 20 per cent. Individual cuts may vary considerably. Meat further contains salts and meat extractives, which add flavor and in the latter case have a certain stimulating value. The latter feature applies to broths made from meats, but the tissue-building proteins do not go into solution. Beef

extracts are good only for flavor and mild stimulation.

2. Fish serve practically the same purpose as meat, namely to supply protein and to a lesser extent fat. The protein content is about the same as that of meat, but the fat averages only 6 per cent. From a practical standpoint the waste, almost one-half, is important.

3. Fats and oils. Usually we assume no essential advantages in the use of one fat or oil over another (barring butter fat). Usage and convenience seem to be determining factors, and within comparatively few years there has been a distinct revolution in feeling in this matter. Substitutes for the more expensive butter fat and olive oil are no longer scorned.

4. Milk. It will be impossible to condense into a few lines all the points of chemical interest in connection with milk. The composition of ordinary rich milk is about 3 per cent protein, 4 per cent fat, and 5 per cent milk sugar. The mineral matter is under 1 per cent. In many communities the legal requirement of 3 to 3½ per cent butter fat is not much exceeded, and the total solids often run below 12 per cent. Although the fat of milk is usually looked upon as its most desirable constituent, the great value of the protein must not be overlooked, and this applies especially to skim milk. Milk, valuable as it is, is a perfect food only for the young of the animal from which the milk is obtained. For the feeding of infants modification is needed. The addition of water diminishes the proportion of protein, while the fat and sugar content are increased by the addition of cream and milk sugar. Cheese includes the protein and fat of milk. Its composition varies considerably, for we know all kinds, from that made of skim milk to that containing much cream.

Ordinarily full cheese may contain about 30 per cent of both protein and fat. The value of this as food is evident.

Butter usually contains about 15 per cent water. The most striking chemical feature of butter fat is that there is present in it about 6 per cent of acids low in the fatty acid series. These may be separated readily and determined. As no other fat contains any considerable amount, this forms the readiest way to distinguish between butter and a butter substitute.

The loss of valuable material for human food by the neglect of skim milk has been greatly deplored. It is said that about two billion pounds, with about 8 per cent of valuable food constituents, fail to be properly utilized.

5. Eggs contain about 13 per cent protein and 10 per cent fat. Eggs are said to supply 3 per cent of the total food of the country.

6. The cereals, barley, buckwheat, corn, oats, rice, rye, and wheat, in the form called air dry, contain about 10 per cent of water. Their protein content averages 11 per cent, fat 2 per cent, and carbohydrate makes up most of the rest. In some of the milled products the more valuable constituents run even higher. Cereals are valuable foods, available as they are at low cost, even if the nutrients are not so fully utilized in the process of digestion as are those of the animal foods.

7. Bread. Wheat has a reasonably high protein content, and on account of the gluten developed in the flour the consistency of the dough is such as to make good bread. It is par excellence the cereal which men prefer. As made up in bread, the food contains 30 per cent of water. The evident lack of fat is made good by the use of butter and other fats.

8. Sugar and starch. The great popularity of sugar in the menu is of comparatively recent development. It is the purest food which we can buy. It is true that it has some peculiar disadvantages. Its good flavor may induce over-use, and on account of its solubility digestive disturbances may be caused by its fermentation. Starch is very pure, but its practical advantages over the cereals are not sufficiently pronounced to give it a peculiar place in the popular esteem. The chemical purity of a food constituent, though interesting in a way, esthetically attractive, is a dietetic disadvantage, for the accompaniments of ordinary foods, mineral matter, roughage, and vitamins, are thus eliminated.

9. Fruits are made up so largely of water that it would not be far from the mark to say that they are used mainly for their flavor. The distinctive features of fruits are sugar, the esters which give the fruity flavor, and acid, varying in amounts and kinds with the different fruits. The water content varies from 77 per cent in grapes to over 90 per cent in watermelons. The solid part is mostly carbohydrates and the nutritious part of this is sugar. Used in such large amounts as grapes and apples are, their sugar content may be of moment in fulfilling the daily requirement for carbohydrates. Fruits are valuable in the general stimulation of the activities of the digestive tract. Bananas are almost in a class by themselves, being as solid as potatoes. A food article which thus combines flavor with substance is a valuable asset to the menu.

10. Vegetables. These should be divided into two classes. Those resembling cucumbers and tomatoes, which are mostly water, and those like shelled beans, peas, and corn, which are comparatively solid. The first class is

comparable with fruit, possessing high condimental value, while the second class has in addition a high food value. The latter, when dried, are in a class with the cereals.

11. Potatoes are only about one-fifth solid, mostly starch. Hence they should be available at low cost to compare with the cereals. They have become very essential in the menu, apparently, and seem to be purchased regardless of price.

12. Nuts are high in fats and proteins and have food value comparable with that of meat.

13. Condiments. Protein, starch, and fat have no pronounced taste and the variety of flavor in foods depends largely upon other substances of little food value, present in small amounts. Sugar is a marked exception to this statement, as it is unique in combining flavor with food value. The food value of the vegetable acids present in foods, as well as that of spices and flavors, is practically negligible. The essential matter of spices ordinarily present is minute. The extracts and the salts of meats must be considered as condiments. When these have been removed from meat, the latter is unpalatable, but is said to be well digested nevertheless. Alcoholic beverages, of the so-called "light" class, have condimental value, and are much used in European countries to round out a rather meager fare. It is clear that alcohol is burned in the system, that is, it is a true food. The objections to its use lie in other directions.

The introduction into our lives of essentially new foods can scarcely be a frequent occurrence. Yet to a certain extent this has happened. The soy bean has been a staple article of food in China, and it has been introduced into this country and utilized for a surprising number of purposes. It serves as a green crop in agriculture, and as a substitute for a hay crop. It is unlikely to assume in our western countries the important place which it holds in the Orient, namely, as flour, sauce, cheese, even milk, although this is all nutritionally possible. It can hardly compete with our present food supply in respect to attractiveness or convenience. Soy bean oil, however, seems to promise usefulness in the way of industrial applications and the magnitude of the crop of soy beans grown with this end in view already compares with that of the grains of lesser importance.

The great climatic range of our country, coupled with better means of transportation, has resulted in a considerable change in our supply of perishable foods. From time to time some interest is aroused in the dewatering of succulent vegetables. Theoretically this is highly desirable, for the transportation of tons of water seems to be a great economic waste. Not much progress, however, has been made in this direction. Except for a few minor instances, the problem still remains to be solved.

Many studies have been made of the amount of the three nutriments consumed in the ration of people free to choose. These dietary studies have been made with groups of people as well as of selected groups, and finally confirmed in studies by means of the respiration calorimeter. From all these studies it is clear that men select their food in such a way that there is an average daily ration of protein, and of fuel-furnishing foods, fat and carbohydrates supplementing one another. The conclusions drawn may be stated thus: In America the daily dietary for a man exerting himself moderately is protein, 100 grams, or 3.6 ounces; fat, a like amount; carbohydrate, 400 grams, or 14.6 ounces. This has a total heat value of

3,000 calories. For absolute rest the ration is less, and for very hard work it exceeds this by more than 50 per cent. Women and children require less, but studies of growing boys have shown an almost startling consumption of food.

Experiments with the respiration calorimeter make it possible to work out the disposal of this food, both as to the material and energy involved. It was learned that life processes consume no energy, but that all the potential energy of the food appears as heat, passes off in the excreta, or is used up in evaporating the water from the body. When the subject of the experiment performs work, he requires more food, but only 20 per cent of the energy of this added food appears in the work done, the rest appearing as heat. That is, the efficiency of the human machine, with respect to the added food is 20 per cent, while the efficiency with respect to the total food is only 15 per cent. This compares with the efficiency of a good steam engine. Such experiments as have been performed to study the energy consumed by brain work have had negative results.

THE CHEMISTRY OF COOKING

Cooking has not developed greatly as a science. It is in the stage of an art, in which there has been much accumulated experience without a full understanding of the causes underlying the results obtained. The chemical points involved in cooking are few, and are touched on in the following brief outline.

Cooking sterilizes food. The modern tendency is to obviate the need of this by proper preparation and inspection, but under certain conditions it is a necessary precaution. Heat accomplishes some chemical changes also. In

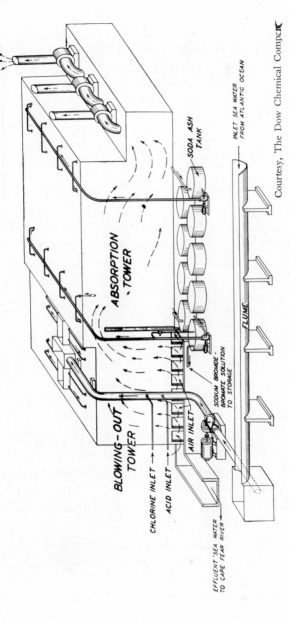

AIR EXIT

SODA ASH
TANK

ABSORPTION
TOWER

INLET SEA WATER
FROM ATLANTIC OCEAN

FLUME

BLOWING-OUT
TOWER

CHLORINE INLET

ACID INLET

AIR INLET

SODIUM BROMIDE -
BROMATE SOLUTION
TO STORAGE

EFFLUENT SEA WATER
TO CAPE FEAR RIVER

Courtesy, The Dow Chemical Company

DIAGRAM OF BROMINE EXTRACTION UNIT

(See page 262.)

SALT WORKS AT STAFFORD, ENGLAND—THE RESERVOIRS OF BRINE

(See page 264.)

the case of meat the blood is coagulated so that the meat is no longer red, the fiber is softened by the conversion of the tough connective tissue into tender gelatine. The fiber contracts due to loss of water, albumens coagulate to form crusts, and there are undefinable changes in the proteins and fats which result in their acquiring an attractive flavor. When meats are boiled, salts and extractives pass out from the meat to the broth. It is probably true that cooked meat is less digestible than the uncooked meat, but the difference is slight. Eggs are coagulated by heat, but the disadvantage of hard-boiled eggs is due perhaps only to lesser mastication. The disadvantage of heating milk in regard to chemical changes is a moot question. The certain advantage of sterilization probably outweighs any disadvantage in other ways.

The cooking of vegetables is more important than that of meats. The swelling and breaking of the starch grains, the rupturing of the cellulose walls, the softening of gelatinous substances, all serve to render the food more adaptable to the action of the digestive juices. Pleasant flavors may be developed and sometimes an unpleasant flavor is removed. Breadmaking is one of the most complex operations of cooking. It involves the leavening of the loaf either by the development of fermentation or the use of baking powders, both involving chemical changes which can be studied in detail. Other changes are not so clear. The proteins coagulate to some extent and make combinations with the starch. The starch on the surface of the loaf is altered, forming dextrin, which, colored by substances on the order of caramel (formed by overheating sugar and starch), helps to form the crust. The final result is a combination of crust and crumb which appeals to the appetite and which is readily permeated by the digestive juices.

The selection of food is as important, perhaps, as the actual manipulation in the cooking processes. Selection involves the proper proportion between animal and vegetable sources, the attainment of a balanced ration, the consideration of digestibility, and the best use of condiments, even consideration of vitamins. Proper comminution, consistency, volume, and temperature are hardly chemical points, but in a full discussion of the matter they must be given a place. In the final result, it is only too apparent that in the present state of our knowledge experience is of greater moment than scientific knowledge. The latter is only slowly making progress in solving the many questions which arise within the field.

FOOD PRESERVING

Men of a grade of civilization past the hunting stage, and living in a temperate climate, must make provision for a winter food supply, while the congestion of our population in great cities introduces the question of food preserving into all seasons. The first solution of the problem is through the selection of the grains, which with their low water content are stable for an indefinite time. Other foodstuffs, as potatoes, may be kept with care for a reasonable period. Fats and oils are very stable. But a conscious act of preserving is necessary for many of our more perishable foods.

Drying comes into the first consideration. Enormous amounts of food are dried, as fruits, fish, and meats. Dried cattle food is in the end for men. Cold storage is so well known that it needs only to be mentioned. Quick freezing has become well established. Sterilization by heat is likely to be confined in the household to the easier operations, such as the preserving of fruits and some vegetables. The more difficult operations, as the canning of meats, require the more complete resources of the factory. There is a possibility of progress, through the more thorough study of household problems which the future will certainly bring. The result may be the extension of household practice; or it may be the relegation to the factory of the few household industries still extant. Associated with sterilization is the use of such substances as sugar, salt, spices, vinegar. Smoking is not very remote from these. The efficiency of these methods is due perhaps to the establishing of a general environment unfriendly to bacterial life.

These methods of preserving are all in high favor. The desirability of chemical preservatives is at least open to discussion. The common inorganic preservatives used are sulphur dioxide and sulphites of sodium and calcium, potassium nitrate, sodium nitrite, boric acid (also called boracic acid) and borax. Among organic substances benzoic acid or its sodium salt is perhaps the most used. The use of some of these is legalized and has many defenders. The whole subject of chemical preservatives has caused much discussion, and some experiments have been made, but no final agreement has yet been reached. The objections raised to their use are as follows: They are substances not suitable for taking into the system and are therefore definitely harmful; they give a false appearance of freshness; they prevent the development of signs with which we are familiar, which we ordinarily rely on as a warning that the food is spoiling; they permit carelessness in preparation. Until the matter has been so thoroughly investigated that all doubt is removed, it would seem wise to assume on the whole a conservative attitude. As the presence of all such preservatives must be declared on the labels, no consumer may be misled into purchasing them.

FOOD ADULTERATION

The national pure food laws, so far as they apply to food adulteration, establish simple principles. Food articles may contain nothing to reduce or to affect injuriously quality or strength; there may be no substitute for, no extraction of a valuable constituent; no addition of deleterious or poisonous matter; no spoiled matter or product from an animal not killed by slaughter. On the whole, so far as safety goes, the law has been effective. Confectionery, interpreted somewhat broadly, is in a class by itself. The essence of this matter is that as long as there is nothing harmful present the article will pass. As the purpose is to please the eye and the palate, no restrictions except those of safety need apply.

VITAMINS AND HORMONES

The functions of the vitamins and the hormones belong to the field of physiology rather than to the chemistry of foods. The importance of vitamins must never be overlooked, however. Moreover the study of their isolation, their analysis and the synthesis of these compounds belongs to organic chemistry, and may be conveniently included in this place.

These two classes of substances are easily confused. Their functions seem to be similar in that they regulate the processes of metabolism, one way or another. The simplest distinction is in their origin, the hormones being built up by various glands of the body, while the vitamins are introduced from without the body as constituents of our foods. The structure of a number of the vitamins has now been determined and, contrary to expectation, nitrogen has not been found to be an essential constituent. The structure of those vitamins which have been established is as follows:

Vitamin A. $C_6H_6(CH_3)_3.C_8H_6.(CH_3)_2CH_2OH$
(a) (b)

Group (a) consists of a six carbon ring, somewhat related to the benzene ring, with three methyl groups attached. Group (b) consists of a chain of eight carbon atoms with alternating double bonds, with two methyl groups attached, and, what seems to be important, one alcohol group. This structure relates it to carotene, from which it is derived in nature by hydrolytic cleavage.

Vitamin B. $(C_5H_4N_2)NH_2 — CH_2 — (C_3HNS)CH_3Cl$
(a) (b)
$— C_2H_4OH$
(c)

Group (a) consists of a heterocyclic ring containing nitrogen, attached to another heterocyclic ring (b) containing nitrogen and sulphur. Group (c) is an alcohol group, and is the only portion bearing some similarity to any portion of Vitamin A.

Vitamin B₂ or G. $C_{10}N_4H_3.(CH_3)_2O_2.C_5H_7(OH)_4$
(a) (b)

Group (a) consists of a triple heterocyclic ring to which is attached the pentose group (b).

Vitamin C, called ascorbic acid, $C_6H_4.(OH)_4O_2$, is a lactone from a six carbon hydroxyacid.

Vitamin D.
$$\underset{(a)}{C_{19}H_{26}(OH)}.\underset{(b)}{C_8H_{17}}$$

Group (a) consists of a modified four ring nucleus (containing a hydroxyl group), to which is attached group (b), a hydrocarbon side chain. The whole is related to ergosterol, which has thus been lifted into a great theoretical and practical importance.

These five compounds seem to have nothing in common except the hydroxyl group. They are built up on radically different principles, involving four important molecular types, open chains, saturated and unsaturated, and rings, homocyclic and heterocyclic.

Interpretations as to structure and function of the vitamins must for the present be tentative. Research is active and each addition to our knowledge properly involves readjustments in our conclusions.

Hormones. It is too early to generalize on the structure and origin of the hormones. Some of them seem to be associated with certain amino acids of the proteins, yet this association must be accepted conservatively.

Thyroxine, $C_6H_2I_2OH.O.C_6 H_2I_2–CH_2–CHNH_2CO_2H$, related to tyrosine, an amino acid of the proteins.

Adrenaline, $C_6H_3(OH)_2.C_3H_8ON$.

Glutathione is made up of three amino acids.

Insulin is a protein of somewhat normal composition.

These compounds do not differ among themselves as radically as do the vitamins. A consideration of all these formulas yields no hint as to the cause of their remarkable influences.

At least seven of the vitamins, or closely related compounds, have been artificially prepared. The industries have been active also, and a number of well recommended preparations are on the market.

Some further progress has been made in the knowledge of the structure of enzymes. The earlier interpretation of their structure as forms of proteins has so far been confirmed. The reasons for the specific characteristics of these three important catalytic substances, vitamins, hormones and enzymes, is not yet explained.

CHAPTER XXVIII

AGRICULTURAL CHEMISTRY

IN the economy of nature, the processes of vegetable life are preliminary to those of animal existence. To some extent modern men utilize the stores of past ages, petroleum and coal, or rely on the energy of the sun as manifested in the power of falling water and the winds. Aside from these instances men are dependent for their existence and activities upon the food and the energy stored up for them by the growing of plants. Men and other animals must rely absolutely upon the vegetable kingdom for their sustenance, and, after using their food, return the spent matter to the atmosphere and to the soil to be applied again to the upbuilding of vegetable matter. Thus these two kingdoms of nature supplement each other. The carbon, hydrogen, oxygen, and nitrogen compounds pass through cycles, mineral to vegetable, to animal and back to mineral, the process being repeated indefinitely. Such a cycle does not, however, exist in regard to the energy development. The energy of plants, after being passed on to animals, is permanently dissipated by the latter, and the plants must draw a new supply from the sun.

It will be well to review the carbon and nitrogen cycles already mentioned in other places. From carbon dioxide and water plants build up carbohydrates, fats, and proteins; animals use these as food and burn them up to form carbon dioxide and water. The cycle is complete, and the process is repeated. Nitrogen, too, goes through a cycle. Plant protein containing nitrogen is built up, serves animals as food, their waste is returned to the soil and thus is returned to the plants. We could imagine plants and animals mutually supplying each other, and establishing a continuous exchange of material without renewals from other sources.

The building up of the carbohydrates from carbon dioxide and water is the simplest of the plant syntheses. Although the following statement is hardly complete, it may be tentatively accepted.

Carbon dioxide with water forms carbonic acid, H_2CO_3. Under the influence of the sunlight, aided by chlorophyll, the green matter of the leaves, a reducing action takes place and formaldehyde is formed, with the loss of two atoms of oxygen, which pass into the air: $H_2CO_3 \rightarrow H_2CO + O_2$. In this reaction as much energy is stored up as would be liberated if the reverse action should take place. This then is the source virtually of the energy by which the animal kingdom lives. The formaldehyde, which for purposes of comparison may now be designated at CH_2O, polymerizes to glucose, or a similar substance, $6CH_2O$, or $C_6H_{12}O_6$, and from this unit all the carbohydrates are built up, including all the disaccharides like cane sugar, $C_{12}H_{22}O_{11}$, and starch and cellulose $(C_6H_{10}O_5)n$, by the loss of water.

The fats in turn are derived simply enough from the carbohydrates. This is illustrated from the fact that starchy foods are fattening.

The following equation:

$$9\tfrac{1}{2}C_6H_{12}O_6 \rightarrow C_3H_5(C_{18}H_{35}O_2)_3 + 2H_2O + 49O$$

Glucose   a typical fat

is not designed to indicate any exact mechanism, but it does show that the change involves a large loss of oxygen which is used up by other molecules, and the resulting fat has therefore stored up much more energy than was represented by the carbohydrate from which it was derived.

The proteins, like the fats and the carbohydrates, are composed of simple units. These units are the amino acids, and they are linked together by nitrogen. It would seem unwise to try to explain their formation from carbohydrates when the matter is far from clear. However, no reactions essentially different from those already shown are involved. Even though the synthesis must involve nitrogen, the amino acid, $C_6H_{11}O_2NH_2$, a protein unit, might readily enough be derived from $C_6H_{12}O_6$, the carbohydrate, and ammonia, NH_3. All these syntheses involve absorption of energy, but that phase presents no difficulties, for absorbing energy from the sunlight is a prime function of plants.

Besides the three groups of compounds just discussed, vegetable organisms include a number of other simpler organic compounds, such as the organic acids, oxalic, citric, malic, and tartaric. There are other groups of substances as the essential oils of the spices, and the alkaloids of certain drugs. Their formation presents no new kind of problem, and we need not follow them any further in our discussion. To these four classes water and mineral matter must be added to make our list of plant constituents complete.

In the composition of plant and animal products the four elements, carbon, hydrogen, oxygen, and nitrogen are usually considered in a group by themselves, as they go to make up the great bulk of plants. Further, when these products are burned, these four elements escape as gases, and all the others remain behind in the ash. These others are included in the name "mineral matter," and their presence is usually shown in the ash and their amount thus determined. The relation of mineral matter to the development of plants is even more obscure than in the case of the same relation in animals, but it is probably much along the same lines. The importance of mineral matter is apparent from the persistence of certain constituents in the ash of plants, and from the absolute necessity of these minerals in available form in any soil in which plants are to grow. As might be surmised, the minerals are compounds of the more common metals and nonmetals. The same five metals which are important among animals are found in plant organisms, namely, sodium, potassium, calcium, magnesium, and iron. Potassium is far more important than sodium. Among the nonmetals, phosphorus, sulphur, silicon, and chlorine are found.

What is the function of this mineral matter? It may be well to repeat in part some of the ideas of a similar discussion in the case of the chemistry of foods. Silicon dioxide serves to stiffen some stalks, as the wheat stalk. Phosphorus serves as a nucleus, like carbon, for the building up of complex molecules, as in certain proteins. The metals seem to form intermediate compounds, necessary to the upbuilding of vital substances. They may be influential in the chemical reactions taking place in the juices, and have some connection with the colloidal nature of the cell. They may have action like catalytic action.

Lastly, the rôle of water is of the greatest moment. It forms a large proportion of the mere bulk of the plant. It holds important constituents in solution, serving as a storehouse and carrier for vital supplies, and as a medium for the process of chemical changes. It is a temperature regulator. It fills all the spaces of the plant, bringing about the rigidity of the leaves which is associated with the highest well-being of the plant. Water has chemical relations to growth, in the first place, as the source of the hydrogen of the plant, and, secondly, in the chemical changes similar to those in animals which take place in the plant, as the changes among the carbohydrates. The chemistry of the cell no doubt involves colloid chemistry, and this type of colloid chemistry depends on water.

The Nature of Soils

Soil is not merely pulverized rock. It is rather rock reduced to fine form, through physical or chemical agencies, mixed with the soluble mineral matter which has been derived from the chemical disintegration of the rock, and with the organic residues from plants which have previously grown in it. The question of rock disintegration has already been discussed in the chapter on geochemistry. The summary of the ideas involved is as follows: Rocks, mostly silicates of a fair degree of complexity, are disintegrated, first physically, through temperature changes, glacial, water and wind action, even through the growth of plants. Upon the extensive surfaces thus exposed there is chemical action, due to water and carbon dioxide, oxygen, the juices of plants, and microorganisms. These chemical changes yield a limited amount of material of some solubility, which serves as the mineral plant food. Vegetation may now start in this mass, and upon the death and decay of the first plants growing, their remains are added to the soil. If this goes far enough, our soil is complete; namely, a basis of inactive insoluble rock material carrying the available inorganic and organic plant food. It may be capable of yielding, by subsequent chemical changes, a new supply of soluble mineral food.

We may for convenience consider the inorganic, or mineral, constituents of the soil in three classes. The first class includes the constituents which are soluble in water and very dilute acids. The plant juices through their acid content are able to exert a more powerful solvent action than water alone. This class represents the most available plant food. The second class of substances includes those which go into solution in acid of greater concentration, about 20 per cent hydrochloric acid. This represents the plant food more remotely available. The third class includes the insoluble material locked up in the chemically unchanged rock material of the soil. This insoluble material cannot support plant life until in the course of time its constituents are so altered that they belong to one of the other classes. In this connection the soils and vegetation on the slopes of Vesuvius are instructive. The solid lava beds gradually disintegrate physically, forming finely divided material, yet barren of vegetation. Near the base of the mountain, where the chemical disintegration of the lava has followed upon the mechanical, vegetation flourishes.

Everyone is familiar with the fact that organic matter, such as dead leaves, roots, and barnyard manure, when mixed with the soil, presently loses its characteristic appearance and becomes merged in the soil as a part thereof. The expression, "good clean dirt," perhaps means that any trace of the origin of a substance, offensive or otherwise, has been obliterated, and it is now all incorporated in the familiar soil. The conversion of ordinary organic matter into the normal organic soil humus involves two constituents, that part containing nitrogen, and that part free from nitrogen, in which the carbon is the center of interest. The nitrogen cycle again comes into consideration. The significant feature of this cycle is that nitrogen compounds, the proteins of decaying animal and vegetable matter, move along through a series of changes, involving a simplification of the molecules, until ammonia is reached, when oxidation begins to take place. In the end the nitrogen is fully converted into nitrates, which serve as the immediate supply of nitrogen for plants. These now rebuild the proteins, and the cycle is complete. The final changes of the cycle have not been completed when the nitrogen compounds are incorporated in the humus. These take place gradually as the nitrates are developed under the influence of bacteria. In the last form they are soluble and easily washed out of the soil and wasted. Hence their gradual formation is an advantage.

The changes by which ordinary carbonaceous organic matter becomes humus are difficult to follow. Some carbon oxidizes to carbon dioxide. As carbonaceous matter decays and ferments, it loses gaseous constituents, darkens in color, and is altered in texture. It is capable of absorbing and holding water. A soil rich in this humus is fertile, for humus from its origin is likely to contain in abundance the materials plants require for growth.

In the process of their growth, plants assimilate carbon, hydrogen, and oxygen from the carbon dioxide of the air and the water of the soil. The other requirements, nitrogen and the minerals, are extracted from the organic and inorganic constituents of the soil. If the plant dies and decays where it has grown, much of that which was extracted is returned to the soil, and the amount of humus is actually increased. Agriculture, however, involves a heavy drain upon the soil when the crop is removed. Hence arises the necessity for the renewal of the available plant food from outside sources. The elements needed by plants for their growth are: sodium, potassium, magnesium, calcium, and iron among the metals, and silicon, chlorine, phosphorus, carbon, hydrogen, oxygen, and nitrogen among the nonmetals. It has been shown lately that small amounts of other elements are essential, among them iron, copper and manganese. Of these, carbon, hydrogen, and oxygen are supplied by the atmosphere and water. The rest must come from the soil. All but calcium, potassium, phosphorus, and nitrogen are so uniformly present in sufficient amounts that they seldom require any attention. These four, and especially the last three of them, may be wanting in a soil that has been cropped. One of the problems, therefore, of agricultural chemistry, is the study of the exhaustion and renewal of these forms of plant food. It has been claimed that most soils have enough mineral food stored up in the less available form to serve plants indefinitely, provided the soils are so handled that these foods become available. Whether this is true or not, it is very apparent that, in a short period of time, soils lose their fertility when crops are removed from them.

Fallowing

The process of fallowing is the simplest manner of renewing the available food. The land lies idle, but during this time the natural changes of rock disintegration go on so that presently there is a new supply of the more soluble plant foods. This is a method now used only exceptionally. The same results are better attained by rotation of crops.

Rotation of Crops

The different crops do not all withdraw the same constituents from the soil in equal amounts. One draws on the nitrogen heavily, another on the potassium, and a third on phosphorus, while in each case the other foods are in a measure spared. If, therefore, through a period of say five years, there is planted a succession of different crops, each will in its turn, while drawing upon its own specific requirement, allow the soil to recuperate with respect to the foods which other plants require. Rotation of crops is not solely a chemical problem. It must be managed with reference to other agricultural needs, such as the use of the seasons for planting, and a convenient distribution of labor.

Fertilizers

To restore the plant food to the soil, to replace a sufficient fraction of that which has been taken away, or otherwise lost, is the purpose of fertilizing. Some soils are said to be capable of supplying the mineral needs indefinitely, but usually plant food must be restored, and the first method for accomplishing this is the use of barnyard manure. A detailed study of this topic is not in order here, but the main point is clear. What comes from the land thus goes back to it. To be sure, through the sale of products from the farm, there is some loss, but these products may be so selected that they bring a maximum of return with a minimum of drain. Dairy and poultry products illustrate this, for what they carry away is of smaller proportionate value than the financial return which they bring. If properly managed, the use of barnyard manure carries back to the land almost all that has come from it, so that the replenishing from outside sources may be reduced to a minimum. Akin to this fertilizer in theory is the use of such materials as tankage and other slaughterhouse products, the refuse of beets at the sugar extraction plants, garbage residue, and everything which has directly or indirectly come from the land. Of course, there is here a change of location, and one farm may be losing what another, even remote, gains.

In the use of artificial or commercial fertilizers, the special chemical nature of the problem becomes conspicuous. Some commercial fertilizers do not suggest any new points over what has already been discussed. Tankage and garbage residues are simply other phases of the theme mentioned under barnyard manure. But in the use of the various nitrogen compounds, phosphate rock, and potash, we are applying our specific chemical knowledge to the problem of soil replenishment. Besides water and humus, soil is most likely to lack nitrogen, phosphorus, and potash, and in less degree sulphur and calcium. These then may be specifically added in forms that are convenient, to supplement the original content of the soil, or to make good the losses through crop removal or waste in other ways.

The recovery of potash from natural sources, the utilization of phosphate rock and the formation of nitrogen compounds from the nitrogen of the air have been described in the chapter on Inorganic Industries. There should be added a word about the natural fixation of nitrogen.

The natural means of fixing nitrogen are confined on the whole to two. Under atmospheric conditions, electric storms, and perhaps other natural phenomena, small amounts of nitrogen are combined with oxygen or hydrogen, and these compounds find their way into the soil. Secondly, certain leguminous plants, by means of the nodules formed upon their roots, induced by bacteria, are capable of utilizing the atmospheric nitrogen. The artificial fixation of nitrogen was a vital question a generation ago. It is now satisfactorily solved.

THE LIMING OF LANDS

Owing to the decay of organic matter and the formation of humus there is likely to be established an acid condition of the soil, in which some plants thrive, but which is unfavorable for the good growth of many others. This phase of agricultural chemistry will be better understood in the future. But one feature is already clear, namely, that some crops must have this acid neutralized. The natural antidote for the acid condition established, or its preventative as the acid gradually forms, is lime. That is, calcium hydroxide for quick action, and calcium carbonate, finely ground, for slower action. This treatment is independent of the requirement of calcium in the normal growth of crops. In some cases this acid condition is studied so carefully that the pH value, properly determined, is a controlling factor in the handling of the soil.

Growing plants without soil is receiving much attention. The plant nutrients are supplied in solution, and the root system is developed either in water or in sand. The chemical questions involved are the same as those of ordinary cultivation.

The nature of most of the vegetable products has been thoroughly studied in the past, and on the whole these are well understood. Carbohydrates, vegetable oils, plant proteins and alkaloids represent well investigated chapters. On the other hand, the phases of plant chemistry corresponding to animal physiology are not nearly so well developed. Much of this remains for the future. The structure of the most important vegetable substance, chlorophyll, the green coloring matter of plants, has been established. It is complex and comparable with that of hemoglobin, the inorganic magnesium of the former corresponding roughly to the iron of the latter. Plant hormones have been found, as is but natural. Various effects of chemical substances upon plants have been studied, this applying to changes of phases of growth and root development.

Unfortunately the various phases of agriculture are confronted with an increasing number of difficulties in the way of blights and insects. To meet these difficulties chemistry supplies sprays and poisons. The vineyards of southern France in June are blue with Bordeaux mixture, and lime-sulphur is manufactured in America on a huge scale. Lead and arsenic sprays, and lately fluorides are successfully used as poisons. It will be necessary to keep careful watch on the products thus sprayed, and on a possibly harmful accumulation in the soil. Some thought is given to the possibility of developing sprays composed of organic compounds. Such compounds would presumably decompose in time, and not accumulate in the soil, as is possible with inorganic materials.

SEA FOODS

The food products of the sea are so much taken for granted that few realize that these in the end involve questions which really belong to agriculture. Without the products of the sea many peoples would be in serious lack of food. In most cases little thought is given to the growth of the vegetation which makes sea life possible. Yet estimates have been made as to the value of sea acreage as compared with land acreage in the production of food. The value is less, but not inconsiderable and has been set as high as one-fourth. It is asserted, moreover, that much of that which the rivers carry to the sea comes back in the way of food. In one country of central Europe the practice of favoring fish life by adding plant fertilizers to the waters of lakes is well established.

CHAPTER XXIX

SANITARY CHEMISTRY

THE recent years have been measured by great progress in the work of sanitation and public health. In this valuable work chemistry has played some part, and what that part is will be here reviewed. The chief lines of its usefulness have been in the investigation of water supplies and the purification of these, of the disposal of the two great wastes, sewage and garbage, in the discussion of the vitiation of air and the problem of ventilation, industrial poisons and in the preparation of disinfectants and antiseptics.

WATER SUPPLIES AND PURIFICATION

Only a limited portion of our population is privileged to use as a water supply a source which has incurred no danger of pollution. The limited population is that of sparsely settled regions, especially in mountain districts, and a few favored municipalities which are so near unsettled regions that they may draw upon them for their water. In another class are cities like New York and Boston, which by the proper precautions keep their watersheds free from danger even in regions adjacent to settled communities. In this class, though the source is very different, come those homes and communities which use ground waters from wells, which are safe because they yield unpolluted waters, or waters whose slight pollution has been cleared up by their long passage through the layers of the ground. The great danger in water supplies lies in the fact that many large communities are dependent upon surface water supplies, rivers, or lakes, which have been polluted either by themselves or by others. No better example can be cited than that of the Ohio River, which serves alternately for the water supply and the sewage receptacle of Pittsburgh, Cincinnati, and Louisville. Surface waters require the most consideration because they are so much used, and at the same time are the most polluted.

Water is likely to take up substances of two classes, the inorganic or mineral, and the organic. The soluble inorganic constituents are mostly the salts of calcium and magnesium, which make the water hard. There is no evidence that they are ordinarily prejudicial to health. Other inorganic substances, like common salt, are unimportant in all but most unusual waters.

The organic constituents, especially the bacteria, are more important. We could perhaps tolerate, upon suppression of our purely esthetic sentiments, the waste products of men or animals, if it were merely dead material. But when these waste products include disease-bearing bacteria, the pollution ceases to be a matter of taste. Cholera, typhoid, and intestinal troubles like dysentery are the specific troubles to be feared, while the general tone of health of a community is said to be generally benefited when the water supply is improved. Of these diseases typhoid fever is the most serious menace. Typhoid fever is not to be feared on account of a general condition of water supply. The danger is due to specific contamination by the excreta of typhoid sufferers. Any water contaminated by sewage is likely to be infected.

It will not be advantageous to tell about the methods of chemical analysis of water supplies. This analysis tells much about the history of the water and its possible pollution, but the particular condition of bacterial pollution is to be found by bacteriological methods. The chemist is then called upon to help the engineer to devise means of purifying water which is contaminated or which may be in danger of becoming so.

There have been various methods suggested in the past for making water safe. On the large scale reliance is now placed almost altogether on filtration and chlorination. Filtration is by the rapid or slow sand filter. Slow sand filtration, suggested by the process of natural purification as water passes through the ground, consists in passing the water downward through a layer of sand about three feet thick. There is soon formed a sediment layer on top of the sand (German, Schmutzdecke) which is a very efficient filtering medium. Any sediment or bacterial matter is retained by this layer, and the effluent is a safe one. In the course of time the layer becomes so thick that it must be removed. The water is then drawn off and the sediment layer scraped off. This is a cumbersome, expensive, and even unsanitary necessity and counts against the process, although mechanical improvements have diminished the objections. More serious are the objections that the filter beds require large areas, and in cold climates must be covered to prevent freezing. Yet London and other large cities use this method with success.

The rapid sand filters are more popular in America. The essential differences are these: The necessary filtering area is cut down to about one-fiftieth by the use of a larger-grained sand. To accomplish the filtration with the coarser sand, a coagulant is introduced which serves to entangle the matter to be removed and to form a filtering layer on the sand. The third essential feature is that through mechanical contrivances the flow of water may be reversed at a high rate of speed, the accumulated deposit washed from the sand layer and thus the filter renewed. This renovation is a matter of a few minutes, and the combination of mechanical manipulation and prompt restoration to use is a very important item. The process of the operation is this: As the water enters the system the coagulant is added. This is either alum (aluminum sulphate) or ferrous sulphate and lime, which are converted respectively into aluminum or ferric hydroxide, substances of gelatinous nature. The water is thoroughly mixed with the coagulant, then allowed to flow slowly through settling chambers for several hours. During this time the greater portion of the coagulum separates out, and the rest is removed on the filters. Insoluble matter including sediment and bacteria are thus entangled and removed first by the settling, finally by the filters. When properly operated, especially in respect to crowding, the rapid sand filters yield a safe and attractive product, which is so nearly free from bacteria that a small dosage of chlorine makes the water absolutely sterile.

Chlorine has been spoken of as a bleacher and disinfectant. In recent years it has been applied to the disinfection of water supplies with marked success. It cannot take the place of filtration with some waters, for example, turbid waters. Any highly polluted water should be filtered. But as an aid to filtration, for the treatment of waters which are almost good enough, and as an emergency measure, chlorine is a great boon and has already saved many lives. The expression "chlorine" is used, although it is applied as the element in the form of liquid chlorine or in compounds in the form of calcium or sodium hypochlorite, all possessing equal efficiency. So called chloramine, that is a mixture of chlorine and ammonia, has been found to be an improvement, both in

A FILTER UNIT

A, represents 12 inches of small stones, ¾—1½ inches. B, graded smaller stones and coarse sand. C, about 2 feet of standard sand, which serves as the filter. The water D, stands 3 feet above the sand. The collecting drains E, lead to the main drain F.

respect to efficiency and the freedom from unpleasant tastes. The introduction of chlorine on its own account or because of interaction with the phenolic compounds of city wastes introduces an odor and taste, which though slight, is objectionable. As yet this objection has not been overcome. It is a disadvantage trivial by the side of the great gain in safety secured through chlorination.

The typhoid death rate is a gruesome but convenient method of determining the safety of a community's water supply. This is the yearly number of deaths per hundred thousand of the population. Roughly speaking, one death represents ten cases of sickness from the disease.

Table I shows the improvement which has been accomplished through a period of years by improvements in water supplies and other means of sanitation. It represents the annual typhoid death rate for the larger cities of the United States through a period of years.

TABLE I

Year	1890	1906-10	1915	1920	1938
Number of cities....	36	78	57	57	78
Typhoid rate........	58	38	8.7	3.5	.67

In 1938, 29 cities reported no deaths from typhoid fever. Table II shows the death rate from typhoid in the city of Cleveland, Ohio, before and after the introduction of a better water supply.

TABLE II

1900-03, annual typhoid rate....................	57
1905-10, with a new supply....................	15.8
1933-39, modern treatment of supply...........	.57

It is probable that even this low rate is attributable in part to other sources than the water supply.

HARDNESS OF WATER

The hardness of water is caused by compounds of calcium and magnesium of two different types. The first type includes the acid carbonates, $H_2Ca(CO_3)_2$ and $H_2Mg(CO_3)_2$. These are considered apart because, upon sufficient boiling, they are decomposed and the calcium and magnesium carbonates deposited and removed from solution. They are called temporary hardness, and the treatment is different from that for permanent hardness, which is due to chlorides and sulphates of the same metals. The objections to hard water are two. Soap is destroyed by these compounds, and there results not alone the waste of soap, but also the formation of the well-known scum of the calcium and magnesium stearates or salts of the fatty acids. This substance adheres to utensils used with soap and remains to a certain extent in clothes washed in hard water. The other detriment in the use of hard water is the sediment of scale which settles out in boilers. This is absolutely serious, and must receive attention by all using hard water. Further, in certain limited fields of manufacturing and in some industrial processes, hard water is undesirable.

The chemical problem of softening is a simple one up to a certain point. We must convert the soluble calcium and magnesium salts into insoluble compounds, which may be allowed to settle out or are filtered off. The first class of compounds mentioned above is thus treated; $H_2Ca(CO_3)_2 + Ca(OH)_2$ lime, $\rightarrow 2CaCO_3$, insoluble and therefore harmless, $+ 2H_2O$. The reaction for magnesium is not quite so simple, but for our present purpose may be assumed to be the same. This assumption that magnesium reacts like calcium will be maintained throughout the discussion.

The softening of a city's water supply increases the attractiveness of the water. So far as the taste of hard water goes, habit differs, and the matter is not serious. But the other considerations are real. The question of municipal softening is complicated by economic and engineering problems. It is likely that it will be solved by individual handling, especially because hardness is objectionable for a comparatively small portion of a city's uses.

A method of water softening adaptable on a scale short of a public water supply has become somewhat common. This is the treatment of the water with natural or artificial zeolites, double silicates of sodium and aluminum. When the water comes in contact with this substance, all the calcium and the magnesium from the hard water go into the compound, and thus become insoluble. The softening operation is perfect, for the sodium liberated in the place of the calcium and magnesium has no hardness effect. The softening agent must be restored occasionally by treatment with sodium chloride, common salt, when the accumulated calcium and magnesium are thrown out and the desired sodium restored.

The use of the new type of soap in a small way eliminates the disagreeable features of hard water. It is conceivable that it may solve the problem from the domestic standpoint. This soap is described in Chapter XXIII.

SEWAGE DISPOSAL

Sewage normally consists of the used city water supply, which has gathered up in its course through the city the various wastes which can be carried away by water. There is likely to be an increase in the mass of the sewage from the ground water, which seeps into the sewers, and in warm weather the loss from evaporation and use on lawns and gardens may cause a definite diminution. Storm waters, when delivered into the common sewers, complicate the problem of sewage disposal. Some communities have separate sewage systems. Until the dilution due to storm waters reaches the ratio of 3 to 1, the sewage is called sanitary sewage, and requires attention. With greater dilution the necessity of treatment for purification is diminished. In addition to human excreta, kitchen wastes, stable wastes, waste from soap and washings, industrial wastes and street washings must be reckoned with. Sewage may be considered 1,000 parts water and 1 part solid matter, of which ¾ is in solution. In America there is a much larger consumption of water per capita than in Europe, and this increases the difficulty of the problem, which depends on the mass of water to be treated rather than concentration of impurities.

From the most superficial standpoint the treatment of sewage has for its aim the prevention of any nuisance. This includes unsightly refuse, odors, danger to bathers and to fish life, and finally pollution of any water used subsequently as a source of supply. The simplest disposal is running the sewage into large rivers or into tidal water under such conditions that no signs of the refuse are ever again apparent. This applies, or seems to apply, in many cases. The sewage of Buffalo once in the Niagara River will not trouble Buffalo again, and a city like St. Louis, or some of the cities on large swift European streams, are not again troubled with their sewage, when it is once discharged into the stream. Whether communities farther down stream notice the pollution is considered more or less a separate question. The same idea applied to lake cities or to cities on tidal harbors has not been so successful, for the flow of the water away is often not sufficiently pronounced. In the Great Lakes and in New York harbor the accumulation of pollution is a problem.

In the last analysis, sewage treatment has for its ultimate object the completion of the nitrogen and carbon cycles already mentioned in another connection, so that the material which has become waste by human use may be so altered that it is unobjectionable, safe, and ready to be taken up for plant growth. The various bacterial methods of treatment have for their immediate practical object the alteration of waste matter, in such a way that it is moved along in this cycle. It must reach such a point, that in the ordinary course of events the process may be completed by nature without any further attention or objectionable features.

Although there are many other features connected with sewage which interest the engineer, the greatest menace to health lies in disease germs present. If these are destroyed, one great problem of sewage disposal is solved, but not all. When sewage is so treated that the nitrogen cycle is completed, and oxidation fully carried out, dangerous bacteria are destroyed. It is therefore only occasionally true that sewage must be treated specifically for bacteria. It is usually treated in a general way and the refinements of bacterial safety left to the finishing touches of water purification when the water is to be used again. It is evident that the making of sewage more pure than the water into which it is to be discharged is an over-refinement.

Running sewage into large bodies of water so that it seems to be removed from our attention, means dilution with so much water charged with oxygen that the operation of oxidation may take place promptly and completely. The Illinois River presents an interesting study. The sewage of Chicago, discharged into this stream, is too great a burden for it to take. Consequently the river is a polluted river, containing no dissolved oxygen and no fish life for many miles. In course of time the absorption of the oxygen from the air rectifies this condition, and the river becomes normal, so that it is not considered a menace to the water supply of St. Louis, farther down stream. Boston meets this problem of sewage dilution by storing its sewage on an island, well out in the bay, for periodic discharge into the sea at ebb tide.

The soil has striking powers in oxidation of waste, and conversion of offensive matter into the innocuous constituents of the soil. In the use of barnyard manures and the disposal of household wastes in the country we see constant application of this. But as soon as people concentrate, the accumulation of refuse is too great for this kind of disposal and the problems of sewage disposal develop. Carrying the sewage out to the country, and applying it to the land is then only logical, and where the winter is open enough, it is not uncommon. Berlin, Paris, and many small English cities use the method of irrigation, which means applying to the soil as much sewage as the soil can dispose of, using the land at the same time for the growing of crops. The land is underdrained, and the process, given favorable climatic and soil conditions, is satisfactory, and the cost is not excessive. The amount of land needed is very large. There are modifications of this method, wherein the growing of crops is left out, and the soil used more in the sense of a filter.

London uses a method of chemical treatment. After screening and some sedimentation, the sewage is treated with ferrous sulphate and lime. The precipitated iron hydroxide carries down with it a considerable fraction of the material, not soluble, and the whole is allowed to settle. This sludge, which is still 95 per cent water, is carried out to sea by steamers, and scattered over so great an area of open water that no signs of it are again apparent.

On the whole chemical treatment is not so promising as bacteriological treatment, which is the natural way of disposal. Disinfection, for example, is only of value in specific cases, as for destroying the disease germs when there are sewage outfalls near bathing beaches. On the whole it delays too much the bacterial changes which are the ideal ones.

At present the methods of sewage disposal of most promise are those depending upon bacterial action, either in tanks without air, or under the influence of air by means of beds or sprinklers, or even by forced aëration.

SEPTIC TANKS AND AËRATION

In these the sewage flows so slowly that it is practically in a state of rest. Fermentation takes place, much of the material changes to gas and to soluble substances, and the effluent is in better condition either for running away or for further treatment. There is no sufficiency of oxygen, and the fermentation must depend upon bacteria of the anaërobic, that is, working without oxygen, order. For small installations this is sometimes all the treatment that sewage receives. The Imhoff tank has mechanical modifications which make action more perfect. A further treatment often applied is the exposure of this effluent to the air, sometimes by sprinkling it as a spray over the surface of broken stone which is covered with the residue of previous contacts. There is abundance of bacterial and insect life on these surfaces and the oxidizing and purifying action is considerable. This double treatment yields

Courtesy, The Dorr Company

SEWAGE DISPOSAL PLANT, SIOUX FALLS, S.D.

Revolving sewage distributors operate in conjunction with trickling filters of crushed stone.

SEWAGE DISPOSAL PLANT ON WARD'S ISLAND, NEW YORK CITY

Ewing Galloway Photo

an effluent which under ordinary conditions is considered satisfactory.

The activated sludge treatment makes use from the beginning of bacterial action favored by an abundance of oxygen. These bacteria are developed by blowing air through a portion of the sewage, until it is apparent that they are present in abundance. After this the incoming sewage is treated with the sediment of previously treated sewage, all the time being exposed to a vigorous circulation of air. The mass becomes brown, and upon standing, the solid matter settles out so completely that the effluent is of satisfactory appearance and "stability," that is, will not putrefy. The activated sludge method is compact, quick, and satisfactory in many respects. But as yet two features are drawbacks. The blowing of the air is wasteful and expensive. And the sludge from the settling tank is still to be disposed of. It promises to have a high fertilizer value, but as obtained contains so much water that it must be dehydrated in order to be applicable. This problem has not yet been completely solved from the standpoint of economy.

In this question of sewage purification it must be appreciated that the chemical side of the question is only one. The engineering question is a very large one, and the whole operation must be carried out so economically that it shall not be an overserious burden to the community. The increasing population of our cities and the higher sanitary ideals demand a solution of the problem. If it cannot be solved at low expense, we must be prepared to submit to a greater expense. The pollution of our river, lake, and harbor banks, to say nothing of our water supplies, will be tolerated less and less as time passes.

GARBAGE DISPOSAL

Garbage, although it must be considered a nuisance, may be looked upon as a definite industrial by-product. It is a product of agriculture which has no further use in the domestic economy. Its outright destruction is a form of waste. The garbage of New York City, for instance, after it is collected and delivered, is worth a million dollars a year. Attention may be called again to the nitrogen cycle. The nitrogen question concerns the placing of the nitrogen of the air, that is, uncombined nitrogen, into combination, thus making it part of the nitrogen cycle. Burning garbage converts the combined, that is, usable nitrogen, into uncombined, that is, useless nitrogen, which is now out of the cycle. Burning of garbage may be expedient, but in the last analysis its utilization would seem preferable.

Garbage disposal takes two forms, mechanical treatment and feeding to hogs. In the former case details differ, but the outcome is that the fat present in garbage is extracted by a proper solvent, and the dried residue is used as a constituent of fertilizers. The other method, feeding to hogs, is also used. Farms where this is accomplished must be conducted in a most thorough manner, to prevent nuisance and disease, but these establishments have not the offensive features which popular ideas associate with them. In this method, as the other, the purpose is to utilize, not to destroy, that part of the food which has not been disposed of.

VITIATION OF AIR AND VENTILATION

It is evident that the air in confined spaces soon loses it attractiveness when it is breathed or otherwise used.

Unless the circumstances are extreme, it can be shown that the harmfulness of such air is not due to an appreciable loss of oxygen, nor is it due to an accumulation of carbon dioxide, for air, otherwise fresh, when mixed with carbon dioxide from chemical sources still retains its freshness. Some years ago a New York State committee on ventilation made a study of this subject, and although the results in some respects were indecisive, several points were well established. These were: The increase of carbon dioxide has no effect on the quality of the air; there was no sign of any poisonous substance in the air of ill-ventilated rooms; the amount of moisture in the air was an important factor, as was also the temperature of the air and its condition of rest or motion. These last features are associated with the heat-regulating power of the body and in this factor the final solution of the effect of bad air will probably be found. Almost a generation later the conclusions from this investigation have been put into partial use by the practice of air conditioning.

Ideal ventilation would require that there should be a flow of air through a given room, so that at every moment its occupants would receive an absolutely fresh supply. Such a condition, when the air must be warmed, is excessive in cost, and in its place a practical program is adopted. This provides for addition of fresh air to dilute the vitiated air until it is sufficiently healthy and comfortable. Three thousand cubic feet of fresh air per person per hour is judged a liberal standard. This is about 1/10 of the amount flowing over a person in the open on a quiet day. There is always considerable passage of air by leakage through crevices or diffusion through the walls. An official standard set by Chicago is as follows: 1,800 cubic feet per person per hour, velocity 2.5 feet per second, carbon dioxide 8 parts in 10,000 (that is 2 to 3 times normal), temperature 20° C. (68° F.), humidity 42 per cent, dust count 100,000 per c.c.; bacteria, 12 colonies per plate.

Vitiation of air by products of combustion, as in illumination and warming, from sewer gases, from industrial operations, as in chemical factories, are problems requiring special attention. Some startling results have been published showing the dangerous condition of the air in auditoriums during epidemics of colds.

Industrial Poisons

Industrial poisons should receive a brief mention. Many substances which may be handled occasionally without inconvenience prove to be harmful when there is frequent contact with the skin or inhalation of dust or vapors. Of the metals which raise questions, lead probably comes first. Its uses, in paints (white lead, red lead), in lead compounds in storage batteries, as lead oxide in enamels, are so many that contacts are to be expected. Copper compounds are used in sprays, especially in the vineyards of France, but, it seems, little harm has developed. The zinc of brass has raised questions of the danger of zinc vapors in brass foundries. Arsenic compounds should be watched carefully; the arsenic in the iron pyrites of soft coal has done damage; arsenic in pigments is spoken of, but today is probably of little danger; arsenic in sprays must be used with care; it is too early in the use of these sprays to pass final judgment as to their harmfulness. Mercury may involve danger, particularly in cases where it is used at high temperatures in place of water in boilers.

Among nonmetallic substances, such highly marked compounds as ammonia, nitrogen peroxide, hydrogen sulphide, and the acids are occasionally harmful. They are, however, so easily noticed that chronic effects are unlikely. This chapter is concerned primarily with effects which, though at the moment inconspicuous, eventually show as injurious. White phosphorus, used in matches, caused much illness; but the use of red phosphorus and sulfide of phosphorus has ended this trouble. The danger of carbon monoxide is well known. Whether its inhalation in unappreciated amounts over a period of time accumulates adverse effects is a question not yet clearly settled. Fluorine in drinking waters has been found in some of our western states to cause dental troubles.

Some organic compounds are serious industrial menaces. Such are methyl alcohol, benzene and aniline. Two new problems have arisen with modern technology: they are, first, the solvents used in lacquers, and, second, the carbon disulphide of the viscose process. Lead tetraethyl, dangerous as it is as an active poison, seems to have no chronic effects as used.

Disinfectants and Antiseptics

A disinfectant is a substance which is capable of destroying bacteria. An antiseptic is milder in its action, perhaps not destroying the bacteria which may be present, but rendering the medium unfavorable for further growth. There can hardly be any distinction between the two except that of degree, and the same substances in different concentrations act as both. Copper sulphate solution of 0.1 per cent concentration acts as an antiseptic, but of 1 per cent concentration it acts as a disinfectant. Certain physical agents, as light and heat, destroy bacteria, but we are concerned here with chemical action. It is often difficult to explain how the chemical reagent acts. The following generalizations are in part somewhat vague, but they are, nevertheless, suggestive. Disinfectants destroy by acid action, by coagulation or precipitation of the bacteria or their food (the heavy metals readily coagulate most forms of protein); by direct poisonous action; by reduction and oxidation. In some cases the action seems nothing more definite than the development of an uncongenial surrounding. Just as higher animals and plants can thrive only within circumscribed conditions it is likely that bacteria are hardy only within narrow limits.

Among the nonmetallic substances the active elements and compounds are naturally in the foreground. Chlorine, bromine, and iodine are very efficient, as are also compounds like chloride of lime which yield chlorine. The acids are efficient, but they are of limited application. Sulphur dioxide is much used, and calcium pentasulphide, lime sulphur solution, is an effective fungicide, although the manner of its action is not clear. Boric acid and borax have marked preserving action, although they are very mild chemical reagents. (Preserving action is akin to antiseptic action.) The heavy metals, particularly mercury in the form of mercuric chloride, are efficacious. After mercury, zinc and copper are the most used. Oxidizing agents like potassium permanganate and hydrogen peroxide are much applied.

Many organic compounds are valuable disinfectants. Their chemical reactivity is low, yet they are very inimical to bacteria. Foremost are the phenols, hydroxyl derivatives of the benzene series, carbolic acid, C_6H_5OH, cresylic acid, C_7H_7OH, and thymol, $C_{10}H_{13}OH$. These are the important constituents of tar and creosote. Formaldehyde possibly reacts chemically with portions of the bacteria. A number of other organic substances are used for bactericidal purposes, but their enumeration would introduce no new ideas. In the present state of our knowledge the efficiency of any organic substance must be determined by direct bacteriological tests.

CHAPTER XXX

DEVELOPMENTS AND TRENDS IN CHEMISTRY

SCIENTIFIC chemistry, based on logical and permanently accepted explanation of phenomena, began with Lavoisier's interpretation of the phenomenon of combustion. His conclusions were made after he learned of Priestley's discovery of oxygen in 1774. The early development in France presently had its influence in other countries. It may be considered that chemistry in the main, in its present form, with knowledge of molecular structure, dates from about 1870. It has been claimed, with a strong tone of reproach, that in the next two decades the physical sciences "rested on their oars" so to speak, assuming that the subjects were reasonably well developed. Any such feeling that the work was finished came to an end with the discoveries of the last decade of the nineteenth century, and just after, when the world was startled, and science awakened, by a number of epoch-making discoveries.

These included:

The discovery of the element argon in the atmosphere.

The X-ray.

Wireless transmission.

Radium.

The vitamins and hormones.

The influence of these discoveries is not to be measured alone by their intrinsic interest, nor in the material benefits which they have conferred on mankind. Almost more important is their awakening effect. They emphasized in a startling way that the limits of the physical sciences had by no means been reached, and that diligence in research might bring wondrous rewards.

In this awakening, chemistry was intimately concerned. One can hardly find a more striking and even romantic illustration in all science than the discovery of *argon* in such considerable amounts in the atmosphere. The atmosphere and its constituents had been studied with intensity for many years, yet this important constituent had not been found. It is true that there had been a certain restlessness about the nature of the nitrogen of the air, but the reason for its seeming abnormality had not been seriously suspected. The discovery of a new gas, in the very air we breathe, in a fairly considerable amount, exhibiting an entirely new characteristic (chemical inactivity) was indeed a revelation. Research became active, and in the end an entirely new chapter was added to the realm of chemistry, the chapter of the inert gases, including names and interests of every day use and applications—argon, helium and neon. This was the beginning of the relevations which in time led to such a dramatic climax— atomic disintegration.

RECENT ACHIEVEMENTS OF CHEMISTRY

The outstanding activity and achievements of the chemistry of today may be referred to three great causes; one may call them events, so clearly outlined were they and so definite was their influence. The first of these three events was the set of discoveries just outlined, which has given to chemistry a new impetus, and has resulted in the greatly increased knowledge of the nature of matter, that is, in the fuller interpretation of the nature of the atom.

The second great event which gave an epoch-making stimulus to American chemistry was the first World War and its aftermath. It soon became apparent, as the war progressed, that our country was far from self-sufficient in ways chemical. In the after years chemists had therefore a powerful stimulus to rectify this deficiency, and their efforts showed most satisfactory results. This paragraph, and to some extent the next, concerns itself with American chemistry, which is of immediate interest, and reflects sufficiently the general line of progress the world over.

The third great event which has given the present powerful stimulus to chemistry has been in the increasing appreciation that the key to progress is research. Fundamental, that is, purely scientific, research is often distinguished from industrial research, and their respective merits debated. These two forms of investigation are so interwoven in their attack on nature's problems, that the benefits of one quickly react upon the other. It is an old saying that any purely scientific development will require a generation for its practical application. There is much truth in this, though the length of time that must elapse is often much shorter in these progressive days. The saying may be turned around somewhat to this effect: Successful practical application of things scientific soon gives to pure science new tools to further its advances.

A brief survey of the growth of research gives a concrete picture of the emphasis which is now placed upon this phase of human endeavor. In 1939, a normal year, 32,000 scientists were engaged in research, besides about half that number of trained helpers. In 1941 the money invested in research increased over that invested the year before by 25 per cent. The number of scientific articles published in a year increased from 9,000 in 1918 to over 30,000 in 1943.

To all these influences is to be added the intense stimulus of the problems of the recent war. To quote a commentator on this situation: "World War II was in essence a war of science in which the brains and industrial techniques of our scientists and engineers were matched against those of the enemy, to produce the most advanced and effective devices of warfare and achieve military supremacy. . . . All this, while primarily intended for the purpose of war, has equal or greater potentialities for commercial progress." Again, quoting: "Never before has science research done so much in so little time as in the years 1941–1946." A summation of the objectives of the research of this period may be stated as follows: Contributions to the national defense; improvements on present products and processes; the providing of substitutes for materials and objects unavailable; development of new products and processes. Even when there is no spectacular new development, such intensive research means an advance all along the line. The objectives just mentioned, and others also, have been reached to a gratifying extent.

The discussions of this chapter involve mainly the scientific progress of American chemical industry. The activities of these years include almost every department of such industry, with results of improvement in almost every field. The research and progress in our American industries are estimated as representing one sixth of our total industrial values. The active period, 1939–45, shows a doubling of chemical production, both war and civilian.

As chemists reflect on the results of the years of the war, the feeling is apparent that the outlook is broader than mere reconversion. "It is certain that the war stimulus will carry us on to a definite success."

PERIODIC TABLE OF ELEMENTS

Mendeléeff's periodic classification of the elements, the greatest generalization of chemistry, was presented to the world in 1869. Its influence increased steadily, despite certain troublesome discrepancies. Most of these were cleared up by the understanding of Moseley's atomic number. Since then the periodic classifications have been a mainstay in chemical considerations. The description of the atom presented in the Chapters XIX and XX, though evidently incomplete, is adequate within limits. The interpretation of the structure of the atom has become increasingly important both in purely scientific studies and in the popular interest. Chemists and physicists have been busy with this question, and the whole world knows its outcome in the atomic bomb. Although a large portion of these studies lie within the domain of physics, chemical considerations have been popularly diffused. Atom, neutron, proton, electron, atomic weights, atomic numbers, isotopes, transuranium elements, atomic disintegration (atom smashing), are terms not so far from public appreciation as they have been in the past.

The writer is reminded of a saying attributed to the physicist Rowland of Johns Hopkins University years ago: "You may think that the atom is an indivisible unit. Some day you will find that it is as complicated as a grand piano."

The classic list of elements in the periodic table ends

with uranium, element 92. It is now confidently reported that four trans-uranium elements of higher atomic weight have been clearly identified—numbers 93, 94, 95 and 96. The first knowledge of these is obtained by observing certain effects produced by the minute traces of these elements present. However, of these new elements, two, neptunium (Np, number 93, atomic weight 237) and plutonium (Pu, number 94, atomic weight 239) have been produced in the form of their compounds in weighable amounts. This is epoch making, namely the production in quantity, even minute, of an element artificially prepared. Names suggested for numbers 95 and 96 are americium (Am) and curium (Cm). Atomic transformations have been established for other elements. Isotopes have been identified for all of them.

This entire subject requires thorough study for its full appreciation. One item, the *fission* of the two elements *uranium* and *plutonium,* has aroused the greatest interest. The hopes and claims for the utilization of this phenomenon in ordinary life are premature. More time must elapse before anything definite may be expected.

PROGRESS IN INORGANIC CHEMISTRY

In respect to the elements and compounds included under the heading of inorganic chemistry and its industries, the period is marked by progress in many lines, although there are no spectacular developments as in other fields. It is worth while to give a number of illustrations of such progress, selecting somewhat more conspicuous examples.

Variations in the forms of glass are seen, in addition to its standard uses, in structural glass, fiber glass, foam and safety glass, which are adaptations to uses new and old.

When, years ago, it was proposed to recover minerals from the Dead Sea, the plan was thought to be fantastic. Yet in the course of the years there has been developed an active industry, employing seven hundred workers and producing bromine, chlorides of sodium, potassium, calcium and magnesium.

Hydrogen peroxide is now produced in car load lots. "Car load lots" is to the industrial chemist the final proof of the success of a process.

The production of one billion pounds of aluminum in a recent year has been a prophecy of more to come. New alloys are looked for and uses in structural operations.

The production of chlorine has become increasingly important. In addition to its sanitary and bleaching uses, it is applied to organic syntheses, to some extent in units for polymerization in the production of plastics and rubber substitutes, and in insecticides and repellants. The much heralded insecticide, DDT, and the weed killer 2, 4-D, both include chlorine in their composition.

The metal *magnesium* has pushed its way forward. Its weight, one third less than that of aluminum, is its first recommendation. While it is conceivable that the ore deposits of copper and iron and other metals may sometime become exhausted, such a fate is out of the question for aluminum and magnesium. The only limitation at present is the availability of minerals which are easily workable ores. The extraction of magnesium from sea water has attracted attention as years ago did the recovery of bromine from that source. "There are nine billion pounds of magnesium in every cubic mile of sea water." But processing that cubic mile is no simple matter.

There has been a proposal to use magnesium to diminish the corrosion of iron in important installations. A mass of magnesium, properly connected with the iron to be preserved, acts as an anode, and the electrolytic corrosion is confined to this more active metal.

The progress of metallurgy from the earliest times has been determined by the ease of the recovery of the metals. This is determined in turn by the relative chemical affinities which must be overcome in the smelting of the ores. The sequence in the history of civilization through the gold, silver, copper and iron ages is very significant from the chemical standpoint. The present availability of aluminum and magnesium adds a new era, foretold in the biblical "feet of clay." The writer remembers the time when a bar of aluminum was shown as an object worthy of attention. Later this interest was transfered to magnesium. There are indications that other metals of the magnesium group, beryllium, calcium and barium, may become available in some measure.

Progress in Organic Chemistry

After the development of the atomic bomb, the most spectacular chemical progress has been in the field of organic chemistry. There are three fields in which this is conspicuous, all three to a great extent depending upon petroleum. These three fields are: the modifications of motor fuel to lead to greater efficiency, especially with respect to aviation; the synthesis of countless organic compounds of the paraffin series, repeating the long established success of the syntheses of benzene (coal tar) derivatives; the building up of the complex molecules which go to make up synthetic plastics, fibers and rubber substitutes.

The main theme of the developments of organic chemistry is *synthesis*. Synthesis is the building up from comparatively simple raw materials, composed of simple molecules, modifications according to a preconceived plan. Such modifications vary from simple changes, through more elaborate structures to the high polymer complexes so much desired for modern needs. So definite are these transformations, both in purpose and achievement, that the terms chemical architecture, or molecular architecture, may be appropriately applied to give an impression of what is accomplished.

Improvements in the efficiency of *motor fuel* has been demanded by the increasing importance of motor traffic, and even more by the war problems of aviation. It has been demonstrated that the presence in motor fuel of certain types of hydrocarbons is beneficial. These types include, (*a*) the olefines, closely related to the paraffins, (*b*) the isomeric forms of the ordinary paraffins, and (*c*) members of the benzene series. The recent problem of gasoline production has therefore been the devising of processes by which these desirable constituents would be formed in the refining.

(*a*) The *olefines* are closely related to the paraffins. The proportion of hydrogen is less. To illustrate, the first three olefines are C_2H_4, C_3H_6, C_4H_8, the corresponding paraffins being C_2H_6, C_3H_8, C_4H_{10}. The significant feature of these compounds is the unsaturated condition, and the consequent "double bond." This is represented as follows: Butane, saturated, CH_3—CH_2—CH_2—CH_3. Butylene, unsaturated, CH_3—CH_2—$CH = CH_2$. Such hydrocarbons can be formed in various ways, among them the overheating of the paraffin hydrocarbons.

The unsaturated hydrocarbons, moreover, are very reactive, and play important parts in the reactions involving the syntheses of paraffin derivatives and the polymerizations which lead to the plastics and rubber substitutes.

(*b*) Practical demonstrations have shown that the *isomeric forms of the paraffins* are more efficient than the normal compounds. This difference was studied, for example, by a comparison of normal heptanes, whose nucleus is represented by the normal chain, C—C—C—C—C—C—C, and iso-octane, whose nucleus is represented

thus,
$$\begin{array}{ccccc} & & C & & \\ & & | & & \\ C & - & C & - C - C - C. \\ & & | & & | \\ & & C & & C \end{array}$$

From this comparison a scale of values has been devised. To normal heptane a value of zero was arbitrarily assigned, and to the iso-octane a value of one hundred. A 100-octane rating of a motor fuel means that its anti-knock value is the same as that of pure iso-octane. The problem in oil refining in this respect is to build up isomeric forms of the hydro-carbons. The details are complicated and must be omitted, but as is well known, considerable progress has been made.

(*c*) A third feature of current oil refining is the conversion of paraffin or similar constituents into hydrocarbons of the *benzene series*. The two conversions of significance are those of hexane and heptane into benzenes and toluene respectively. C_6H_{14} to C_6H_6
$$\left(\begin{array}{ccc} & C & \\ C & & C \\ | & & | \\ C & & C \\ & C & \end{array} \right)$$

and C_7H_{16} to $C_6H_5.CH_3$ (
C
C   C-C
C   C
C
). This operation on

a commercial scale is comparatively recent, although it is
apparent that such changes take place in bituminous coal
distillations. Toluene thus formed is also of use in the
preparation of trinitro-toluene, TNT.

The *synthesis* of organic compounds of the paraffin series, especially those based upon constituents of petroleum
as the raw material, has made striking advances. The
preparation of compounds of the benzene series, such as
photographic chemicals, drugs and dyes, has been a practice of many years standing. The reasons for this can be
readily appreciated. The chief benzene hydrocarbons are
liquids, and are easily obtainable in sufficiently pure form.
They react readily with sulphuric and nitric acids to form
intermediates which can be converted to other compounds. Finally, the benzene nucleus, C_6H_5— (from
C_6H_6) is very persistent, retaining its individuality and
acting as a chemical framework to which many other elements or groups of elements can be attached.

Until recently none of these conditions applied to the
simpler and more important paraffins, and few synthetic
operations were attempted. Today, the situation is very
different. The industries have learned to handle gases
physically and chemically, and to obtain them in sufficiently pure form. It is stated that seventeen individual
hydrocarbons of the paraffin and related series are now
available commercially. Means have been found to overcome the proverbial sluggishness of the paraffins.

By persistent devotion to this problem, science and industry have succeeded in preparing an impressive list of organic compounds, including members of practically every type. Such a list includes alcohols, aldehydes, acids, ethers, esters, ketones, amines, chlorine compounds, as well as almost endless combinations of these types, which on account of their varied structure serve broader purposes. Announcements of commercial compounds thus synthesized read like chemical dictionaries. "It is conspicuous that petroleum is becoming more and more chemically minded." "Petroleum is a partnership between science and industry." All this is in striking contrast to the petroleum industry at the beginning of the century, when the distillation and purification of merchantable hydrocarbons represented the whole of the industry.

To the methods of attack on petroleum constituents indicated on pages 276–278, namely action by chlorine, addition to the dehydrogenated paraffins and controlled oxidation, the formation of nitro compounds by the direct action of nitric acid has been added. In one way or another the intermediates thus formed are converted into the many compounds now available.

It is difficult to make clear to the layman what the final disposition is of the products of this outstanding industry. Their applications are often highly technical. However, some impression may be obtained from the following captions:

Intermediates: to be the material for other compounds.

Solvents (quotation from a chemical journal): "The development of solvents has been of the greatest influence in the development of chemical industries in this country." The industries require a variety of solvents for purposes not easily appreciated by the outside world. Small differences are often very significant in their efficiency.

Disinfectants, fumigants, insecticides and insect repellants, weed exterminators.

Accelerators, anticorrosives, catalyzers, plasticizers.

Building materials for synthetic plastics, fibers and rubber substitutes.

Further, fifty million pounds of chemicals were used in the preparation of vitamins.

Thirty million gallons of alcohols, ethyl, isopropyl and higher alcohols, were manufactured in a recent year by one of the larger petroleum refining companies.

The third great department of organic syntheses is that involved in the preparation of the famous synthetics, *plastics, fibers* and *rubber*. Although in some respects the pressure for such substitutes ceases with the end of the war, the scientific attainment is permanent, and its results will be of moment in ordinary times and in times of stress. A resumé of the whole subject is in order, with a discussion involved in the chemistry of the raw materials, their polymerization and the products. (Consult pages 290–294.)

The preparation of these artificial substitutes falls into two divisions. One division is illustrated by rayon, cellophane and celluloid. Useful as these are, they are really only modifications of the complex substance cellulose, a natural synthetic, and from the point of view of the chemist are less profound and less interesting than the synthetics about to be described.

The model which the chemist has sought to imitate, both in respect to physical properties and chemical composition, is to be found in the three great types of natural synthetics, the polysaccharide cellulose, the polyamide protein (wool, silk, leather) and the polyterpane rubber. These consist of complex molecules, made up of simple building stones, combined into a whole by special chemical affinities. The units, the building stones of cellulose, of one kind only, glucose, $C_6H_{12}O_6$, are held together by oxygen atoms. The building stones of the proteins are the amino acids, about twenty in number, which, though varied somewhat, are of the same pattern. These are linked into a whole by nitrogen atoms. The units of rubber are probably of one kind only, isoprene, C_5H_8, or its "dimer" $C_{10}H_{16}$. These units are linked together directly. A schematic representation may be helpful:

Cellulose:

$C_6H_{10}O_4$—O—$C_6H_{10}O_4$—O—$C_6H_{10}O_4$—O—$C_6H_{10}O_4$, etc.

Proteins:

Am. Ac.—N—Am. Ac.—N—Am. Ac.—N—Am. Ac., etc.

Rubber: C_5H_8—C_5H_8—C_5H_8—C_5H_8—C_5H_8, etc.

The number of units in each case is large, in the hundreds, or even in the thousands.

In the formation of these synthetic complexes two conditions must be fulfilled. One is the procuring of simple units which are capable of combining to form the complexes desired. The other condition is the linking of these units by polymerization, co-polymerization or condensation, often with the help of a catalyst. The activity of the simple units is the essential feature, but they must not alone be active, they must be at least doubly active (multiple function), in that they can form combinations at more than one point. To illustrate: A simple combination between A— and B— would be A—B. The possibilities of action are exhausted. If —X— and —Y— have several points of activity, they can form complexes almost indefinitely, thus: —X—Y—X—Y—X—Y— and so on.

The simple compounds of multiple function are not too many, but they are adequate. They are aldehydes, amino compounds, as urea and phenol, and especially in connection with rubber, they are unsaturated hydrocarbons obtained directly or indirectly from petroleum. These, furthermore, are available from the economic standpoint, a very essential feature.

In respect to the artificial synthesis of the three types of "poly" compounds—cellulose, proteins and rubber—the synthesis of cellulose has aroused no practical interest. The natural abundance of this material (cotton, wood) obviates any such necessity. The striving has been for the other types, and products have been sought and obtained in great variety. Nylon, which has aroused so much interest, is a polyamide. It has been an outstandingly satisfactory product, and has served as a model for polyamides produced in other countries. Synthetic rubber substitutes (not actually synthetic rubber), as is well known, have been produced in a number of forms. Among the units leading to these, isoprene, butadiene and styrene are conspicuous. When more than one type of unit is involved, the process is properly termed co-polymerization, but the action is not essentially different. The processes of polymerization, co-polymerization and condensation have yielded a multitude of plastics, which have served so many purposes and have been so generally accepted by the industries.

Edward Slosson, a chemical commentator, made about 1920 these two criticisms, which in the light of later years amounted to prophecies: "Chemists have been able with great success to take a complex like starch, and to resolve it into its constituent units. The real challenge now is to start with constructive units and to build up the complex." Also, "The chemist has yet to investigate the reasons for the gummy residues left in his experimentation flasks." Modern synthetics have met the challenge.

The tremendous drain upon the *natural petroleum* resources naturally turns men's thoughts to a possible eventual exhaustion of these supplies. The estimates of the time of their lasting vary from a definite optimism to estimates less hopeful. A statement that at present twenty billion barrels of petroleum are in sight seems encouraging until one realizes that the present annual consumption is well over one billion barrels. Although at present (1947) the situation may not be considered acute, some attention is paid to the possibilities of future substitutes. Accordingly, there has been a revival of interest in bituminous shales, in the tar sands of Canada and in lignites (low-grade coals), all of which are abundant and can conceivably yield motor fuel. These minerals, along with the great abundance of bituminous coal, are, it is claimed, sufficient to guarantee a source of gasoline indefinitely. It is worth noting that even if the sources of petroleum yield diminishing amounts, they will still be of great value, as they will automatically be devoted to materials like chemical products, which in lesser abundance than motor fuel will serve many needs of a different order.

An entirely new chapter of organic compounds and syntheses has come into prominence. This is the chapter of the *organic silicon compounds,* and of their polymerization products, the polysilicones. These resemble, both in composition and products, the plastics and rubber, and due to their greater stability toward heat may develop a considerable usefulness. The analogy of silicon compounds to the organic compounds based on carbon is not unexpected, for silicon is next to carbon in the periodic list. A recent announcement includes the following details: These silicon complexes offer a liquid which flows at —70°F., a stable lubricant and a stable rubber substitute, developments of importance comparable to that of high octane gasoline and synthetic rubber.

Agricultural Chemistry

Agriculture has had its problems, the growing of more food and the finding of sufficient fertilizers. It would seem that the chief requirements of the commercial fertilizers, nitrogen, phosphorus and potash, had been adequately met in spite of the added strain. With the war ended, nitrogen compounds will be more available, and the developments of Carlsbad, New Mexico, promise adequate supplies of potash.

The standard insecticides and fungicides of the past have involved arsenic, copper, lead, fluorine and sulphur. There is always the question whether there may not be an undue accumulation of these mineral substances in the soil and in the food. In the latter respect it has become advisable to set legal limits to the amounts which may be present. Attention has naturally been given to organic products, as they lack that menace. Rotenone, pyrethrum and nicotine are standard. DDT (dichlorodiphenyltrichloroethane) has now come in with an enthusiastic welcome, of value in sanitary ways as in ways agricultural. It has developed that it is not a cure-all, but no doubt it will serve many purposes. If it fails to meet all expectations, it will nevertheless be a stimulation to further research. Akin to this much heralded insecticide is the weed exterminator, 2, 4–D, (dichlorophenoxyacetic acid). If its promise is fulfilled, it will be a great boon, not alone to economic agriculture, but also to the lighter province of horticulture.

It is worthy of note that the increase in soy bean culture is tremendous. The yield of oil is measured by the hundreds of millions of pounds, the greater portion being applied to food, lesser amounts to such uses as soaps and paints.

PHARMACEUTICAL CHEMISTRY

The chemistry of synthetical medicines has made considerable progress. There is a constant striving to connect the composition of medicinals with their therapeutic effect. A conspicuous example is the reaching out to this end by the sulfa drugs, which have been synthesized and tried in great variety, but the variations are always based upon a definite structural foundation of the molecule. In a general way the enthusiastic claim that this is the golden age of therapeutics has some meaning. The most conspicuous product of the immediate past, penicillin, in a sense does not belong in the chemical chapter, although the chemist claims a considerable contributory credit.

War Gases and Chemical Warfare

The public waited with great apprehension for any announcement of the use of war gases, a feature so important in the war of 1914–1918. Such news never came. On high authority it was stated that "our opponents did not challenge us on this score because of our high state of preparedness." This preparedness was both offensive and defensive. For a time, at least, the chapter on war gases may be dropped out of consideration.

Other phases of chemical warfare, usually well publicized, such as screening smokes, flame throwers, incendiaries, RDX, a more powerful explosive, and finally the atomic bomb are evidences of the tireless activity of the chemical profession, and chemists have received much credit for all that they have done, and the results have been inspirations for work to come.

GLOSSARY

GLOSSARY

Acid.—A compound made up of a nonmetallic group and of hydrogen, so constituted that this hydrogen is replaceable by metals with the formation of salts. It is neutralized by a base, with the formation of a salt and water. When dissolved in water it yields positive hydrogen ions and negative nonmetallic ions.

Adsorption.—The retention on the part of a solid by surface attraction of gases or liquids, as the adsorption of gases by charcoal.

Alcohol.—A general name for compounds of the paraffin series formed by the introduction of one hydroxyl group in place of hydrogen. Ordinary alcohol is the best known example.

Aldehyde.—Any compound containing the group $-C\!\!\diagup\!\!\diagdown\!\!_H^O$. This group is very reactive, and especially sensitive to oxygen.

Aliphatic.—A general name applied to the paraffin series of hydrocarbons and their derivatives.

Alkali.—An active basic compound, usually the hydroxide, of the metals of the sodium group. The term is applied also to the metals of this group and to their compounds in a general way.

Allotropic Forms.—The various forms of the same element, as oxygen and ozone, diamond and charcoal, differing by a varied number or arrangement in the molecule of atoms of the same kind.

Amalgam.—An alloy, one of the constituent metals of which is mercury.

Amide.—A compound obtained by replacing the hydroxyl group of an organic acid by means of the amino group, as acetamide.

Amine.—A compound derived from ammonia by the replacement of its hydrogen by certain radicals.

Amino.—A prefix applied to the names of certain compounds containing the group—NH_2, as amino-acid.

Amorphous.—Without crystalline form.

Anhydride.—An oxide of a nonmetal (or of an organic acid group) capable of uniting with water to form an acid. Sulphuric anhydride with water forms sulphuric acid.

Aromatic.—A general name applied to the hydrocarbons of the benzene series, and their derivatives.

Ash.—The noncombustible and nonvolatile residue from the burning of animal or vegetable matter representing approximately the original mineral content. It may be an essential constituent, as the ash of milk, or an admixture, as the salt of butter.

-ate.—A suffix applied to the names of salts of the oxy-acids characterized by the suffix *-ic*. Nitric acid forms nitrates.

Atomic number.—The ordinal number of the elements determined by their X-ray spectra. Almost, but not quite coincident with the order of the atomic weights.

Atom.—The smallest particle, portion or proportion of matter which enters into chemical reactions or compounds. It is the unit of chemical relations.

Base.—The hydroxide of a metal capable of uniting with an acid. The name is also applied in a broad way to the positive metallic or nonacid portion of a salt.

Benzene.—The name of the fundamental member of the second hydrocarbon series of organic chemistry. The term is applied as an adjective to designate a relationship to this series.

Bond.—The conventional assumption of the unit of linkage among atoms and radicals. The hydrogen atom is used as the basis for estimating its value, and it is conveniently represented by a dash, —, but this must not be interpreted as a material or rigid connection.

Calorie.—The unit of heat, being the amount needed to heat one unit of water one degree. The gram and centigrade degree give a convenient unit for small quantities of heat, and 1,000 times this amount for larger quantities. A calorie can also be computed in the English system of weights and measures.

Carbohydrate.—An organic compound composed of carbon, hydrogen, and oxygen, the last two in the proportions of water, as $C_6H_{12}O_6$. They are all composed of similar simple combinations called monosaccharides, or of unions of two or more of these simple combinations. The various forms of sugars, starch, and cellulose make up this carbohydrate group.

Carboxyl.—The acid group, $-C\overset{/\!/O}{-}OH$ of organic acids.

Catalyst.—A substance which accelerates or retards a chemical action without entering into the final products. Sometimes called catalyzers.

Chain.—A term applied to a number of carbon atoms linked together, forming the main portion of an organic compound of the paraffin series.

Chromophor group.—The particular arrangement of atoms which gives color to molecules thus making it possible for them to serve as the basis of dyes.

Colloidal.—The relation between two substances in which one holds the other in a dispersed state evenly disseminated throughout its mass, but not in the form of solution. Jellies and emulsions offer good illustrations.

Compound.—A substance formed by the definite chemical union of two or more elements. In the union the elements lose their individuality and the compound possesses its own characteristic properties.

Condensation.—The building up of complex molecules from dissimilar units. This is frequently accomplished by the presence of hydrogen in one unit and of oxygen in another.

Determination.—The measurement in any expedient manner of the amount of a particular constituent of a compound or mixture.

Disaccharide.—One of the sugar groups, containing two of the simple sugar units. Ordinary cane sugar, milk sugar, and maltose are the most common.

Dissociate.—To separate into parts in such a manner that these parts may unite under changed conditions to re-form the original compound.

Double Decomposition.—The reaction between a salt and an acid, base, or other salt, involving the simple interchange of the positive groups (metal or hydrogen) and the formation of a new pair of compounds. Illustration: sodium chloride and silver nitrate yield silver chloride and sodium nitrate.

Drying oils.—Liquid fats, which on account of their unsaturated condition unite with oxygen and undergo polymerization, both changes tending to establish the solid state.

Electrolysis—(Decomposition by electricity.) Acids, bases and salts in aqueous solution conduct electricity, and when a current is passed, the positive constituent is liberated at the negative pole, and the negative constituent at the positive pole. This process may also be carried out on fused bases and salts.

Electrolytes.—Substances (as acids, bases, and salts) which are capable of conducting electricity. The name suggests both conductivity and electrolysis.

Electrochemical Series.—The list of the metals placed in the order of their reactivity in certain respects; it gives an approximate idea of the general nature of the metals.

Electron.—The unit of electricity (negative), present in the shells of the atoms, and by their number and arrangement determining the atomic number and chemical properties of the element. The electrons in the nucleus do not assert themselves.

Element.—A substance which is incapable of being resolved by any known means into simpler parts. It is the basis of the compounds.

Enzyme.—A complex chemical compound, secreted by various plant and animal organisms, capable of catalytically bringing about certain changes which are more frequently hydrolytic than otherwise.

Equation.—An expression borrowed from algebra, used to indicate the nature of a reaction and the proportions of the reacting substances.

Ester.—An organic salt, made up of an organic base and any acid, more usually an organic acid. Ethyl acetate.

Ether.—A compound formed by the linking together of two alcohol radicals by means of oxygen. C_2H_5—O—C_2H_5. The oxygen marks also the place of separation of the two groups. Complex sugars have a somewhat similar structure.

Ethyl.—C_2H_5—, the second and most important radical of the paraffin series of hydrocarbons. C_2H_5Cl, ethyl chloride.

Fat.—A mixture of esters made up of the organic base, glycerol, and three fatty acid groups. Glyceryl stearate. The liquid fats, or oils, are also included under this term.

Ferment.—A living organism, which by its growth brings about chemical changes, as the production of alcohol from sugar.

Formula.—The group of symbols used to indicate the composition and structure of a compound. The symbols are sometimes so arranged that they show the exact relation of the atoms in the molecule. The formula is then called graphic, or structural. Formula, HNO_3. Structural formula $H—O—N\begin{smallmatrix} O \\ O \end{smallmatrix}$

-gen.—A suffix indicating producing or generating. Hydrogen = producing water.

Glucose.—$C_6H_{12}O_6$, also called dextrose, grape or starch sugar, is the most important simple sugar or monosaccharide, and is the constituent or one of the constituents of the more common complex carbohydrates.

Gravimetric analysis.—Quantitative analysis by methods of weighing.

Group.—(*a*) Same as *Radical.* (*b*) A number of substances which are considered together on account of their similarity.

Halogen.—A general name given to the elements of the chlorine group, fluorine, chlorine, bromine, and iodine, indicating the readiness with which they form salts with the metals. (Greek, hal = Latin, sal, salt.)

Halogenation.—Introduction of a halogen.

Hardness.—(*a*) The comparative readiness with which a solid may be scratched. This is determined by reference to an arbitrary scale numbered 1 to 10. Hardness and specific gravity are not related. Lead is heavy but soft, glass is light but hard.

(*b*) The soap-destroying power of water, caused by the presence usually of calcium and magnesium salts.

Hydro-acid.—An acid of the type, hydrochloric acid, HCl, containing no oxygen.

Hydrogenation.—The addition of hydrogen to organic compounds, especially the fatty oils, which contain less than the normal amount of hydrogen.

Hydrolysis.—(Decomposition by water.) The resolution of a compound made up of two or more individualized groups, into these groups, by the addition of water. The linkage between the groups is broken, one group uniting with hydrogen, the other with hydroxyl of water. Hydrolysis applies only to substances which may be assumed to be formed by the union of these groups by the loss of water.

Hydroxide.—A basic compound, containing the hydroxyl group, —OH. The terms base and hydroxide are often synonymous.

Hydroxyl.—The group —OH, derived from water, present in many compounds, which contain both hydrogen and oxygen, as bases and acids.

-ic.—A suffix applied, (*a*) To the name of most important oxy-acid derived from any given nonmetal. The suffix *-ous* indicates an acid with less oxygen.

(*b*) When an element combines with another element or group in more than one proportion, the suffix-*ic* is applied to the name of the first element to indicate the compound containing the greater proportion of the second element or group, as *-ous* is used to indicate the smaller proportion. CuCl, CuCl$_2$, cuprous and cupric chlorides.

-ide.—The suffix applied to the name of the second constituent of a compound indicates that it contains only two elements; it is applied also to compounds made up of groups which are considered as single units, as ammonium chloride, (NH$_4$) Cl.

Indicator.—A substance which by color changes shows the progress of a chemical reaction.

Inorganic.—Pertaining to any chemical discussion involving compounds which are not organic; from the standpoint of the natural sciences associated with the mineral kingdom.

Ion.—A group, carrying one or more positive or negative electric charges, derived from acids, bases, or salts dissolved in water. Ions are either positive hydrogen or metallic, or negative hydroxyl or nonmetallic.

Ionization.—The dissociation of an ionogen into its constituent ions upon solution in water.

Ionogen.—A convenient term applied to acids, bases, and salts, because upon solution in water they yield ions. Ionogen and electrolyte ordinarily denote the same substances.

Isomerism.—The condition exhibited by different compounds which are composed of the same elements in the same proportions as C$_2$H$_2$ and C$_6$H$_6$. The more interesting phases of isomerism involve identical similarity in the absolute number of atoms, and a similarity in nature of the compounds, but a distinction due to a different arrangement of the atoms in the molecule, as ethylene and ethylidene chlorides, $CH_3.CHCl_2$ and $CH_2Cl.CH_2Cl$.

-ite.—The suffix applied to the names of salts derived from acids designated by the suffix *-ous*. Sulphurous acid yields sodium sulphite.

Kinetic.—Pertaining to the motion of molecules.

Latent Heat.—(latent = concealed.) The molecular or kinetic energy of the liquid or gaseous state, appearing in the form of sensible heat when the physical state is changed to one of lower molecular energy, gas to liquid, liquid to solid. An equal amount of sensible heat must be applied in order to bring about the reverse changes.

Metal.—An element capable of replacing directly or indirectly the hydrogen of an acid, of forming a base, and of forming by itself a positive ion. The popular idea of a metal includes more than half of these elements, but the metals of the sodium and calcium group must be included to make the list complete.

Methyl.—CH_3—; the first radical of the paraffin series of hydrocarbons, CH_3Cl, methyl chloride.

Mineral.—(*a*) An element or compound as found in a natural state. Rocks may contain several minerals, but each mineral is a definite chemical substance.

(*b*) The term applied to the constituents of animal or vegetable matter aside from carbon, hydrogen, oxygen, and nitrogen. They are present in the ash of such substances.

Molar Solutions.—The solution obtained by dissolving the gram-molecular weight of any substance, usually in water, so as to make a total of one liter of solution. The molar solution of calcium hydroxide contains 74 grams. $Ca(OH)_2$, $40+2\times16+2\times1=74$.

Molecule.—The smallest units of which any substance is composed. These units are composed of several kinds of atoms, as the molecules of water, H_2O, of one kind of atom, as oxygen, O_2, and in some cases, as argon, of single atoms. The molecule is the physical unit, as the atom is the chemical unit.

Monosaccharide.—See *Carbohydrate.*

Neutron.—One of the hydrogen units of the nucleus of the atom. In some manner it contains both the positive proton and the negative electron and is therefore neutral.

Nitro.—(*a*) The name applied to the group —NO_2, derived from nitric acid by the elimination of its hydroxyl group.

(*b*) A prefix applied to organic compounds containing this group, as nitrobenzene, $C_6H_5NO_2$.

Nonmetal.—An element possessing characteristics in a sense the opposite of those of a metal. Nonmetals combined with hydrogen alone, or with hydrogen and oxygen, form acids, and are included in the negative ions. They lack the usual external characteristics associated with metals.

Normal Solutions.—Molar solutions so modified that they represent one valence or combining weight. The molar solution and normal solution of hydrochloric acid, HCl, are the same, but in the cases of sulphuric acid, H_2SO_4, and phosphoric acid, H_3PO_4, the molar solutions must be diluted to one-half and one-third concentration, respectively, in order to convert them into normal solution.

-ol.—A suffix applied to hydroxyl derivatives, alcohols among the paraffins, phenols among the benzenes.

Organic.—Pertaining to compounds included under the head, hydrocarbons and their derivatives. The name is derived from the fact that in the early years of chemistry, the compounds included in this study were assumed to be of necessity products of organized life. Although such a limitation is incorrect, products of animal and vegetable life are very important in organic chemistry.

Oxidation.—Primarily the process of adding oxygen to any substance; it has however been applied more broadly to increasing the valence of certain elements and even to subtracting hydrogen.

Oxide.—The compound of an element with oxygen. The oxides of metals and of nonmetals are of very different character.

Oxy-acid.—Inorganic acids containing oxygen, as sulphuric acid. They may be assumed to be made up by the union of nonmetallic oxides with water.

Paraffin.—The name of the first series of the hydrocarbons; the name indicates that these hydrocarbons possess a low affinity for acids. Also called the methane, marsh gas, aliphatic or fatty series.

Per.—A prefix indicating a higher degree of valence than the usual. In lead oxide, PbO, the valence of lead is 2, in lead peroxide, PbO_2, its valence is 4.

Phenol.—A general name for hydroxyl derivatives of the benzene hydrocarbons, corresponding to some extent to the alcohols of the paraffins.

Plastics.—Synthetic solids. Two features are associated with plastics. First, they are capable of molding while soft and they subsequently harden. Second, they are complexes built up from simple units by polymerization or condensation.

Polymerization.—The building up of complex molecules from similar simple units, with or without a catalyst. The units must possess a special activity such as that of the aldehyde group or the unsaturated condition.

Precipitate.—The act or product of forming an insoluble solid from ingredients which were soluble. The formation and nature of precipitates formed under known conditions are so characteristic that they are the readiest means of detecting unknown substances.

Protein.—Complex nitrogen compounds common in animal tissue. Egg white and horn are typical.

Proton.—One of the hydrogen units of the nucleus of the atom. It lacks the electron of the shell and is therefore positive.

Pyrolysis.—(Decomposition by heat). A term more general than destructive distillation, including particularly the splitting off of hydrogen from paraffin hydrocarbons to establish the unsaturated active condition.

Qualitative analysis.—This concerns the nature of the ingredients of a compound or mixture.

Quantitative analysis.—This concerns the amounts of the various ingredients of a compound or mixture.

Radical.—A group of elements, as ethyl, C_2H_5, or sulphate, SO_4, preserving its unity through various reactions. Often called group or residue.

Reaction.—The action between two chemical substances. Also a change caused in one under influence of physical force. It is so frequently represented by an equation that the terms are easily confused.

Reagent.—Any active chemical substance; more exactly one applied for the accomplishment of some specific purpose.

Reduction.—The opposite of oxidation in its various meanings.

Residue.—The same as group or radical.

Ring.—A combination of carbon (or other) atoms in which, besides the linking of adjacent atoms, those somewhat remote are linked together, thus forming a ring. The benzene ring

is the most important example.

Saccharide.—See *carbohydrate, di-* and *poly-saccharide.*

Salt.—The product obtained by replacing the hydrogen of an acid by means of a metal; by the mutual action of a base and acid; by the union direct or indirect of positive metallic and negative nonmetallic groups. The statements represent the same facts from somewhat different aspects.

Saponification.—(Soap making.) The decomposition of an ester, especially a fat, by the action of a strong base. This base unites with the acid, and the base of the ester, the alcohol, is set free.

Series.—A group of similar substances, which differ in such a way in respect to composition and properties that they exhibit a regular progression. The series of organic compounds are conspicuous examples.

Shells.—The series of imaginary cubes about the nucleus of the atom, at the corners of which the planetary electrons are located.

Solute.—The substance dissolved in a solvent.

Solvent.—There are two main types, represented by water for inorganic substances and by a large number of organic liquids suitable for the solution of organic substances. The simple alcohols to some extent fall into both classes.

Specific Gravity.—The ratio of the weight of solids and liquids to that of equal volumes of water. For gases the standard is either air or hydrogen.

Specific Heat.—The ratio of the heat capacity of a substance to that of water.

State, Physical State.—The solid, liquid, or gaseous condition.

Synthesis.—In a narrow sense the union of two aproximately equal organic groups, usually by the intervention of inorganic units. In a broader sense the artificial preparation of any organic compound from simple materials, organic or inorganic.

Unsaturated.—(*a*) Physical, as of a solution, capable of taking up more of a given substance.

(*b*) Chemical, the condition of hydrocarbons or hydrocarbon residues containing less than their normal content of hydrogen.

Valence.—The combining value of any element or group, compared with that of hydrogen, which is taken as unity. Each such unit considered as one linkage and may be represented by a bond. Valence 1, H—Cl, valence 2, Ca $=$ O, valences 1 and 2, $H\!\!>\!\!O$. 8 is the highest valence known. The valence of any element or group may usually be recognized by inspection of the formula of its hydrogen or oxygen compound.

Volumetric analysis.—Quantitative analysis by the use of solutions of known concentration.

TABLE OF ELEMENTS

INTERNATIONAL ATOMIC WEIGHTS, 1947

BASED UPON LIST PUBLISHED BY THE JOURNAL OF THE AMERICAN CHEMICAL SOCIETY

Elements	Symbols	Atomic Numbers	Atomic Weights	Elements	Symbols	Atomic Numbers	Atomic Weights
Actinium ...	Ac	89	...	Mercury	Hg	80	200.61
Alabamium ..	Ab	85	...	Molybdenum .	Mo	42	95.95
Aluminum ..	Al	13	26.97	Neodymium .	Nd	60	144.27
Antimony ...	Sb	51	121.76	Neon	Ne	10	20.183
Argon	A	18	39.944	Nickel	Ni	28	58.69
Arsenic ...	As	33	74.91	Nitrogen	N	7	14.008
Barium	Ba	56	137.36	Osmium	Os	76	190.2
Beryllium ...	Be	4	9.02	Oxygen	O	8	16.0000
Bismuth	Bi	83	209.00	Palladium ..	Pd	46	106.7
Boron	B	5	10.82	Phosphorus ..	P	15	30.98
Bromine	Br	35	79.916	Platinum ...	Pt	78	195.23
Cadmium ...	Cd	48	112.41	Polonium ..	Po	84	210
Calcium	Ca	20	40.08	Potassium ..	K	19	39.096
Carbon	C	6	12.010	Praseodymium	Pr	59	140.92
Cerium	Ce	58	140.13	Protactinium .	Pa	91	231
Cesium	Cs	55	132.91	Radium	Ra	88	226.05
Chlorine	Cl	17	35.457	Radon	Rn	86	222
Chromium ..	Cr	24	52.01	Rhenium ...	Re	75	186.31
Cobalt	Co	27	58.94	Rhodium ...	Rh	45	102.91
Columbium .	Cb	41	92.91	Rubidium ..	Rb	37	85.48
Copper	Cu	29	63.57	Ruthenium ..	Ru	44	101.7
Dysprosium .	Dy	66	162.46	Samarium ..	Sm	62	150.43
Erbium	Er	68	167.2	Scandium ..	Sc	21	45.10
Europium ...	Eu	63	152.0	Selenium ...	Se	34	78.96
Fluorine	F	9	19.00	Silicon	Si	14	28.06
Gadolinium .	Gd	64	156.9	Silver	Ag	47	107.880
Gallium	Ga	31	69.72	Sodium	Na	11	22.997
Germanium .	Ge	32	72.60	Strontium ..	Sr	38	87.63
Gold	Au	79	197.2	Sulphur	S	16	32.06
Hafnium ...	Hf	72	178.6	Tantalum ...	Ta	73	180.88
Helium	He	2	4.003	Tellurium ...	Te	52	127.61
Holmium ...	Ho	67	164.94	Terbium ...	Tb	65	159.2
Hydrogen ...	H	1	1.0080	Thallium ...	Tl	81	204.39
Illinium	Il	61	...	Thorium ...	Th	90	232.12
Indium	In	49	114.76	Thulium ...	Tm	69	169.4
Iodine	I	53	126.92	Tin	Sn	50	118.70
Iridium	Ir	77	193.1	Titanium ...	Ti	22	47.90
Iron	Fe	26	55.85	Tungsten ...	W	74	183.92
Krypton	Kr	36	83.7	Uranium ...	U	92	238.07
Lanthanum .	La	57	138.92	Vanadium ..	V	23	50.95
Lead	Pb	82	207.21	Virginium ..	Vi	87	...
Lithium	Li	3	6.940	Xenon	Xe	54	131.3
Lutecium ..	Lu	71	174.99	Ytterbium ..	Yb	70	173.04
Magnesium ..	Mg	12	24.32	Yttrium	Y	39	88.92
Manganese ..	Mn	25	54.93	Zinc	Zn	30	65.38
Masurium ..	Ma	43	...	Zirconium ..	Zr	40	91.22

The trans-uranic elements are: Neptunium (Np) No. 93, Plutonium (Pu) No. 94, Americum? (Am) No. 95, Curium? (Cm) No. 96.

Comparison of Centigrade and Fahrenheit Temperature Scales

Centigrade	Fahrenheit	Centigrade	Fahrenheit
—150°	—238°	50°	122°
—100	—148	60	140
—30	—22	70	158
—20	—4	80	176
—10	+14	90	194
—5	+23	100	212
0	+32	150	302
5	+41	200	392
10	50	250	482
20	68	300	572
30	86	350	662
40	104	400	752

The Metals in the Order of Their Specific Gravity

Lithium	0.53
Potassium	0.87
Sodium	0.98
Calcium	1.6
Magnesium	1.7
Strontium	2.5
Aluminum	2.7
Barium	3.8
Arsenic	5.7
Antimony	6.6
Chromium	6.7
Zinc	7.1
Tin	7.3
Manganese	7.4
Iron	7.9
Cobalt	8.6
Copper	8.9
Bismuth	9.8
Silver	10.5
Lead	11.3
Mercury	13.6
Gold	19.3
Platinum	21.5

The Metals in the Order of Their Fusibility

	°C.	°F.
Mercury	—39	—38
Potassium	63	145
Sodium	98	208
Tin	232	449
Bismuth	265	510
Lead	326	620
Zinc	419	786
Antimony	630	1166
Magnesium	630	1166
Aluminum	655	1210
Calcium	800	1472
Silver	960	1760
Gold	1060	1940
Copper	1080	1976
Manganese	1250	2282
Nickel	1450	2640
Iron	1500	2730
Platinum	1750	3180